What people in the healin

Sexual Abuse
Sacred Wound

In focusing on creativity as the crucible for transformation, *Sexual Abuse / Sacred Wound* goes beyond much of the literature for survivors of sexual abuse; it points to liberation and out of victimization. Both the simplicity and sophistication of this book make it accessible and useful for lay and professional audiences.

Dr. Peter Levine
author of the forthcoming *Waking the Tiger: Healing Trauma Through the Body*
founder of Somatic Experiencing™

According to Dr. Mines, the experience of sexual abuse is a direct attack on one's essence and integrity. *Sexual Abuse / Sacred Wound* provides resources and techniques to reestablish inner contact with both and shows how the resolution of trauma can be a major source of spiritual growth and a major milestone on the spiritual path. Dr. Mines' book is an evolution of the pioneering work of Peter Levine, and provides a needed component in the treatment of sexual abuse trauma. I found *Sexual Abuse / Sacred Wound* to be informative and inspirational, and consider it "must reading" for anyone who has been traumatized or sexually abused, or for anyone who treats sexual abuse or other traumas.

William R. Emerson, Ph.D.
Pioneer in the treatment of pre- and perinatal trauma
Director, Emerson Training Seminars (Petaluma, Ca.)

This is a very important book which contributes to the resolution of the controversy over the recovery of repressed memories of abuse.
Dr. Mines' methodlogy is a combination of Eastern and Western approaches. Her focus on a somatic orientation is precisely what is missing from the literature on trauma/abuse therapy. She conveys with compassion, clarity, and clinical expertise a very creative path to healing based on her personal experience as well as that of her clients.

Marjorie L. Rand, Ph.D.
Co-author of *Body, Self & Soul; Sustaining Integration*

Sexual Abuse Sacred Wound

TRANSFORMING DEEP TRAUMA

Stephanie Mines, Ph.D.

STATION HILL OPENINGS

BARRYTOWN, LTD.

Published under the Station Hill Openings imprint by Barrytown, Ltd., Barrytown, New York 12507.

Distributed by Consortium Book Sales & Distribution, Inc., 1045 Westgate Drive, Saint Paul, Minnesota 55114-1065.

"The Story of Zorah Lambowski," p. 65 and following, is printed here by permission of Zorah Lambowski.

Cover design by Susan Quasha.
Typesetting by Alison Wilkes.

Library of Congress Cataloging-in-Publication Data

Mines, Stephanie.
    Sexual abuse/sacred wound : transforming deep trauma / Stephanie Mines.
        p.   cm.
     Includes index.
     ISBN 1-886449-11-2 (pbk. : alk. paper)
     1. Adult child abuse victims—Rehabilitation. 2. Focused expressive psychotherapy.   I. Title.
    RC569.5.A28M56   1996
    616.85′83690651—dc20   96-24397
                                                     CIP

Printed in the United States of America

CONTENTS

ACKNOWLEDGEMENTS

I would like to begin by acknowledging my husband. His patience and loving kindness give me my greatest hope for the ability of human beings to survive this toxic age with good values intact. Next, I acknowledge my children, Rachel and Sierra, for all the ways they teach me and for giving me such good reason to live and create. My women friends, whose spirits are each like shiny sesame seeds, nourish me and inspire me with a belief in the powers of creativity and perseverance. My publisher, George Quasha, encouraged me to complete this manuscript. His belief in me helped me enormously to believe in myself.

I would also like to acknowledge Dr. Peter Levine who has synthesized essential information and organized it to provide me with a unique understanding of the nature and impact of trauma and its patterns in sexual abuse. Peter's awareness and awakening language have stimulated my own creativity. His work has been crucial for me professionally and personally.

Finally, I would like to acknowledge my family of origin. My mother and father launched me irrevocably onto a path of healing. They gave me no choice but to evolve profoundly, and to discover a well of compassion, the sacred drink for survivors of trauma. I am grateful to have this opportunity to recognize Muriel Newman and Sidney Bernard Mines whose suffering far exceeds mine. May my efforts free their souls. I am grateful to my brother Alex for his valiant efforts to grow strong, and I acknowledge myself, along with my family members, for my power to continue, to move on, and my desire to be of service.

INTRODUCTION

This book is the fruit both of my years as a psychotherapist working with women and men who have suffered from sexual and other forms of abuse, and of my own self-therapy and personal transformation. I write not only as a therapist and healer, but as an abused person. I offer my own healing history as encouragement and, I hope, inspiration for those who continue to suffer from wounds inflicted in their past.

Through the application of the methods of expressive therapy that I provide in this book, it is possible for the individual to undertake his or her own healing process. Though in many cases work with a therapist can be extremely valuable, appropriate therapy is not always available, and, when the method of therapy involves the creative arts, the intervention or supervision of a therapist may not be necessary. When the individual is truly dedicated to his or her own healing, expressive art work in the form of writing, drawing, or creative movement can provide the "feedback" otherwise required of the therapist.

This book contains basically four kinds of material: numerous case histories that document the different ways in which expressive work can be instrumental in healing; instruction in methods and ideas for the self-implementation of expressive therapies; resources for going further with expressive therapy work, as well as access to alternative healing practices; examples of expressive work by myself and others undertaken in the context of our own healing.

It is my purpose and intention in writing this book to demonstrate the courage of people who have been sexually, emotionally, physically, and spiritually violated. That is why this book opens with case histories written to reveal the many permutations of sexual abuse, and some of the key facets in its transformation. The many healing stories I have witnessed have communicated to me a deep respect for the human capacity to confront trauma without denial and to determine to live outside of its shadow. Profound commitment and self-dedication are required to see this task through. It is work without end, but it offers the greatest reward — self-knowledge. Stories of lives lived in this way are needed to encourage others. The case histories that open this book are based on the experiences of the people I have seen in my practice and on my own experiences of recovering from sexual abuse. Frequently one case history merges several stories and is combined with my own additions and discoveries. None of these stories is therefore purely biographical, but all of them are based on actual experiences that serve as real models of recovery. It is also my purpose in each case history to demonstrate the role of creativity in holistic healing.

It is important to me not to retraumatize my readers. For this reason, descriptions of severe violence are *not* emphasized. I believe it is possible to be of help in renegotiating trauma without recreating traumatic experience for the reader. Being a survivor of abuse myself, I am acutely aware of the impact of reading about abuse. In softening my stories, without compromising truth one iota, but by using language gently, slowly, and gradually, I hope to allow an ever–deepening healing to occur.

I seek a way to inform that does not employ shock. As an integral part of the trauma experience, shock invites a horde of nervous system confusions that ultimately create devastating, though highly renegotiable, damage. Almost all discussion of trauma, of necessity, evokes some shock response. I don't think that I can completely circumvent this, but I can at least try to reduce the magnitude of that shock by the way I communicate. As long as abuse continues, we remain, to some extent, conditioned to shock. The truly preventive measure, I believe, is our work on ourselves, which, in its cleansing, empowers us to make abuse of any kind impossible. It is with a prayer for this possibility that I offer these stories and my commentaries, observations, and suggestions.

Inherent in this book is the value of the arts and expressive, creative work in healing from sexual abuse and related deep trauma. I cannot imagine my own recovery without the joyful, vitalizing, and exciting experience of writing, movement, visual, and performing arts. In each story presented here, as well as the sections of this book that provide resources, the arts play a role. I have long been committed to the belief that we are all artists, and I do not mean this in the trite sense that dilettantes might employ. Rather, I mean we all have a right to enter the field of creative expression in order to discover the scope of our experience — the tragic as well as the joyful. This birthright to be expressive, creative, and to expand into the arts is my way to transcend depression, transform anger, deeply experience grief and forgiveness, and plunge mightily into the well of collective truth. The arts, with their broad scope, are the only containers I know capable of holding the magnitude of feeling that erupts in the process of healing from abuse.

For many people the arts seem a distant land, one they cannot reach because their voices have been battened down, their hands tied behind their backs, and their muscles stripped of their spontaneity. For this reason, I have provided the TOOLBOX and RE-SOURCE sections of this book — to give jump starts to those who can't get going creatively, to suggest structure for those who fear the unboundaried realm of expression, and to list resources for those who can more easily begin by doing research, charting their way with caution and wisdom. Trauma and abuse rob us of the ability to be wholeheartedly expressive, but we can reclaim that treasure as we reclaim our selves, our human nature, our right to be dramatic, artistic, open, spontaneous, and child-like.

I believe we have a great deal yet to learn about the impact of abuse and the ways our particular cultural configuration can intensify or heal the cycles of trauma. We are still at a juncture of human history when we can look at these issues and make choices. I don't know how much longer we can remain at this turning point before we are overcome by shock waves. I want to make my contribution to preventing this inundation by increasing the awareness we now have about trauma. As a survivor, as a healer, and as someone who continues to work on herself, I believe I can do this.

This book represents my effort in this regard. It was written while I maintained a busy practice, mothered my children, and nurtured the powerfully transformative relationship I have with my husband. I wanted very much to write this book without abdicating any of my relational responsibilities and without disturbing what balance I can create in my busy life. It remains important to me that this book *not* be a source of trauma for anyone, including myself, but that it be a source of renegotiation and evolution. I feel obligated not only to model but to thoroughly LIVE a life of balance and health, not just for what such an experience can mean for others, but because of the healing implicit *for me* by living in a healthy way. I need *ongoing* healing and I believe *all* survivors do.

Without being an alarmist, I can say that I am sensitive to a planetary healing crisis and aware that there is something I can do about it. The main way, it seems to me, that I can be helpful is in the way I live, write, and express myself. In my own process, what has been particularly significant is defining health for myself, and maintaining it with balance and creative expression. For me, health and creativity go hand in hand.

I cannot say often enough that it is creativity that allows me to truly know the depths of my own transformative power. Just talking will not, no matter how deep the level of communication, reveal to me the full extent of all that I know and am. My collective and my most intimate truth is known and experienced in art — writing, movement, sounding, and the use of color and form. Expansion into the full potential of human possibility is, I believe, what healing is about, and I see that expansion most directly portrayed in creativity, in art, in all its forms.

Trauma is simultaneously an obstacle and an alchemical force that fires us into the realms beyond survival. We, the wounded healers, can grow into the magnificent loving kindness and creative geniuses we are each capable of — this is not unlikely, and not in any way impossible. But in order to truly embody this idealism, I believe we need health, creative expression, and creative opportunity — vehicles for transformation and deep knowing.

This book is NOT a comprehensive statement about either sexual abuse or the ways in which it can be healed. There are many aspects of sexual abuse and incest which I have *not* discussed (such as an in-depth study of the impact of sexual abuse by mothers on their daughters, or the impact of sexual abuse by psychotherapists on their clients). It is not that I am avoiding these topics, but they have not presented themselves enough in my practice to give me the kind of experience I think necessary for me to discuss them with expertise. I hope that others who feel motivated and inspired will undertake the task of addressing the subjects, and the many others related to the transformation of sexual abuse.

It is the deepest desire of my heart to make the pain I have experienced useful for others. I believe I have done a great deal to disperse the suffering I have known from abuse and trauma into tears of joy. If those tears can water the glorious plants of human development, I will feel gratified and humbled. Having been used poorly, I want now to be well used by all who can benefit from what I write.

Aspects
of
Healing
from
Sexual Abuse

Five Case Histories

Psyche, Soma and Healing from Addictions

The Story of Shelley Cleveland

Shelley Cleveland was wide-eyed, apparently astounded by what she saw in the world. And while she wasn't particularly thin, she nevertheless appeared drawn. Her look of shock or fear carried with it a kind of passivity. Her body was held tightly as if in terror.

Initially, Shelley came for therapy because of psychosomatic illnesses. For several years she had suffered from extraordinary fatigue, failures in her immune system, and allergic responses to most foods. She had been diagnosed with candida albicans (a fungal infection which results in an unusual reaction to a wide host of foods) following the birth of her daughter two years earlier.

In her twenties, Shelley had used alcohol, marijuana, and cocaine regularly, and in substantial amounts. It wasn't until she became pregnant that she decided to stop these addictions. Now she had withdrawn completely from their use. As she went through the subtle and sometimes agonizing process of detoxification, she found herself inundated with guilt. "Why," she asked herself obsessively, "have I been so weak and indulgent?"

I sensed in Shelley a passion for life and the power to heal. On the outside, however, only her exhaustion showed. She had dark circles under her eyes and her complexion was grey. I saw her somatic situation as a plea for help. Shelley had done a great deal to help herself, but a macrobiotic diet, a program of vitamins, supplements, cell salts, homeopathics, elixirs and various approaches to exercise had not proved thoroughly effective, though they had helped her regain some strength. Shelley's depletion involved her entire being — body, mind, and spirit — and this whole being had not yet been addressed. Some portion of this depletion reflected the way her substance use had taxed her physical, emotional, and spiritual self. To a certain extent, Shelley was still withdrawing from these substances.

As we met weekly, Shelley revealed more and more about herself. Together we uncovered a background permeated with abuse. Shelley was the child of an alcoholic father and a neglecting, selfish mother. Her parents had separated when Shelley was quite young. Her brother, taking advantage of Shelley's vulnerability to release his own anger at his loveless existence, had abused her relentlessly, both sexually and physically. Shelley's efforts to get help from her mother and grandmother were ignored. Gradually, feeling hopeless, she had withdrawn from her own vitality and youthfulness, sacrificing her power, integrity, insight, and creativity in order to survive. In her late thirties she at last hit rock bottom. Emotionally and physically drained, she had nowhere to go but within. The drugs she used no longer excited her. She had become bored with the artificial stimulation that marked her daily life.

I don't know where Shelley found the courage to stop using, after so many years of habitual intoxication. The desire to have a child and to be a healthy mother, I think, was one of the most powerful pulls in the direction of her sobriety. The magnitude of her motivation to be a good mother became clearer and clearer as we worked together.

For the first year and a half that I worked with Shelley, we focused on building her physical strength. We knew that we had achieved success when Shelley could feel, for more than one day, that she was energetically capable of meeting her duties as a homemaker and mother. The approach that worked in building Shelley's physical strength consisted of Jin shin* treatments on a weekly basis, bi-monthly acupuncture** treatments, nutritional support, and weekly psychotherapy. While this may sound like an onslaught of therapy, it was, in fact, entirely appropriate and necessary. An extreme neglect and abuse of body, mind, and spirit requires extraordinary attention to bring balance. In our early therapeutic sessions, I was amazed as each week Shelley revealed another story in her history of abuse. What impressed me, along with her survival, was

---

*Jin shin is a Japanese approach to healing, calling for a subtle, intentional touch. See the Resources section of this book for further information.
**See the Resources section of this book for a description of the use of acupuncture in healing from trauma.

the extent of her repression. She had been violated repeatedly, physically, sexually, emotionally, and psychically, and yet she had great difficulty protesting. No one had attended to her pain, no one had believed her or observed her suffering, so, as a child, she had just stopped asking for help and eventually she negated her own needs. In our conversations, she discussed her abuse with incongruous dispassion.

Shelley discovered that much of her thinking and her beliefs were based on denial. First, there was the belief that her childhood was happy. When the truth began to emerge, and slowly grow larger, this denial became riddled with holes and through these holes came Shelley Cleveland's tears. The next layer of denial specifically involved Shelley's mother. Shelley had idolized her attractive mother whom she believed to be the sweetest, most delicate creature. But, as the wounded part of Shelley began to have a voice, we learned something quite different about Shelley's mom. Shelley herself stated that she could see how she had used drugs and alcohol to numb herself to her own suffering. As we proceeded, she felt more and more.

Recollections of neglect caused Shelley to feel endless grief. She mourned nightly for the suffering child within her and when she wasn't mourning, she raged. She raged at the mother with the pretty face and the steely heart who went out on dates and left her child with careless baby-sitters. She raged at the brother who tormented his sister without remorse. She wailed and raged against the baby-sitters who ignored her screams. All of this was extracted from the wall of Shelley's denial and that wall had been maintained by her passivity. Shelley Cleveland had come to believe in her failure. She had accepted the place where she felt her mother, father, and brother had put her, a place where the wounded must sit condemned to self-doubt, confusion, and fear.

Ultimately, after many years of work on herself, Shelley would come to see her brother with compassion, and even offer him resources from her own process. Shelley lovingly tended to both her father and her mother on their deathbeds, but her work on herself continued. Shelley was determined to remake herself from the rubble of family dysfunction.

Shelley had learned to identify with her abused self. She had worked hard to become unseen, someone who did not express herself, someone you would overlook. Yet, Shelley retained a spark of faith in her own potential. She looked as if she was lost in a forest of dullness, condemned to a listless emptiness, but she had the desire to explore beneath her fatigue, beneath her desperation. Desperation can be a platform for transformation. This was surely the case for Shelley. Though nutritional support and dietary change did prove useful, it was only in the context of deep, purposeful self-awareness, energetic balance, and expression that healing finally took place. And the healing that unfolded for Shelley Cleveland was a thorough one. Her commitment to herself proved to be extremely powerful, and she met every challenge to her integrated well–being like an authentic warrior of the spirit. After five years of therapy the Shelley who continued to meet with me weekly looked nothing like the fragile, tired woman I first met. Curly–haired, bright–eyed, vivacious, and resonant with vitality, Shelley Cleveland grew year by year into her womanly wisdom, ready to use what she had learned in the world. But this took a lot of work, and time.

Conscientiously releasing herself physically, psychically, and emotionally from addictive behaviors was crucial to the reclaiming of Shelley's true, essential self. The flatness of her affect was, in part, the result of the way the substances she had used had robbed her of her authentic responses. Cocaine used to get her up; marijuana and alcohol used to bring her down. Without these, for a while, she felt she was nothing, and this revealed itself in our sessions.

At first Shelley was reluctant to be expressive. The suffering of the child within her was too painful to be heard or seen, to be objectified or named. Our first entry into the hidden territory of the masked past was done while Shelley and I held hands. She clutched my fingers as she drew back the curtains she herself had protectively drawn over the truth. She peered into her own childhood as one would peer into a dank and swampy pool. I, too, was saddened and awed as I shared the poignant territory of her pain. Night after night, day after day, the young Shelley was victimized by her brother's overbearing physical invasion of her body and her spirit.

Thus she came to live in fear, to feel unprotected, to believe (as women often do who have been sexually abused by members of their own families) that there was no help, that the world is threatening and that she had nowhere to turn. It was from this feeling of hopeless abandonment that the drugs had provided her some relief. The identification of herself as one ignored and despicable stayed with her for a long time, even as her health improved and her appearance became striking, increasingly more vibrant and upright.

Extricating a damaged individual from the chasm of abuse is a long process, requiring patience and fortitude. The strenuousness of the work must be combined with a certain lightheartedness and faith in the future. These latter qualities are the very ones that the survivor usually lacks. Humor is hard to come by in abusive households. It is of crucial significance that the survivor develop some access to her own child nature and that she be encouraged to play joyfully, to have friendships, and to be loved by others. This is particularly true during the most difficult stretches of therapy, such as when the realm of abuse is being traversed therapeutically for the first time. Camaraderie and an enjoyment of simple things during these times becomes the greatest antidote to the bitterness of the past. In this case, Shelley's husband had the endurance to stick by her side as she went through dramatic shifts and swings in feelings and behavior. Her daughter was healthy and vivacious, giving Shelley a distraction from her depression and an opportunity to view her own childhood through the multi-colored prism of mothering.

Only when Shelley's physical strength increased so that she experienced weeks of feeling her own capacity could we introduce expressive modalities. Anger dominated powerfully over grief when Shelley became stronger. She was filled with a retaliating rage for her brother. We found ways to allow her body some healthy satisfaction for her urges. Shelley wanted to rip and tear and crumple. Tearing the pages out of telephone books was a ready solution. We also tried tearing up old sheets and rags. Shelley herself found great relief in throwing darts at a dart board, while making the sounds that released her chest and throat. We used drawing — drawing the family in all of its disarray, tearing the drawings, scattering them, stomping them, crumpling them. Shelley wrote letters to her brother and burned them. Shelley cut up photographs of her brother and threw darts at them. Both inside and outside of the sessions Shelley herself was remarkably creative in uncovering different ways to express the indwelling fury that had been held within her for most of her life. She was ready to explore anything that would heal her and allow her to feel her wholeness. Her enthusiasm was impressive and was an indicator to me of the extent of the power within her.

All of our expressive explorations were done with careful attention to Shelley's overall health and integration. Screams that she felt she had to release were let out slowly, with sounds coming from deep within the belly, so as not to damage the lining of the throat. Each release was explored energetically* and carefully titrated, so that the experience of big feeling was never overwhelming. I was a careful guide, tracking always the balance in Shelley's nature. She had accommodated the repressed trauma for so long — I didn't want to radically distort her energetic state. Shelley never left my studio office without feeling grounded and without first making sure that the feelings she had released and expressed were replaced with a reflection of her own healing vortex.

It took great courage for Shelley to go on this journey into the labyrinth of her mysterious life. She spent months at a time facing nonstop cycles of fear, anger, and grief. She discovered deeper and deeper layers of abuse. She was shocked to recall her mother's punitive and cruel cleansing of her genitals in the bath, contrasted sharply by her inability to discuss the details of sex. She felt great sadness recalling the loneliness of her childhood, the emptiness and neglect she had come to accept as her past.

---

*When I use the word "energetically" or "energetic" I mean "pertaining to energy," not, as they are often used, to mean "powerfully" or "powerful."

The Victory of Sleep

As she realized the magnitude of her fear, Shelley experienced a kind of paralysis regarding her activity in the world, her relational life and even her sleep patterns. This made her cling desperately to her husband as her security. When he was gone, she was certain that someone would abuse her. She relied on him to do the work she couldn't do and to be her backup if she had a week of sleepless nights. Sometimes, however, even her husband's presence in the house was insufficient to block her anguish. I was moved by her willingness to live with her terror and to use the skills we developed together to tap into her own resources for calm and understanding. During her sleepless nights, she used every creative, meditative, and expressive ally she had to get to the core of her unrest. Never giving up, and resorting to chemical supports only when there was no other choice, Shelley persistently searched deeper and deeper within herself for solutions to her sleep dilemma, and finally she found a combination of natural remedies and emotional and spiritual resources that allowed her to have consistent nights of normal, restful sleep. She expressed a great deal of pride, and I seconded it, in finally being able to sleep well, regardless of the events of her day-to-day life. This took years of work. The victory of sleep, being able to let herself rest, was not a small one for Shelley. It represented her ability to love, nurture, and support herself, in her own way, in her own time. The tools she assembled were of her own choosing. I made resources available, but she made her own decisions and, in the end, her choices worked for her.

Writing was an important tool for Shelley in her search for peace. She journaled, wrote letters to the individuals in the history of her abuse, to her own body, and to different aspects of herself. This writing did not always result in sleep, but it did give her a document to review and consider as she sought to make sense of her restlessness. She felt sometimes that there was a whole cast of characters within her and none of them could get along. She wrote:

> There's an enemy living within me that prevents me from everlasting happiness. It transmits messages throughout my

being, such as 'Don't let me sleep. Don't let me get too healthy. Don't let me meditate. Don't let me get conscious.' If I get real healthy, this enemy says, in my body, my mind, my spirit, then I might be successful and happy and productive and that's too threatening for me. Fear of success, fear of failure, I don't know which one is stronger.

Writing allowed Shelley the chance to reclaim the expression that she had been denied by fear. In a letter to her deceased mother, she writes:

Oh Mom, where were you when I needed you oh so much? You were out on the town with your date dancing, drinking, laughing, ya, getting your needs met. You looked so pretty when your date came to pick you up, all dressed up in your frilly dress, high heels, and beauty-shop hairdo. But before your date arrived you didn't look so happy, you said we could have popcorn and soda and then you were gone in a flash. My needs were never considered, much less met. I was stranded, so I spent the night alone. My brother stayed in his room except when he came out to beat me. Then I was even more alone. How could you have done that to your child? Well, you did it and I wonder if you ever felt guilty about leaving us so much? Probably not, since your priorities were all mixed up. Thank you mom, for abandoning me, for ignoring me, for withdrawing your love.

Her writing reveals how pervasive was Shelley's feeling of vulnerability:

I feel an open wound in my being. It is a cavern of pain and inside it I can see my mother yelling at me, giving me the silent treatment, going out on dates, leaving me alone, coming home from work in a bad mood, having no food in the house, getting yelled at, criticized. I want this gaping hole of a wound to close and heal but how can it? I feel queasy with so much painful emotional stuff coming up. It really hurts. I feel like the child inside me is dominating my being, she won't go back to her designated place. My adult needs to step in and take over, but she seems to be watching all this in the distance. She's numb and useless, her strength is taken aback from watching the little girl writhe in agony. The adult in me feels her heart going out to this rejected child, but the adult is paralyzed with horror as if looking at a gory scene.

Shelley sought the source of her fear by writing at night, from the center of the cyclone:

> I feel my brother's presence in the darkened room. He is sinister as he creeps towards me. He is very still as he looks me over with desire and repugnance. He is crouched on his hands and knees so that he can crawl out if he has to. I can see it so clearly, it is incredibly frightening. My brother is waiting for me to go to sleep so that he can get me and hurt me. But if I don't fall asleep, he won't touch me and I will be spared the pain of him ever hurting me again. I have to stay awake and that's so hard for me now, in the middle of the night.

Shelley Cleveland's process demonstrates the magnitude of the humiliation that the sexually abused individual endures. In one piece of writing she says:

> This anger is a pretty wonderful thing because I care for myself now. I have more self-respect and more love for myself since I've allowed myself to be angry. But the humiliation is something I can't seem to shake off. I have this urge to wash my hands, my body and especially my genitals. I feel so dirty and used but I know I can't wash myself enough because the filth, degradation and humiliation is in my mind and my mind cannot simply be washed. It has to be cleansed in a complex process. It takes time and I want to be rid of this humiliation NOW. Can my soul possibly help lift me out of this hard state? I want to be free of this ugly burden. I know one thing I must do and that is — I must allow myself to feel the sorrows of the past, for the first time as if they had just happened.

Perhaps the most empowering development for Shelley was the discovery that she could look at her pain, anger, humiliation, and sorrow and face it. She found that she did have the strength to confront and, in fact, embrace her emotions and to respond creatively and honestly. This full–bodied, whole–hearted acceptance of all her feelings and her ability to take responsibility for her own transformation was the key to Shelley's rebirth into worthiness and self–respect.

Shelley's history of substance abuse added a significant dimension to her healing. We had to wait through the necessary periods of detoxification, as the remnants of the drugs in her system slowly separated from her body, sometimes causing disorientation and confusion. We had to be patient together, giving this cleansing the time it needed and honoring whatever Shelley experienced as an aspect of her transformation. Whenever she wasn't lively or motivated, she tended to judge herself harshly. Each time she did this, I met her at this place of self–doubt with support, modeling a dependable commitment to Shelley and her process.

The Body Tells the Story

Shelley had lichensclerosis, a fungal infection of the vulva, as well as vitiligo, a random spotting of the skin due to a pigment imbalance. The vitiligo was an obvious component in Shelley's physical appearance and the lichensclerosis was a severe irritant. Both somatic conditions aroused Shelley's deep feelings of shame. The vitiligo gave Shelley the striking, unique appearance of a multicolored being, a creature of many shades, chameleon–like, changing with the seasons.

One of Shelley's most joyful experiences was when she and her husband, as a team, bathed her vulva to relieve the bothersome itching. This was in lieu of sexual intercourse when it was too painful for Shelley to bear. Her husband's willingness to open himself to his wife's psycho–physical– emotional realm was *his* act of courage. Don Cleveland claimed he had no personal familiarity with the territory of pain and stress that his wife was travelling in her life. On the contrary, Don came from what he described as a "happy home." He couldn't really comprehend Shelley's suffering, but he came to believe her and honor her process. Don participated with Shelley in ongoing therapy and was responsive to unconventional, expressive techniques despite his conventional background.

Facing the lichensclerosis was a major challenge for Shelley. She addressed it by engaging in a written dialogue with her vulva. I quote from this dialogue to demonstrate the level of Shelley's creativity and courage.

Vulva: I am inside a body that has been mistreated and without love. I am not happy living in this body. My owner doesn't like me and is confused about my existence.

Shelley: But you don't like yourself either so what am I to do to integrate us?

Vulva: You could start by being loving and tender towards me. You could show me respect and acknowledge my presence as the physical presence of your sexuality.

Shelley: And what can you do to help me? Can you stop the itching?

Vulva: No, I can't stop the itching until you love me. You must reject your mother's and brother's shameful influence on you. It was only a test to make you a stronger and wiser person anyway. Also you must use me for what I was created, for lovemaking. I need that love you see, for I get lonely without coupling with your loved one.

Shelley: So it's all up to me, is it? I have to do all the work and all the changing before you will give me any peace?

Vulva: Yes. For the constant itching is a catalyst for you to change. One of your lessons is to not give in to the itching. The scratching makes me feel very bad and it makes you feel weak and destructive. I'm ready to be your ally. We can work together and solve this dilemma but please, first accept me as part of you. Ultimately you must love me just the way I am. I've missed your love so much. I need you so much. Only you can heal me.

As Shelley developed her expressiveness, her whole life was touched. Her interactions with her relatives and friends changed. She began to crave relationships that would not deny her unique expression. She came to accept her feelings more and more and she wanted to share them with others.

Shelley's story is an ongoing one. It can't be concluded. She acknowledged, after her first year of therapy, that she had set out on a journey. She was committed to working with herself. She returned repeatedly to realizing that she had to stand on her own two feet. Gradually she became more and more outspoken, less fearful in groups, and more and more committed to loving herself. Everyone I've met who has been sexually abused must confront their passivity. For Shelley, passivity had become a shelter. It allowed her to avoid the consequences of being heard and noticed. Slowly she shed layer after layer of passivity; she risked more in conversations; she dared to be herself.

Our therapeutic relationship reached a noticeable turning point one day in a group session when Shelley could not resolve her feelings about her mother. Her hatred, despair, and anger were locked in place and would not budge. Solo movement work and supportive group movement did not make a crack in the logjam. As the time approached to conclude the session, I looked at Shelley's confused face and said, "I'm sorry, but I can't bring this to a healing conclusion right now." Shelley's reply revealed how far she had come in her own development. "I guess I have to accept that this is the way it is right now and I just can't make it better immediately."

As we heal from sexual abuse, we learn patience and trust in a process that always seems to have its own energetic schedule. One of our most compassionate acts is the choice for self acceptance before we are "perfect". Shelley had always hoped that someone would save her from the horror of her experience. She wanted a formula for healing. She wanted a map, a route to regeneration. But on the day when neither I nor the group she was a part of could make her better, Shelley stepped into a reality she could never have faced before. This admission of responsibility was an empowerment for Shelley Cleveland — one of many.

Eventually Shelley's health improved so much, she became a resource for others seeking drug–free self–healing. She returned to her job as a Special Education teacher and began to tutor other children, in addition. Her vibrant face and form were so compelling, no one really noticed her remarkably multicolored skin. She remains in therapy, going deeper inside herself and simultaneously expanding into the world around her. Her relationship with her husband thrives as he increases his sensitivity to her process and her sexuality, and she allows herself to receive more and more of his love and support.

Our work together succeeds, I believe, because of three significant factors:

1. Shelley's tireless devotion to healing and her willingness to explore every resource she can access.

2. The bond of trust we built together. Shelley's felt sense of my support offset the excruciating experience of her mother's abandonment.

3. The implementation of expressive mediums (writing and movement, in particular), which Shelley used authentically in her work with me, on her own, and in group therapy.

In terms of her struggle to overcome the effect of her long involvement with addictive substances, Shelley showed remarkable courage and determination. In her committed way, she devoted herself to using every healthy means possible to cleanse her system of the toxicity she had once so eagerly imbibed. Her zealousness resulted in increasing vitality, substantiating for her the value of her own chosen approach.

Instead of disliking her body for the way it showed her the depth of her pain, she began to appreciate, accept, and make space for the symptomology that revealed her body's story. Eventually, these symptoms decreased and she could admit that she was becoming healthier and healthier.

But this was not easily done and I'm not at all sure that Shelley acknowledged her own courage and creativity *while* she was feeling listless, afflicted by herpes or a maddening sugar craving. It was only later, when only one or two symptoms remained, that she could see how far she had come somatically as well as psychically and emotionally.

There is still more to be done. Shelley has difficulty believing in herself professionally and she still clings to her patterns of underachievement to hide her power. But she is no longer involved in substance use, she greets the challenges of her life with enthusiasm, she has real intimacy, including vital sexuality, with her husband, and she is more appropriately open to other people, men and women, than ever before in her life. She is a model of authentic healing — a woman moving into her mature years with vigor and increasing strength. I feel a bond of true sisterhood with her because together we have stopped the lineage of abuse in her life.

Masculinity and Overwhelming Emotion
The Story of Luke Overhill

Located on the picturesque back roads of rural mid–America, Luke Overhill's home contained all the seeds of alcoholism and abuse necessary to sprout severe traumatic response. His mother and father had allowed their relationship to become an endlessly stratified geology of non-communication and alienation. The cruel, vast distance that described the unresolved territory of their relational problems inevitably impacted and even defined the way their children were raised. The two boys Abe and Daisy had once yearned for when they were young and eager for family were shoved into the corners of life by the tension between mom and dad. Alcohol was the solvent Abe and Daisy chose to find relief from their despair. Without resources and without knowing how to define their needs, Abe and Daisy were caught in a doomed–to–failure attempt to guide their children through a life that they themselves could not handle.

Luke spent most of his time out of doors. He found solace in the woods and with the animals. In his fantasies, he called the animals his true family and made up stories of how he lived with them. He burrowed into the ground with the badgers and swam under water with the beavers. He soared in the skies with the eagles he loved best of all and he called the earth itself his mother, for she could hold him in his grief when he lay down upon her body. Luke could run for hours, swirling and twirling alone in the shelter of the trees or ride his bike down the rural avenues, going further and further away from his own sense of homelessness. Emotion ruled his life in a way that was natural for children. His body, particularly his developing musculature, became the ready carrier for his feeling.

Luke's house was not his home. He was frightened of his mother. Occasionally he sensed his father's concern for him, but this always produced a negative reaction from his mother, so even that comfort was forbidden. Lonely, he tried to justify his solitude by a sense of mystical uniqueness, thereby explaining the distance between him and everyone else, though his explanation offered only superficial satisfaction. It did not give him the companionship for which he secretly longed. His feelings of confusion and isolation could not so easily find an outlet as did his desire to run and spin. Here, emotion imploded and distorted itself as a youngster sought inwardly for an explanation that he had no tools, other than imagination, to find.

When he became a teenager, Luke developed an obsessive attraction to the motorcycle gangs that ran the back roads of his town with their nasty show of authority. Their garb and their demeanor had a magical power over him, and soon this became the power of desire. He wanted to look like them, walk like them, and feel the way he fantasized they felt. Most of all, he wanted to ride with them, but he knew that was impossible. His parents would reject him completely if he in any way revealed his passion for the brutal, for the wild, and for what was obviously rebellious. This emotion imploded, was held at bay until a moment Luke yearned for, the moment of his emancipation.

After he graduated high school, Luke decided to leave home. This was acceptable since he had fulfilled Abe and Daisy's expectations and they longed to be free of the responsibilities that prevented them from being fully immersed in their lives of alcohol, cigarettes, and television. Their sadness hung in the lined crevices of their faces. The bags under their eyes held the grief they could no longer feel. At night, drunk and lost, they would batter one another with words, and thereby vent the rage and blame that were their only explanation for unfulfilled dreams and lost hopes. They wanted to be left to do this final flailing, and be done with it, to die of the only "treasures" they knew, the substances of their escape. Luke and his brother had long listened to these nightly repetitions, which filled them with inexpressible grief, rage, despair, and guilt. Their feeling of being trapped in hell with their parents had long been bottled up inside them, a secret fury and longing to escape that they didn't share with anyone, not even each other.

It would take many years of experience and healing for these brothers to speak to one another of their early life together. Survival demanded alienation, isolation, and containment, but eventually they would connect and reflect on this troubled formative time and grieve together. So Luke left home, and within a few years, his younger brother, Teddy, left home too. The two boys had survived through separation. Their environment had made them apparently inarticulate, expressionless. Abe and Daisy were finally alone with each other and their addictions, and so the house filled with smoke and vituperation. Gone were the sounds of little boys tinkering and telling their small stories of friendships and fights. Gone were the voices of young, new life, beginnings and promises, questions and hopes. At last, Abe and Daisy surrendered to the bitter emptiness they had chosen, and the boys went out to find out if life had meaning or not.

Luke moved West, and there he found another group of bikers, looking and acting remarkably like the gang at home. Free at last to follow his own inclination, he joined them and saved his money for a bike to ride the beautiful tree–lined byways of the heartlands of America, flying around among his nature friends, the trees, the eagles, the rivers, and the creatures that scurry through the woods. But there was something here he hadn't anticipated — the violence and lust of these men toward each other. On one road trip, the leader of the group picked Luke as his sexual release. Drunk on cheap beer, sweaty from the long, dirty ride, he bedded down with sandy–haired, wide–eyed and passive Luke, who was never asked if he wished to explore his manliness or his sexuality in this particular way. In the morning, the older man forgot Luke, and the group of men went their own ways, with casual plans to reconnect. Luke got on his bike and went back to town, where he worked for the Farm Bureau as general gopher, running out to the farms in the Farm Bureau truck to get information, deliver packages, and keep track of Farm Bureau regulations — the orders and controls that the Bureau enforced.

After that incident, Luke never said anything about it, but he also never went back to the bikers. He sold his bike, wanting to hide all evidence of his involvement. He became even more isolated from people and carried within himself a shame he could not articulate or even identify. At night, though, he had strange dreams and would wake in an acrid sweat that soaked his sheets. His memories would become entangled then — and he was lost in a bizarre but unforgettable sense of his father sucking on his penis. He thought for sure he was going crazy, this couldn't be true, why was he dreaming it? And he would run into the fields for comfort, laying his body down on the moist ground as he did as a youngster, and letting the sounds of the animals busy about their survival come into his distressed mind. But he would never cry, rather he would sink into a kind of trance where only the smells and the sounds of nature were present and all memories of Abe or Daisy or Teddy or the bikers were gone. If upon rising from his supine meditations he would see a bird flying, he would say to himself that this was a good omen and that he was blessed by the birds and would return one day to their land from whence he truly came.

When he was 25, Luke met Melinda and they liked each other. She was sweet–faced, chubby, simple, and sincere. Melinda too was strongly drawn to nature, and, importantly for Luke, she had a great love of bird watching. She wanted to grow her own food, and she wanted to have children. They moved in together, and eventually they married. Sharing his bed with Melinda, Luke could not hide the recurring night sweats, the longing to run out of the house, and the difficulty he had in maintaining any kind of intimacy. Whenever he and Melinda reached a place of difficulty, Luke just wanted to leave; he couldn't stay to work through things, and he couldn't bear to be told how he was letting Melinda down. At work, he did well and was promoted, but whenever there was any criticism, Luke couldn't stay to hear it, and thus, ironically, his running away actually held him back, kept him from advancing to a management position, though he knew he was always being considered for that.

Abuse Interferes with Intimacy: How to Break the Vicious Cycle?

Melinda wanted to have children, but Luke was terribly frightened of the responsibility. Something haunted him. He found himself not wanting to sleep with Melinda, and he found himself unable to talk with her about his distance. The degree of closeness she wanted sent waves of terror through Luke's body, and all he could think of was immersion in the world of nature, of his desire to be lost in the woods, and to return to his true family, the family of the animals. Secretly, he began to believe in this return more and more, to dwell on it and to hold to its promise, the way a small child holds a teddy bear or a blanket. He became constantly more preoccupied, lost in his fantasies of escape, but mild, almost passive, unresponsive to Melinda's inquiries, until she was furious with frustration and confusion. Melinda feared for their marriage. Luckily she had a strong sense of self and could speak up honestly and clearly. Melinda suggested that Luke get help, and because he desperately wanted to maintain the love he had with his wife, the first true relationship he had ever known, Luke went into therapy.

At this juncture, Luke's being was layered with so many unexpressed feelings, almost all flowing out of traumatic episodes, that emotion had reached the boiling–over point. He had reverted to the mystical coping mechanisms that had so successfully rescued him in the past. His traumatized nervous system was burdened with more unresolved experience than he could handle. It was with desperation that he once more became enmeshed with the fabrications that had previously been his saving grace. His unique and resplendent creativity was the super hero for the abandoned child within him. How could I help him find his way through the sticky and coagulated mud of unresolved trauma to an understanding of himself, where he had come from, who he was, and where he wanted to go? Our starting point was that he wanted to find a way to continue with his wife. This made him willing to open more to himself, and to risk doing something new.

When I first started working with him, all Luke wanted to do was to tell me about his forays into the woods and the visions he had there. He didn't want to talk about the difficulty in his relationship or his struggles with intimacy. He wanted to talk about his escape from his relationship. What I sensed in his obsession was an unresolved creative instinct that had never found a community in which to exist. My hypotheses came from the combined awarenesses of my own life as a survivor of sexual abuse and as an artist, and my memories of my childhood, which Luke stimulated. Something about Luke reminded me of how I felt as an adolescent, lost in fictional scenarios that, while they were clearly escapes, were also comforting coping mechanisms. Eventually my visions became stories and poems that were periodically validated by a teacher or a friend, allowing me to feel heard and appreciated. I never mentioned this to Luke, but I used these thoughts. Taking a chance, I decided to act on what I felt and perceived, a similarity between Luke's experience and mine that resonated with me.

I suggested to Luke that he tell his nature tales into a tape recorder, or perhaps type them on a computer, that he listen to them, read them, and illustrate them with photographs of nature taken at the very places where he loved to hide. I also encouraged him to share his stories and his photographs with Melinda and some other friends. I suggested that he bring his secret world into the world of the living and that what was hidden become a cause for enjoyment and not a place he retreated to out of despair.

Luke was intrigued by my ideas, they were unlike anything he had ever heard. Since he loved to take pictures, he set off with his camera, full of curiosity for this new option I had presented. But he came back with pictures of devastation. He didn't know why, but he felt irretrievably drawn to photographing not the places in nature that were intact and radiant, but the damaged places — the rot and putrefaction, the burned and charred land, the ravaged places where man had mercilessly and disrespectfully torn into the environment for his own greed. His subjects became the dams flooding over pristine wilderness, the roads hacked into elegant mountainsides, the ski resorts forced onto raw high mountain land, the debris cast thoughtlessly by the hordes of people who thought the land was their living room and not the temple of the Goddess Nature. The grief and rage Luke felt when he showed me the photos was impossible to suppress and he found himself sobbing and frightened. This was not the outcome either of us had anticipated, but indeed it brought us closer to Luke's dilemma.

Overwhelming Emotion

As I tried gently to hold a place of safety for Luke, who sobbed beyond his own understanding, he sank into the nightmarish place that he hid from his wife Melinda and which made him feel so ashamed. The sweat poured out of him, heat was followed by chills and shaking, as the photos lay around him, and Luke was very confused. I slowed him down by giving his emotion enough space so that it did not have to become chaos. I did not encourage him to intensify his feeling through sound, or any other emotive act. Rather I sought a way to witness with him the authentic feeling arising in him. If crying or sobbing emerged, I let it be, but I said nothing to intensify it. My support was held within my silence and my patience, a willingness to let the truth have its space. I wanted to give Luke an opportunity to know what was happening, and to feel that he could manage this outpouring without being overwhelmed by it. So much in Luke's life had been overwhelming. And he had been the passive victim, the helpless grain of sand in the face of the uncontrollable wave. He needed another option now. You might say that the subject of our meeting at this time was the pattern of being overwhelmed, rather than the contextual issues of sexual abuse or emotional abuse or family of origin dysfunction.

The slowing down worked. Little by little Luke began to feel that he was in the center of this release rather than at the bottom of it. We breathed and stepped back together. Luke could feel that I was with him and that I could be trusted to oversee this pattern of becoming overwhelmed by his feeling. This in and of itself had been part of what drove him away from Melinda and made it difficult for him to believe that resolution was an option. His emotions, despite his great effort to eliminate them, had in fact accumulated to become so overwhelming that his whole life was dominated and restricted by them.

When Luke let his emotions become present during our time together, he made a great deal of healing possible. He may have felt that he was out of control, but, in fact, he was permitting a quality of his experience and an aspect of himself that had always been a secret to show up and be seen. The pattern of hiding deep feeling and the pattern of feeling shame in front of others for having feelings was broken *for the first time in his life*. Even without dealing with the content behind Luke's emotional release, he and I together found a new way of allowing him to experience emotion and titrate* the overwhelming aspects of it. The technique was astoundingly simple: slowing down without repressing, and with a calm awareness. I wanted very much for us to mark this event as important, and as a new perspective applicable for his future.

It wasn't long after this that Luke was able to tell me of his experience with the bike gang leader and of his nightmarish memories of his father. Just the telling was enough for the time being. I didn't try to interpret these experiences or to link them. I just allowed these moments, which were part of Luke's life, to be spoken for the first time, to be known, and for the pain surrounding them to be recognized, and, in fact, honored. This intricate process of allowing, feeling, and slowing it, pacing it; of not judging or interpreting, of not blaming or naming, but of just witnessing was clearly and unmistakably both necessary and transformative. The look of calm surprise, delight, and comprehension on Luke's face when he acknowledged the benefits of this pacing was the indicator I looked for to know that this approach was correct for him.

It soon became clear to me that Luke wanted desperately to please me. He was perplexed because his desire to be pleasing to me was stronger than his desire to avoid his own overwhelming emotion; and pleasing me meant, little by little, allowing emotion to be part of his life. Thus, our relationship itself provided a vehicle for shifting this terrible imbalance that Luke suffered from — an imbalance caused by an enormous repression and secrecy. But what I was determined to reveal to him was that I simply represented a part of

---

*Titrate: This word is used here in the sense of allowing feelings to be felt in increments rather than in doses too large to be integrated. In this sense you might say that the opposite of titration is catharsis. Titration is intended to produce integration and awareness. Feelings become graspable and there is enough space and solitude around the titrated experience to accrue understanding and completion. The client meets his/her own experience of release from his/her own center. Peter Levine is the originator of this term in this context, and I want to acknowledge his contribution, not only by suggesting the word, but also by suggesting all the word implies in the process of healing trauma.

himself that he longed to meet — the part that accepted, acknowledged, even applauded, his feelings. The most frightening feelings
of Luke's life were stuffed in a bag and hidden from the world,
where they exploded in the secrecy of a solitude witnessed only by
a natural world that, while it could contain Luke's secrets, could
not always respond to them. The challenge Luke faced was the challenge of being a powerfully feeling human being, carrying the scars
of abuse and neglect, and remaining in relationship with me, while
sharing and expressing that feeling directly. My job was to find ways
to modulate the release of that feeling so that it would not be so
overwhelming. The very fact that Luke and I could work so smoothly together was evidence of his readiness to bring his feelings and
his experience into the world of people — to build for himself a
community of support.

All survivors of abuse carry this burden of overwhelming emotion. The nature of abuse is that it places a weight too large for anyone to bear on the victim — an overload of experience and feeling
which the human nervous system cannot integrate all at once. For
the survivor of abuse, space, enough space to feel and integrate, is
one of the antidotes to the terror of overwhelming emotion. The
knowledge, hard to accept, often initially resisted, that there is
enough time and space and patience for the survivor to feel and
integrate all there is to feel and integrate is a simple but magnani-
mous healer. In the unconditionally accepting environment of pure
time and space, the survivor comes into a gentle, sometimes serene,
power. Witnessed by caring, accepting eyes, the integration necessary for each traumatized being can happen gracefully, resembling
the way a dancer finds completion in good choreography.

As Luke began to tell me the stories of his childhood and his adolescence, his memories, dreams, and fears, I simply gave him the
space to feel while he spoke, to slowly, often with eyes closed, allow
the truthfulness of his experience to be known by him, and to be
heard and accepted by me. I quietly highlighted the moments of
charged feeling, asking him to pause sometimes when he wanted
to rush on. I listened, attuned to him, and that is how I served him.

Sometimes I would ask a question or make a comment while Luke spoke, but those questions and comments were always from within an energetic environment that totally accepted Luke and his telling, and that completely supported him, was completely for him, and sought no other motive, no other purpose. Thus the years and years of being ignored by his mother and father, the years and years of being discounted and shoved into the corner of life, were offset by being heard and believed.

It surprised him at first — how certain I was that he had been hurt. Long before we broached the question of the image of his father sucking on his little boy penis, long before we looked at the trauma Luke experienced when he was raped by the bike gang leader, long before we looked at any suggestion of any kind of sexual abuse, I made it clear to Luke that in my estimation the stories he told of his childhood were stories of neglect, and within that neglect, an unquestionable abuse occurred. I also let him know that his parents' alcoholic rages were horribly abusive experiences for Luke. To watch the people he depended upon for nurturance and support violate each other, verbally and physically, was an unbearable torment. The witnessing of these scenes, hearing his parents thrashing at each other in the night, seeing his mother's bruised arms and hearing her vituperative outbursts, seeing the ugly shadow side of both his parents rise up and strike, aroused in Luke a terror that haunted him. And that terror usurped the place in him that should have been occupied by a sense of safety and security, a sense of trust and well–being. Safety, security, trust, and well–being — these were words that had little meaning for Luke. The foundation of ego and self–esteem that these words represent when they are truly experienced by a child had not been built in this genuine, sensitive young man, so full of yearning and rage. My clarity about his suffering was a mirror he had *never* seen. As he looked into it, he began to believe the image he saw, and that image allowed his experience to make sense to him in a new way.

I wanted to find a way to bring together the split parts of Luke — the Luke who wandered, who ran from relational maturation into the only place where he knew freedom and felt the safety to be and feel, and the Luke who wanted to be close to another human being, to feel a completion in contact with another. I wanted to find some way to mend this splitting in Luke BEFORE we explored the subject of sexual abuse. If these abuses had occurred, they had occurred when he was too fractured to know what to do about them. To renegotiate these traumas, the fractures had to be repaired to some extent so that Luke could be a container for his own overwhelming emotion, so that feeling could have time and space to be, and so that the appropriate and natural responses to those abuses could arise and be known, simply, slowly, and purely, in a safe, spacious environment.

This integration of the fractured parts of Luke took a long time. In the meantime, we built a relationship based on trust, truthfulness, and interaction. Not all of this time was spent talking about trauma. We also talked about poetry, about things we had read in the newspaper or things we had seen. We talked about jobs and bosses and exchanges between employees, about cars and rent, about food and health. We found a way that we could talk together that created a relational net, so that we could sustain long pauses, long silences, long still moments when integration was occurring, when the nervous system and the emotional structure of Luke's being shifted, delicately rearranging itself, adjusting to his new being.

Luke softened a great deal in the years we worked together. He accepted other people more as he accepted himself more — the bad drivers on the freeway, parents who were short with their children, people who didn't pay their bills on time — the people he used to condemn furiously. And he ran away from Melinda less and less. He stayed more and more when they had a disagreement, and if he had to leave, he told her why, and where he was going. Sometimes he could even tell her when he would be back.

When his relationship with Melinda had stability, and when Luke had been promoted in his job to a position he really liked, when life had a rhythm for him that he found both comfortable and yet stimulating and vital, then we approached his issues of sexual abuse.

In the context of his strong sense of self, these issues could be tracked and witnessed and the inroads they had made into Luke's psyche could be seen as his personal map of devastation. Then, clearly, we could see why the photos of violated nature had aroused such a strong release in Luke. These were indeed pictures of himself, the visual depiction of his internal reality. Thus did he feel — like a raped earth, and his tears were for himself, an outburst of compassion and grief.

By joining forces with Luke, and by inviting his partner and friends into the process of reconstruction, healing seemed to both of us to be inevitable. By working together slowly and deeply, gently, carefully and with great awareness, we came eventually to a time when Luke could handle his recurring moments of emotional inundation on his own. He came to a place where the feelings he used to run from became a resource and he could directly prepare for himself a space into which he could welcome his feelings, and then share them with those close to him.

Regaining the power and energy of his own feeling experience made Luke smile. His return to a fully–feeling state brought with it a delight in living that restored to this gentle, caring, and passionate man the ability to be actively engaged in life in a creative and meaningful way. He could grieve for his parents who traded their vitality for substances, and he could celebrate his difference from them. He genuinely acknowledged that he had said yes to life, over and over again, and he joined Melinda in a desire to have children, because he had successfully given birth to himself.

In my work with Luke, I often returned to some of the crucial interventions that supported him and provided the options for him to contain successfully, without repression, his overwhelming emotion. These were:

1. Giving him enough room to feel, and encouraging him to express feeling slowly and authentically.

2. Reminding Luke of his creative and human resources — his skills at photography *and* communication, his wife and the friends who loved him. These people, unlike his mother and father, wanted to know about Luke's unique experience. Connecting with his truly supportive community was a great discovery for Luke. He

needed to be reminded of this resource. It was still so new for him.

3. Pointing Luke in the direction of creative expression was one of my most important interventions. A talented photographer, storyteller, naturalist, and writer, Luke tended to forget his artist self, but when reminded and encouraged, he turned to that part of his identity warmly and with excitement. Once again, this was new. In his early development, no one had noticed how talented he was. But now, with just gentle and repeated reminders, he was refreshed and rejuvenated by his artistry. Avenues of expression were avenues of release, and release did not allow his emotion to stagnate and overwhelm him.

4. Acknowledging that emotion deserves and demands expression and release is new self-care information for everyone. Once we had to learn to brush our teeth regularly, later we learned to floss them. We had to learn about sunscreen to protect our skin, and the foods we could eat to be healthier. But very few of us learned about emotional and spiritual care, and the value of releasing and allowing feeling rather than accumulating it. Therapy can fulfill the function of awakening this habit, without which we find ourselves all too often on the brink of depression, violence, self-abuse, and addictions. This is the path of overwhelming emotion, but it can be changed. I believe emotion is a sign of health — the more, the better, but only if it can be channeled, expressed, and appreciated. Expressive and holistic therapy honors this part of selfhood and knows that artistry and deep feeling walk hand in hand.

The Role of Confrontation in Healing From Abuse

The Story of Jeanette Bailey

Jeanette Bailey is pleasant and mature, a woman in her early 50s, the mother of three grown children. She was married for 25 years to Dick Bailey, a successful engineer who was always too busy to get very involved at home. Jeanette had taken a momentously independent step by legally separating from Dick when the children were out of the roost. Breaking the "normal" mold of her contemporaries, Jeanette acted, probably for the first time in her life, for herself alone. Prior to her marriage she had been ruled by the heavy hand of her conservative and severe mother. With her mother dead, her children secure in their own worlds, and finally free of Dick's abusive temper, Jeanette surveyed her life with her own eyes.

It was a surprising landscape for someone who, to all appearances, was a simple, gentle, and kindly figure. Despite the trappings of suburban housewifery with its patina of contentment, the convolutions of Jeanette's past were intricately labyrinthine. The twine had been twisted and knotted repeatedly in the weaving of her life, so much so that Jeanette was almost strangled in the swirl of lies and betrayal interwoven throughout her "proper" upbringing and her marriage to a minister's son.

Nothing is what it appears to be: that was the phrase that underscored Jeanette's story. Confusion seemed to have been born with her. The woman she thought to be her mother was not her mother. The man she assumed was her father was not her father, and the girl she thought was her sister was not her sister. One truth, however, was unchallenged — Jeanette's twin brother Joe was truly her twin brother and the tragedy which was his life was their shared tragedy — a story of thorough abandonment. And Joe's sudden death was the addict's tale, one all too common in this country strewn with the shards of spirits torn by family lies; spirits left to suffer in bodies that lie in the arms of substance abuse — a cruel, uncaring mother.

Jeanette, unlike her brother who died of alcoholism, was someone who seemed to cope amazingly well. She was truly a good Christian, a woman of caring. Perhaps her smile was her addiction — her bright eyes shining no matter what distortion crossed her path. This capacity to cope was not entirely a lie, though it was Jeanette's mask over her pain. In truth, she had a good heart, and the sweetness she offered to others did indeed return to her.

Jeanette was the only one in her family with the courage to break the chain of abuse, dysfunction, abandonment, denial, and addiction. After her twin brother's death, Jeanette could no longer hold within her body the lie of their origins. With courage drawn from a deep well of spiritual waters, Jeanette set out to uncover a truth she had long suspected.

Jeanette and Joe grew up in a large stone house in the Midwest. The people they called "Mother" and "Father" were highly respected in their churchgoing, middle class community. Cleanliness, good manners, Christianity, and propriety were requirements in their household. Mother, in particular, was regarded as an embodiment of the good Samaritan, opening the doors of her impressive home to needy, white Christian boys and girls who had been left, for any number of reasons, without family. So, the house was always full of young people, and while Jeanette and Joe were raised to believe they were Mother and Father's children, they were frequently treated as less important than the foster residents. They were encouraged to sacrifice their rooms for new recruits or to "share" their clothes with more needy householders.

Jeanette, in particular, felt Mother's rejection. Nothing she did was ever good enough. Especially after Father's death, Jeanette felt desperately, though quietly, lonely. It would have been difficult to explain this isolation, given her crowded surroundings, but the truth was Jeanette grew up feeling abandoned.

It was many years before this feeling of abandonment found resolution in the discovery of her true history. Long after the merciless beating Jeanette received at Mother's hands, long after the abuse and sexual taunting she tolerated without protection from the boys at school, Jeanette decided to seriously address the unavoidable sense she had that her Mother was not her real mother. Freed of the watchful eye of her Mother and the continuous onslaught of angry demands from her husband; freed of the necessary needs of her children, Jeanette could at last be with Jeanette. And honoring her own self led her to relentless questioning and research, which resulted in the discovery that she had been an adopted child, and the woman she was told was her sister and with whom she shared a home, was actually her mother. This was shocking enough, but there was more to the mystery. Who was her father and where was he?

Daring to defy the history of repression in which she had been steeped, Jeanette set out on a course that no one else in her family had taken, awakening yet more complication, but nevertheless creating order in her mind. She had a passion for truth, and all the avoidance of truth that surrounded her had served only to increase her passion. Jeanette decided to contact her true father, a man she'd never seen. Her first foray into contact, once she located her father, was met with rejection. He didn't respond to her letters and phone calls, even when they were announcements of her brother's imminent death. After Joe's passing, Jeanette determined she would find her father, and she organized a plan to travel 800 miles just to set her eyes on the man she longed to call "Daddy."

Jeanette was born during World War II. Her parents were young people brought together suddenly and unexpectedly, flirting with adulthood and sex, the way young people have played for centuries. The result of their encounter with exploration and innocence was conception. The war forced Jeanette's father into service, and Jeanette's mother only discovered her pregnancy at six months. Lily Ann, Jeanette's mother, was herself the result of a tragic family condition, so hidden all the details were lost. Because of these unrevealed circumstances, Lily Ann lived in the foster home run by Emma Sewickley rather than her birth parents' home. It was into the Sewickley home that the twins borne by Lily Ann were delivered and raised — Jeanette and Joe. So Jeanette was raised as her mother's sister, and the woman who played the role of mother for both of them, Mother Sewickley, ran her household with an iron hand. As matriarch in a home for foster children, she used the opportunity to rule as Queen, making law, imposing rules of conduct and morality, threatening expulsion and cruelty at any hint of violation of her God–fearing code.

In Mother Sewickley's home, Jeanette said, "It was mother's way or the highway." For a brief time Jeanette could remember being pampered and adored, snuggling under the covers with "daddy," who was Father Sewickley. But then Father Sewickley died, and Mother's cruel, controlling streak intensified. Jeanette learned to obey, but the rules were demanding and without explanation, and the house was full of foster children. If one of the boys asked her to stroke his penis, what was the right thing to do? No one ever said a word about sex. It was a mystery within a mystery, avoided to the point of total deception. And if a boy followed Jeanette home from school and caressed her breasts in an alleyway, was it his fault? or hers? Where did responsibility truly rest? Once, after going to a dance with a boy, Jeanette was horribly beaten by Mother Sewickley. Her legs were covered with welts and she had difficulty walking upstairs. Once, after Joe playfully tripped her, he was sentenced to isolation in a windowless room for a week. And Mother Sewickley was regarded as an exemplary figure; she was named Mother of the Year. Her home full of foster children was considered a model of Christian service.

Jeanette remembers the threats of the boys at school, the feeling of being unprotected, and giving in, always giving in, accepting that she had no advocate, no support. Why not give in? Who would defend her anyway? And what was right, what was wrong? Robbed of her sense of self, subjected to the rule of totalitarian, cruel authority, it was difficult to know the intention and meaning of attack. Abuse brought with it confusion and confusion generated passivity. And always in the back of her mind, especially when she needed comfort, Jeanette treasured the memory of daddy, Father Sewickley, and his protective presence, the man who was no longer there, except in her recollections, which brought smiles to cover up tears.

When Dick Bailey proposed marriage, Jeanette felt her deepest prayer had been fulfilled. While she loved Dick, she admired his father even more. This patient man honored Jeanette in a way she had never known. She felt safe with Dick's father — protected. She relished this feeling. It was almost intoxicating. She couldn't remember having it since Father Sewickley died, and she longed for it, craved it, desperately. In fact, experiencing this safety made Jeanette painfully aware of how unsafe she had felt most of her life. Jeanette became so attached to the protective aura that seemed to surround her bond with the Bailey family that she gave up college for marriage without a second thought. It never occurred to her to ask for both — surely a sacrifice was required for the joy of being in the Bailey family.

Because of this feeling of sanctuary and completion engendered primarily by the devoted behavior of Dick Bailey's father, Jeanette was shocked and overwhelmed when she first experienced her husband's abusive temper. But her denial mechanisms turned on automatically and remained in operation for almost twenty–five years. Until their marriage was over, Jeanette never revealed how Dick verbally tormented her, physically attacked her, threatened her life, and sexually used her. For as long as her three children remained at home, Jeanette hid her experience as best she could, never admitting her despair to anyone, hiding her grief deep inside her body. Within the ample folds of her hips and arms, she kept the feelings waiting until the children were grown and safely on to their own lives. Then she sued for divorce.

And when she walked away from the lie of her marriage to Dick Bailey, Jeanette was a woman finally able to articulate her own story. This possibility had been masked for her entire life. One year after the divorce, her brother died of alcoholism, but not before the truth of their parentage was revealed and Jeanette had the address of her true father.

The Confrontation

What is the role of confrontation with a parent or abuser in the healing process? Is there a time when confrontation is recommended or even beneficial? What are the consequences of confrontation? What are the benefits? The process of Jeanette Bailey's confrontation of her father, Stuart Langerman, explores many of these questions, and her story provides a context within which the advisability of confrontation can be evaluated.

After all her years of passivity and hiding, confronting her true father with his abandonment of his children was a demonstration of Jeanette's courage and spirit, long suppressed. It followed naturally on the heels of her separation from her husband, and the very naturalness of this process is the testimony to its rightness. The timing is also a function of the death of her brother Joe, who died longing to see his true father. What was stunning about Jeanette's form of action was the loving context in which it occurred. Despite countless acts of abuse she had experienced, oftentimes in the name of "religion," Jeanette remained a spiritual being. Behind her passivity was the kindness, tolerance, and compassion never practiced by any of her abusers, but nonetheless alive in her. And she herself felt the value of her own loving kindness as she practiced it.

In the years I have been working with survivors of sexual abuse, I have been struck by the persistence of the human spirit to remain compassionate despite abuse. I am amazed and humbled by the way women who have been tormented and sometimes tortured by their mothers and fathers become loving and respectful mothers themselves. I have been awestruck by the way in which men who have been cruelly wounded by their mothers and fathers become supportive and healing partners. This human demonstration of commitment to loving kindness inspires me more than tales of saints because it's this natural appearance of our divinity in the way we live our lives which is, from my perspective, the source of authentic hope. The story of Jeanette's confrontation with Stuart Langerman illustrates and provides a model of compassionate renegotiation.

Jeanette thought, reflected, meditated, and prayed for a long time after Joe's death. His inability to break the chains of addiction was directly related to the despair he felt about feeling the love of his true birth father. In his last years he was able to be with and speak to his birth mother, the woman he had always thought of as his much older sister. This mom, who reached out to him finally, revealed the location of Stuart Langerman. But his father persisted in his abandonment and rejection, never answering Jeanette and Joe's pleas for contact. So, without knowing either the touch or sight of the man who fathered him, Joe died of his own toxicity, his imploded grief and despair.

Still grieving the loss of her twin brother, Jeanette determined to end the lineage of lies, betrayal, deception, and secrets that had been the pattern of her life since birth. The courage and confidence she generated at this moment mirrored the surge of empowerment she felt when she separated from her husband, saying, "No more!" to his abuse of her. Similarly, now she said, clearly, "No more" to her birth father's attempts to avoid his spiritual and emotional responsibility to his children. Without vengeance or resentment, but with clarity and understanding, Jeanette Bailey determined to set the record straight.

Jeanette prepared well for her journey. She thoroughly researched her feelings as her first step into this demanding venture. Why did she want to meet her father and talk to him about their life, their bond? If he hadn't responded to Joe's deathbed pleas, why should she walk right into his rejection? She did this exploration and research with the co–participation of her therapist, from whom she requested a deep, supportive relationship. The real support was for Jeanette's discovery of her own truth. What did *she* really want? Could she identify and express this clear intention and manifest it? As her therapist, my job was to support and mirror back to Jeanette *her* true experience.

The death of her brother Joe was a turning point for Jeanette, and somehow out of the agony and chaos of his loss, she received a powerful healing inspiration, which led directly to her decision to find and confront her true father. Such a confrontation is a matter of deep significance requiring extraordinary courage and energetic resources. Even though the purpose of confrontation is freedom from the burden of deception and secrecy, the passage to that point of release is rather like a pilgrimage. Massive change of any kind requires thoroughgoing consideration and evaluation and should not be undertaken casually. Jeanette's years of being a solid support for three children had taught her constancy and stability. It was one thing, however, to be constant for others, and quite another challenge to provide constancy for oneself in the face of emotional earth-quakes.

And that's what confrontation is, no matter how you look at it — it is an emotional earthquake, reorganizing the strata of one's life and identity. Even the idea of participating in a confrontation must come from deep reserves of awareness and support. And while it appeared to everyone that Joe's dying days, his death itself, and the period thereafter were periods of enormous chaos requiring a demanding performance from people like Jeanette who can cope so well, there was something that occurred in that period of time that offered an opening no one could have predicted.

Joe's first marriage had been to a native Canadian woman. As her partner, Joe had been introduced to the spirit and culture of the Ojibways. Their particular approach to spirituality was quite different from the puritanical Christianity of Mother Sewickley's home. There was something in the community and culture of the people Joe met through his first wife, Amelia, which gave him permission to be in pain. They were the only people he ever encountered in his short, alcohol permeated existence who acknowledged without judgment the ongoing grieving which was his life. Silently, with eyes that bore witness to constant loss, they abided by him and gave him the spiritual nourishment no one else could muster for his unbroken and persistent sense of abandonment and disappointment.

Without a word, they held him, though his arms never could reach out. Without a gesture, they wiped his tears and drank his truth, along with the liquid of their own travail. And when Joe died in the Midwest, these people came for him. Clothed in their own placid mystery, they drove silently down from Canada and parked outside the funeral home to continue to this last moment to witness Joe's pain. Even though Joe had divorced Amelia and died married to another woman, they did not forget him. Death was a crucial transition, and Joe's spirit called out to them from his silent heart. Spirit touches spirit, and families of the spirit are sometimes more enduring than blood ties.

Jeanette saw and felt the Ojibway caravan when it arrived at Joe's funeral. Perhaps more than anyone else, she noticed the depth of knowledge pouring out from this silent group that appeared out of nowhere to attend the passing of Joe Sewickley. And Sewickley was hardly Joe's name anymore, though it was carved on his tombstone. He was a man with a secret history and secret historians, and the ones whose faces are lined with the unspeakable attended his spirit with more empathy, perhaps, than anyone inside the stately church. Jeanette felt this from them because she too was cloaked in mystery. While everyone cast quick glances at the big cars and pickups parked in front of the church, uncomfortable with this unforeseen attendance, Jeanette was touched and awakened. Somehow these people gave her the strength to be true to herself. Their reservoir of quietude, she felt, was filled with compassion, and their compassion became *her* food. She ate it to find strength for her own quest.

Healing from abuse, trauma, and betrayal of the magnitude which Jeanette Bailey experienced is never easily done, but what makes such a pilgrimage not only bearable but possible is spiritual support. What is spiritual support? Is it just belief in a particular kind of God or a particular kind of practice? Not really. Spiritual support can happen in moments such as the moment when Jeanette Bailey paid attention to the caravan of the Ojibway people at her brother's funeral. That spiritual support was given to her in an unseen transmission, undocumented, perhaps utterly unrecognized by anyone other than Jeanette Bailey and then mirrored back to her as truth by her therapist when she told the story. Spiritual support comes in many forms, sometimes known only to the recipient, and it is a wealth uncountable. It shores up the weakest hearts and provides inspiration even to the cynical. In order to receive support of this nature, you simply have to be present and available. Jeanette Bailey was available at her brother's funeral for this transmission and support, and she took in with her eyes and her heart the ancient spirits of endurance and transcendence, wisdom and sanctuary. Her heart open and her soul strengthened, Jeanette was thus able to envision confrontation. The Ojibways, without knowing, inspired Jeanette to take her own journey.

Building Resources

If confrontation is a healing tool you choose to employ, build your resources in preparation. You will need them. And these resources must be solid, not newly won. Their stability is also a model of the stability a survivor needs if he or she is considering confrontation. Here's a checklist of questions to answer to assure those resources:

1. **Spiritual support** — how do you nourish your spirit? Where are your spiritual resources? Are you cultivating them? How will you recall them when you need them? Examples of spiritual support are: meditation, walks in nature, prayer, self-reflection, reading inspirational books, or listening to music that uplifts and soothes your soul.

2. **Human support** — who are your friends? Can you really count on them at all times? Who is unquestionably there for you? List them. Talk to them. Tell them about the confrontation you are planning. Post their phone numbers near your telephone so you can call them whenever you need to — and know which friends are the most comforting, the most tolerant and the kindest.

3. **Physical support** — how is your health? What can you tolerate in terms of emotional upheaval, confusion, and anxiety? Do you eat properly to support and nourish yourself? What can you do to build your health so it will sustain you during the emotional upheaval that accompanies a confrontation? How do you manage stress? Write these techniques down and post them so they are there to remind you, to use them. If you don't have stress-reducing methods built into your life, find them and practice them long *before* the confrontation.

4. **Emotional and expressive support** — what creative outlets, expressive mediums, and activities nurture you? What reminders can you give yourself to access these avenues for emotional nurturance? Do you play a musical instrument, keep a journal, dance, or paint? How will you remind yourself to use these resources? What do you do when your emotional dam

overflows? Do you write in your journal, sing, or run? Cultivate healthy, expansive containers for your feelings.

5. **Your home** — do you feel safe and comfortable in your home? Is it a sanctuary for you? If it is not, how can it become one? When you return to it after your confrontation, will you be able to rest there, to regenerate yourself, and to reassure yourself that you have done well?

These support systems and resources must be well established if you plan to engage in a confrontation with an abuser or perpetrator. It is worthwhile to consider *where* a confrontation will occur. Will you be more empowered if the meeting is on neutral ground? How will you arrange it? Do you want to meet on your turf, or theirs? Think this through carefully. Do not be hasty. Visualize the confrontation in a variety of settings and evaluate, based on your body's responses, where you will feel the strongest.

There is no real final chapter to the story of Jeanette Bailey's meeting with the man who is her father, Stuart Langerman. The meeting occurred, and the story unfolds, continuing. In some ways the confrontation itself was unexpectedly disappointing. Jeanette Bailey appeared unannounced on her father's porch. The man who answered the door was unquestionably her father. He looked exactly like Joe Sewickley, and he mirrored back to Jeanette her own eyes. A kind, passive man whose life was in shambles around him, there was little he could do to reach out to Jeanette or comfort her. Surrounded by his deteriorating environment, he had nothing to offer, and no excuse for his abandonment, even to the moment of his son Joe's death. Jeanette's longing for his tenderness coursed through her body but remained unsatisfied. He was so distracted by the demands of a manic depressive wife, one son an alcoholic and the other a paraplegic, that he had no room for his daughter Jeanette, no energy for her, nothing to offer. Stuart Langerman was deeply incapable of being a wise and protective father. On the contrary, he himself was needy and helpless. The fantasy of finding the father–friend was shattered, but Jeanette Bailey wasn't shattered. Her strength of spirit was deepened by her pursuit of the truth, and while her father could hardly be present for Jeanette, Jeanette had created a confrontation in which she was present for herself. She returned home somewhat dazed but prepared to take the time to integrate the truth. She would not get the father she longed for, not ever. Lasting, dependable masculine support and connection had yet to evolve in her life. But Jeanette, by her own determination, had named and witnessed her truth.

In many regards, Jeanette could really begin her therapeutic work *after* her meeting with her father. The mystery of her origins solved, Jeanette now had to focus her attention on herself. The issues that glared at her now were the same ones that were in place before the confrontation, but now *nothing could distract Jeanette from her work on herself*. These were the questions we formulated for her therapeutic future:

1. How could Jeanette express the rage and grief she experienced now when she had just fully realized she had never felt the love and support she needed to be a strong, healthy individual? I explored this dilemma by reminding Jeanette of the abilities she already had developed and that had sustained her thus far. Jeanette's secret passion was singing and throughout her life she had sung to express herself. I pointed her in that direction again now, reminding her of a resource she tended to forget when overwhelmed by a sense of abandonment. This pattern is unfortunately all too familiar for survivors — we forget our gifts and our abilities when we need them the most — when we face retraumatization. But at just such a juncture, an ally in the healing process is critical. I reminded Jeanette of the release and empowerment she experienced by singing, and pointed her in the direction of experiencing herself through her voice.

2. Jeanette had sacrificed power by repressing her feelings, stifling her angry responses, quietly coping and keeping a stiff upper lip when confronted with abusive experiences, such as her husband's raging attacks on her and their children. How could she regain her

physical strength when her doctor told her that her immune system was not up to par, that her blood pressure was too high, and that she was dangerously overweight? The answers were manifold. On the physical level, Jeanette needed to re-evaluate her eating patterns and her exercise patterns — her lifestyle as a whole. She had eaten what others told her to eat; she had moved as she thought she was supposed to move. Rebuilding a sense of self meant not only eating differently and exercising differently, but being willing to move into the world differently. Jeanette faced the challenge of individuation at every level of her life.

3. How could Jeanette build a future career for herself after years of being a housewife? How could she regain skills and confidence? This question posed the natural next step for Jeanette — facing her fear of being in the world. She didn't feel capable of competing with others, of being assertive, and she didn't know if she was smart enough to be reeducated. After all, she wondered maybe she was too old. But the answer to this question is, was, and always will be SUPPORT. Support paved the way for Jeanette to talk about her fears, and to discover the resources she could access to face them.

4. How could Jeanette reclaim her sexuality, which had been stifled by her feelings of worthlessness, her mother's puritanism, and her husband's demanding, abusive intrusions, made without sensitivity to Jeanette? By retracing the sexually traumatic events in her life, Jeanette could discovery her own true sexuality and acknowledge her need to be in a vital, responsive, and sexually alive relationship. Once this need was consciously claimed, the chances of its fulfillment were much greater, and Jeanette's body and demeanor would follow the awareness of her mind. When Jeanette accepted herself and her sexual needs, life would respond.

The confrontation between Jeanette and her father put to rest Jeanette's concern over parentage and cleared the way for her ownership of her future. Now the real work began, the work of building Jeanette's foundation for a future, a new life, in which her needs were the centerpiece. I had to provide the inspiration that it was not too late to do this. I had to mirror back to Jeanette that the confidence and courage it took to navigate a confrontation with her father remained with her and was her primary resource as she moved into the unknown, freed at last from the restrictive influences of the controlling mother Sewickley, the abandoning mother and father, the abusive husband and the needy, addicted brother. Jeanette had survived them all. Now she could live her *own* life.

Before I end the story of Jeanette Bailey, for the purposes of this book, I want to be sure that you hear more about Jeanette's love of singing. Unfortunately, you will not be able to hear her voice, but song, especially spiritual songs, when sung by Jeanette, were the perfect manifestation of her healing journey. The complexity of her story, with all its layers of betrayal and loss, could not be easily expressed in any medium. But, the multi-dimensional power of song, with its alchemy of breath and tone, carried innately the foundation of faith that sustained and motivated Jeanette Bailey. When Jeanette sang, her body told its tale to an omnipresent listener, the Divine Love that Jeanette knew for certain had never abandoned her.

Pacing in Therapy: What Comes First?

The Story of Leslie Ann Sweborge

Pacing is a crucial awareness in therapy, particularly when trauma has presented itself. Knowing how and when to proceed, when to stabilize, when to extend, when to support and when to challenge is wisdom born out of experience and maturity.

All of the stories in this book are, in one way or another, about pacing. Shelley Cleveland's story, for instance, contains an important description of pacing in terms of detoxification from substance use. Shelley's physical strength could not build until both the drugs she had used and the addictive patterns that supported their use were released. It would have been poor judgment to encourage vigorous expressive work, such as movement, for instance, until this strength was in place. At that juncture, however, Shelley was naturally eager and truly ready for unique and powerful movement. A mature therapist will be able to attune to the survivor's energetic rhythm and access the appropriate pace for working effectively.

Luke Overhill had to learn that it was okay to have feelings and to share them with others before he could talk about the content of his memories and sensations. Jeanette Bailey had to clear up the mystery about her mother and father before she could begin to build a life for herself. In each case, the pacing is dependent on the individual survivor.

Leslie Ann Sweborge's story, which follows, reveals the importance of building a foundation of financial, familial, and professional security as a basis for deep emotional work. Look at your own situation to see which of these models most resembles your own needs to consider how you might pace your process. Most importantly, whether you are a therapist or a survivor client (or both), know that pacing is essential. Pacing allows you to have perspective on your healing, to provide boundaries for yourself, and to give yourself support and spaciousness when things become too intense. Your own needs and feelings are the best indicators for how to pace. When you feel overwhelmed, slow down and soothe yourself, do comforting things. When you feel strong, allow yourself to expand — be creative. When to rest and when to stretch — you *will* find your own best timing through trial and error and successfully navigate your passage. Trust yourself in this.

Leslie Ann's face had the elegance and angularity of a Native American woman, though she was of European descent. The control her life demanded had constructed a set jaw and an abrupt way of gesturing, characteristic of many people who carry in their bodies a history of violation. Her long dark hair moved quickly with her face, framing it in flashes, especially when her darting gestures cascaded before the viewer to avoid too long an embrace of the eyes: Leslie Ann's intensity was felt in the energy pulsing between her movements, in her downcast eyes, generating a mystery, waiting to be uncovered.

Sexual abuse teaches us to hide, to withdraw, and to keep secrets. It forces us to create disguises and masquerades to cover the pain and terror we feel. It makes us careful to the point of paranoia — testing to see if there is any chance of trust, any hope for honesty. Survivors of abuse learn the dance of the saboteur, avoiding pleasure (the hallmark of betrayal) at every turn. Survivors are vigilant, anticipating the sudden move that marks loss, perhaps attack.

Middle class New York and New Jersey are breeding grounds for abuse and trauma. Family problems stay locked within the walls of apartments where lives unfold with little room for expansion. It was in one of these neighborhoods that Leslie Ann was born and grew up, part of a sprawling family of six, managed by a working couple, Mom and Dad, Rose and Jack.

The world around Leslie Ann was full of chaos and chattering. Her brothers and sisters, her mother and father, her neighbors, her schoolmates, were always talking about what they ate, what they saw, what they wanted, what they needed. Leslie Ann felt like she lived in a madhouse, or as a witness to the building of the Tower of Babel. None of this talk included her. It seemed odd to her that so much could swirl about her and that she could feel so markedly the weight of isolation. From too early in her life, she carried within herself the burden of the unspoken, the dense silence of abandonment, the quiet that stretches endlessly into dreamlike emptiness. Even as a child, she had the look of someone with a distant preoccupation, uncommon for her years. Just as side canyons of massive rock structures contain pools of water that remain unmoving for months, even years, so did Leslie Ann's grief over her father's violation of her remain untouched, a secret stuck between eroding geology, damned by a timeless and unspoken rule that forbade her from speaking.

It may have been her countenance of unutterable pain that created in Leslie Ann the elegance which was her beauty and her isolation. This was an elegance held rigidly against the organic fluidity of her feminine structure — an elegance that knew no gestures other than quick, defensive ones. Leslie Ann had secrets, and a fortress of fear to contain and house them.

Leslie Ann was the middle child in the family, the quietest one, sandwiched between three girls and two boys. And while the others resembled Rose, the German mother, with their round faces and fair coloring, Leslie Ann stood out as unique. She took after her father's side of the family, but she was the only one of all the children to look like him. How curious! Leslie Ann treasured her distinctive difference — her slenderness, her darkness. When she looked in the mirror, she was pleased, even proud. And this was worth a great deal to her. There was little else for her to take pride in but her difference.

As she grew up in the bustling, ceaselessly active East Coast town, Leslie Ann came to hoard the admiring glances she got when the family went out. At home, no one was special. The household was lorded over by Jack, though he was gone more than he was home, and when he was home at night, he was frequently drunk. Rose, her mother, was absolutely docile. Her eyes were always downcast, as if ashamed of her place in life. But she cast her eyes away even when Leslie Ann needed her help, or when she just needed someone to talk to. Like her, Leslie Ann's brothers and sisters were terrified — terrified of Jack's alcoholic rages and terrified because of Rose's inability to protect them. So they too averted their eyes. No one was available to help anyone else. This was a secret agreement, a deal they all made covertly, for survival. They formed a silent conspiracy of avoidance, often in the midst of a chattering activity. This was their only safety. It was also the cause of extraordinary pain, a pain that seemed part of daily life, but which would have been denied with horrified cries if it had been addressed directly.

It was under cover of this avoidance and lack of communication that the abuse occurred. Despite his alcoholism, Leslie Ann remembered admiring her father up until that Saturday afternoon in her fifth year. But from that day forward, she detested him and intently nurtured within herself a rage so enormous it breached the barrier of violence, though she never revealed it openly or expressed it in any way other than withdrawal. Thus was the pattern made.

The abuse itself happened swiftly and was never repeated. The other children were shopping with Rose, and Leslie Ann was left alone with her father. It had been a pleasant morning. Jack slept while Leslie Ann watched cartoons on television. She enjoyed the specialness of being alone with Dad, even though he was asleep. Then he called her into bed with him, and she cuddled under the sheets, feeling good with his closeness which she so rarely knew. But when he began to touch her in places she instinctively knew were private, hers, then her enjoyment ended abruptly, and her entire body became rigid with fear. This rigidity would remain with her for a long time past this morning. As his hands explored her more, a revulsion built within her until she could no longer contain it, and she bolted from the bed to the bathroom and began throwing up. He left her alone there and never spoke. Long after her small breakfast of cereal and milk had been washed away, Leslie Ann continued to retch, the dry heaves failing to eliminate her disgust and outrage. This day marked her life with betrayal, and even though she had the courage to flee, instantly and powerfully, the scene of her violation was branded in her memory forever as a scar. She would never be the same again.

Leslie Ann avoided her father from that day on. She spoke to him only when necessary, and the curiosity was that no one noticed this distance or commented upon it. Everyone in this family had come to accept distance. It never occurred to Leslie Ann to tell her mother of the betrayal. Her mother simply was not available. Neither did it occur to her to share this horrible experience with her siblings. They, she felt, were too intent upon their own survival to be concerned about hers. Only after she began therapy did the story unfold, with its history and its related events. And perhaps without therapy, the story might have remained forever buried in Leslie Ann's body.

Yet, in the larger view, repression does have a limited life span. These stories must eventually seep out like fresh water in a canyon cul de sac, whether they are told verbally or somatically, whether they are overt or covert, the stories of abuse *cannot* be forever hidden. The tears restrained under the guise of hardness, resistance, spill out, in their own time. The deep inner core that shouts LIFE must erupt from the hard rock of depression.

After two failed marriages, the single mother of two children, Leslie Ann found her way to therapy simply because she was crying all the time now — crying at work, crying over dinner, crying in the car, crying in the bathroom. If she didn't find out why she was crying, she soon wouldn't be able to function. She could hardly function now. It was all she could do to get the children to school, go to work, and come home. Her lonely, hard battle against her story had reached its limit.

Entering Therapy

When Leslie Ann made an appointment to visit the therapist a friend suggested, she felt she was utterly helpless. This was a last gasp move. Even worse, she felt disoriented, unsure of why she was going, or even what therapy could do for her. How did it work? What was her relationship to the person she called "therapist?" When she walked into the room where the therapist sat, all she could feel was that she was rather like a little girl, a little girl who had been hurt very very badly and didn't know where to turn for help. It was like being lost at the department store or the parade and watching wide–eyed while strangers tried to determine your name and address. The confusion was overwhelming. She was reduced to tears before she said a word beyond the introductions, and she was humiliated by her weakness, ashamed of her childishness. In this condition of being overloaded, which in itself is quite similar to being traumatized, pacing does not exist. It's up to the therapist to introduce the concept. Then, the client can integrate it as a way to manage and understand the inundating experience of being overwhelmed by one's own feelings.

From my perspective, when Leslie Ann entered the room where we were to do our work, I immediately recognized the magnitude of her despair and her sense of confusion. As a survivor of sexual abuse myself, I understand these symptoms to reflect not the permanent condition of the sufferer, but a temporary, transitional state, a state of release, almost inevitable in the process of healing from abuse of such enormous proportions as incest. Encompassing this awareness, I could be with Leslie Ann's "disintegration" (really an unraveling) and support her journey through it, tenderly, without much interference initially. Some words of support, an encouragement of boundary, and a gentle beckoning into the present (such as, "It's natural for you to feel like this after the pain that occurred when you were young, but now we can look at that pain and find healing.") allows the emotionality to subside, even if temporarily. Then, two adults can be together, problem solving, finding comfort, recognizing human kinship.

None of this, however, was easy for Leslie Ann. She felt like she was falling apart, losing it, and she didn't really know why or how. But, there was a safety she felt as I listened attentively and compassionately to her, acknowledging her tears — that began to calm her, to allow her to believe that change was possible. She took a deep breath and looked at me. I looked back, smiling into her eyes. Being heard allowed the first instance of pacing. By mirroring belief back to her, Leslie Ann organically slowed herself down.

This was the beginning of Leslie Ann's therapeutic process, but while the beginning contains the seeds of the future, it is still only the introduction to the story. A developmental threshold was crossed, but there was a long healing distance ahead. In therapy, the client's power and essence begins to shine forth, little by little, and builds a foundation for emergence. As that essence emerges, it slowly becomes itself utterly. This is an unpredictable journey and the therapist's job is to nurture the unfolding, always, in a variety of ways, many of them unpredictable.

Depression and Isolation Are Not Pacing

Depression was Leslie Ann's coping mechanism, the place she went when she felt frightened, and depression is a stranglehold on feeling. While it slows the process of release, it is not pacing. Depression brings things to a dead stop. Expressionlessness, unresponsiveness, distance, withdrawal — all these mark depression as a barrier to others as strong and as long–lasting as the Berlin Wall. But the Berlin Wall came down, and the walls of depression too come down, with time, patience, hard work, courage, and a love of liberation.

In the environment in which Leslie Ann grew up, almost everything that should nurture a child's growth was missing. There was little comfort, little sanctuary, little opportunity for communication. Development was stunted, crippled, but this disabling was not permanent. The losses of the past were indeed losses, but acknowledgement is the wound's balm, and the beginning of healing. Pacing begins with acknowledgement, and acknowledgement marks the end of depression, the withholding of feeling, and shutting down.

Relationship had not been carefully cultivated in Leslie Ann's life. Despite being surrounded by a large family and living in a crowded city, full of potential resources as well as potential harm, Leslie Ann's primary coping tools of depression and withdrawal made her isolate herself, and pacing is not possible in isolation.

Isolation implies and is usually bonded with depression. Because depression and isolation were such strong patterns for Leslie Ann, I suggested she become part of a therapy group I was initiating for women survivors of sexual abuse. She agreed, and even the agreement was a big step for her, a step towards a willingness to relate.

I was interested in creating a multi–modality experience for women survivors of sexual abuse, a place where interaction and expression could weave themselves together, and where the underlying traumas we had experienced could be brought into the light of community, where we could be comforted for our pains and encouraged in our capacities, so that ultimately we could move beyond trauma into our unfolding lives. I wanted the group environment to be a place where resolution could be experienced in the presence of others. The group was a medium to renegotiate the trauma patterned in the family of origin.

The family is the system whose structure naturally provides pacing skills, when that family is healthy. Through interaction, discussion, feedback, and shared problem solving, the family members put overwhelming circumstances into a positive perspective and recommend steps for managing difficult situations in all realms of life, from relationships to physical problems; from financial stress to educational or career planning. But hardly anyone I know or work with professionally had this experience of family as teachers of pacing. I knew that group therapy was one of the important ways for Leslie Ann to have a firsthand experience of learning pacing skills in a collective situation, from her peers, interactionally.

Successful pacing demands interaction with one's body. The body teaches us pacing if we know how to listen to it, attune to it, read it, and decode it. If we can find the body's rhythm and follow it, pacing will happen naturally. But we need a structure within which to do this, and we need feedback and discussion to explore this process.

Authentic Movement is one vehicle for investigating and decoding the body's storehouse of information. The group to which I invited Leslie Ann would use the stimulating and insightful tool of Authentic Movement in its meetings, along with processing, communication, and whatever expressive avenues (writing, sounding, visual art) would extend our awareness.

Authentic Movement, Group Therapy and Pacing*

Imagine yourself in a big room with softly carpeted floors, high ceilings, and pillows. The only other occupants of the room are a small group of people who know how to observe compassionately, with detachment, and who watch only to support you, only to encourage your authenticity. And even more importantly, these witnesses are people with whom you feel a kinship, people who you know share your pain. Your intention in this room is singular, focused — it is to allow the truth of the moment to come through your body in the form of movement. There is nothing else to do. Can you feel the silence and the reliable authenticity of the environment? Can you feel the accumulated power of everyone's combined intention, everyone's attention to healing?

This is the context in which Authentic Movement functions to help us experience the truth of our bodies. Authentic Movement is one instrument in the medicine bag of holistic healing, a healing that encompasses the body's reality and interweaves it with our thoughts and our feelings. To carefully read the messages of the body, we slow down and become attentive, finally, to the whole truth. We listen to the language of our organs and limbs, our bones and our muscles, our skin and our hearts. Pacing is about prioritizing, determining what comes first, and even who comes first. You or your children? You or your employer? You or your therapist? You or your partner? You or your schedule? Your body or your mind? As we move, all these pulls are felt, and gradually we find ourselves surrendering decision making to our bodies.

If your ankle is sprained, a priority is established. If your sinuses are infected, a priority is established. But do we honor our body's priorities, or do we override them, by pushing ourselves, by using drugs and chemicals to stifle and mute our body's message? If we listen to, and even write down, our body sensations, and share our impressions with like–minded listeners, we can decode our own

---

*See both the "Tools" and "Resources" sections of this book for more information on Dance Therapy, Authentic Movement, and Genuine Movement Process, as well as information on the therapeutic applications of other art forms. Resources for locating literature, agencies and therapists are contained in these sections.

self-talk, our own communications to ourselves. Thereby a body–centered rhythm is found, and pacing occurs, not through behavior modification, but experientially, organically.

The group Leslie Ann joined was restricted to women to allow a greater sense of privacy and safety, not because men are in and of themselves dangerous, but because the gentle sisterhood seemed a good place to *begin* to build trust, and trust is a cornerstone for pacing. For women who have been abused by other women, of course, there are additional implications to such a sisterhood. And Leslie Ann's situation was not uncommon — one in which the perpetrator was actually a man, her father, but the betrayal was compounded by her mother's lack of presence. Yet even with this all–too–common history, starting with women alone allowed a higher level of safety, particularly when movement, exposing the body, revealing its sensuality and its vulnerability, was on the agenda.

Trust is a puzzle piece that must be in place for pacing to occur at all. Pacing implies that it's okay to slow things down; it's okay to manage feeling. Overwhelming inundations of feeling are reckless, and it's a now or never rush. Without pacing, we experience desperation and panic as feeling and expression go helter skelter, madly seeking orientation, focus, comfort, and response. Pacing is providing that orientation. Since most of us did not learn this kind of management in a healthy way at home, someone must show us. That someone is often a therapist.

To introduce pacing means to become part of a natural order in which all things have a time and place. This does not in any way suggest a loss of spontaneity. Rather, it suggests that we and our feelings, our questions, and especially our needs have their own space, and that we can find that space, even if we have to wait for it. We do this through self–awareness and self–responsiveness, but we have to learn to cultivate this selfhood. This takes some time, but it can and must be done.

Pacing flows naturally out of self–confidence and atunement to the body. If we are not given these qualities in our upbringing, in our family of origin, we must find them for ourselves. Group work, when well–facilitated and organized, replicates some of the dynamics of a healthy family where pacing is a natural event. This is what

I intended for the group Leslie Ann joined. Together we could explore and discuss different ways to pace, the ways each of us had found to work with our own emotional states. Authentic Movement in a group context is rather like being lovingly witnessed while engaged in play, something that occurs naturally in healthy families.

Invisibility was Leslie Ann's key to protection. She had found safety under the cloak of isolation and nonresponsiveness. How would she ever learn about pacing if she didn't share her process with others? The group was a place to participate, to join in the revelation of individual and collective truth, but it also evoked Leslie Ann's fear and resistance. At first, she just didn't want to do it. Not doing was her movement. Hiding in quiet and stillness, paralysis, in timidity and shyness, terror and unspoken desire, had been her pattern.

When she watched other group members move and interact, Leslie Ann experienced a confrontation within herself between stubborness, holding, and her yearning to reach out. She kept to herself, caught in the stranglehold of her own struggle, desperately wanting connection, but without the self–confidence or trust to move from what seemed a safe and familiar stasis into the frightening world of free flowing, participatory human interplay.

Because she didn't yet know about pacing, Leslie Ann's first venture into expression was explosive. In the format of the group, Leslie Ann's statue–like holding one day erupted in a run and then a piercing scream. This was her statement. It spoke for years of repression. It was her breakthrough to herself and others. At that moment, it was the first item on *her* agenda. It was met with objectivity and compassion. The members of the group watched, accepted, heard, witnessed, and made no comment until the time for speaking arrived. In the ground rules of Authentic Movement process, only after all movement is completed does each participant speak. Everyone speaks from the standpoint of their own experience. The caveat applied to all is that comments not reflect any projection, any assumption, any interpretation of the mover's impact. Each person speaks only for themselves, and there is a Quaker–like silence that holds these personal utterances in a sacred container.

In this tender quietude, Leslie Ann reviewed not only the intensity of her own experience as it was revealed, but she saw also how she responded to the other women, and how each of them became projections of her mother and her sisters, and that within these projections there was both a positive and a negative side, a healing pattern and a trauma pattern. On the positive side, there was companionship with her sisters, camaraderie that brought smiles and joy into life. She had almost forgotten that! In her home of origin, there had been evenings of laughter, shared observations, double dates, dress swapping, adventures in the open air, book lendings, whispers in school hallways, birthday parties, jokes, special gifts, and a million other treasures that represented a great healing resource Leslie Ann had almost overlooked. Now, in the context of this group, these resources came back to her and supported her, encouraged her, as she moved in front of the others or shared an experience. And as this possibility of connection began to penetrate her being, so long locked against penetration, Leslie Ann found herself inevitably softening, little by little, to the possibility of humans comforting one another, imperfectly it's true, but possibly, on occasion — not always, but sometimes.

As the possibility of being heard and witnessed with respect increased, Leslie Ann allowed herself to move more and more. *In other words, the coping mechanism of repression was gradually replaced with expression.* She moved to express her anger at her father, and she named her movement as such, for herself and by herself. And as she released this anger, *little by little*, in the presence of her protective and attentive witness–sisters, in an agreed–upon time frame with boundaries and limits, she carried less and less of it within herself, *and this made pacing possible because the overload of feeling came into balance.* Her burden of emotion was lightened, little by little, and what remained was more of Leslie Ann and less of her abuser father. Leslie Ann acknowledged more of her own anger — the fiery, energetic, spontaneous, righteous indignation of the abused child, the fury of the protective woman, the power of the strong person she was — and she noticed that her anger felt less and less like the secretive, resentful, vengeance-impacted bitterness of her father, Jack, the drunkard, who, as the fates would have it, died of a heart attack within a few years after Leslie Ann began her therapeutic journey.

The group existed not as a social gathering, but as a laboratory in which patterns of resistance and projection could be exposed and explored, with the hope of replacing the coping mechanisms that evolved from trauma with healthy resources. This unwinding from the vortex–like grip of trauma is not easily done, and quick methods of relieving trauma should be questioned, as the vortex winds its way deeply into the nervous system like a corkscrew and must be extracted precisely, gently, and slowly.

In the laboratory of a movement space occupied by a group of women, all of whom have been sexually abused, and all of whom have come to look at their patterns of disharmony, some difficulty and discomfort is to be expected. The intention is not necessarily to make things pleasant, but to make it possible and safe for those issues we have been forced to hide to come to the surface, to be seen and acknowledged, and gently released, over time.

The impact of the group, unavoidably, is to bring out some of our relational distress. The group comes to feel, of necessity, somewhat like a family, if only by virtue of the fact that we are all there together consistently, in this one space, and there is a need to communicate. Feelings about one another proliferate, and the group members sit in the midst of one pacing crisis after another — what shall we say, what shall we NOT say? Feelings become quickly entangled with projections, and suddenly we are all humbled to discover that it is very difficult to know what we actually do feel about another person. Not only that, it is very difficult to know how to express whatever we feel.

It was a shock for Leslie Ann to find that her experience as a survivor of trauma resonated with almost *everyone* else in the group. Realizing she wasn't alone created waves of grief/relief, as she acknowledged, much to her amazement, how much she had longed to connect with, and be contacted by, the members of her family, to feel their support and understanding. This was not a simple admission — it was an admission withheld for over thirty years; the feelings of a young child who wanted to be comforted and heard by her mother, the feelings of an adolescent girl who wanted to be honest with her sisters, the feelings of a young woman whose body had been violated, who wanted to speak of her needs, and who had been afraid to talk for far too long. Fear and indescribable, wordless longing were behind Leslie Ann's resistance and repression, but it was a fear so impacted with history, that it needed a big space to come out, it needed a well–established safety in order to unfurl from the knotted place deep inside Leslie Ann's being.

In a group dedicated to honoring feelings of this magnitude, real healing *can* occur, and with a facilitator who has the responsibility of tracking not only the impact of this process on Leslie Ann, but the impact on *all* the other survivors present, transformation can happen successfully within a group context. And there is something about this kind of occurrence in a group that is qualitatively different from a similar experience in a private session, or when one is alone. The witnessing, the being held by the eyes of the whole group, is a special and crucial intervention for survivors, renegotiating many layers of trauma simultaneously.

Leslie Ann was ready to take in the support of the group, the space they voluntarily gave her; she was ready to take in the possibility that her needs and her feelings could be held, genuinely and lovingly. The experience of expressing her feelings and having them met, honored, and acknowledged by a group of women did not forever solve the issue of communication with others for Leslie Ann. But, it was an important and resourceful experience in the context of a whole history of rejection, and *did* help create the self–confidence necessary for Leslie Ann herself to use pacing in her life.

Job and Profession:
Pacing, Process, and Making It in the World

Leslie Ann wanted to sustain herself in the world financially and professionally, and she had children to support. As a woman with low self–esteem and an average education, she did not feel confident facing the professional world. It took immense courage for Leslie Ann to work and to compete with others for work. It took immense courage for her to accept the responsibility of motherhood and parenthood and simultaneously create work for herself that she would enjoy and in which she would be respected. All of this was linked in every conceivable way to the fact that Leslie Ann was a survivor of sexual abuse. Every disrespectful look, every rejection, every criticism that she received triggered* in her memories connected with abuse and betrayal. Every day she had to overcome countless moments of discomfort generated by the way she was related to as a woman and as a person in a secretarial role. This is precisely where pacing is a required tool for making it in the world. Pacing demands the ability to separate the past from the present, and to know how one can be triggered and NOT react, without repressing feeling, but by witnessing it and allowing it.

The abuse that occurred in childhood must be honestly acknowledged but it *is* over, and it is possible for the survivor to know this

---

*Trigger: A trigger is an event, an experience, or an impression that evokes for the survivor a memory or a flashback of an abusive or traumatic experience. For instance, the abuse may have occurred in a basement, and the trauma survivor may be triggered by walking into a basement. Or, the perpetrator of the abuse could have been a blonde woman , and the trauma survivor feels agitated at the sight of a blonde woman. Another example is that the abuse was experienced as being fondled by a school teacher in a classroom and the survivor feels threatened when left alone with a school teacher in a classroom. Dates and seasons sometimes function as triggers. For example, the abuse occurred in the winter, so the approach of winter makes the survivor nervous. Whatever the trigger, it reveals itself as being a cause of agitation which seems unequal to the circumstances. For this reason, experiencing apparently unrelated symptoms (agitation, nervousness, dry mouth, sweaty palms, feeling threatened, etc.) should not be thought of as a fluke or something to be ignored or overlooked, but as a potential source of healing information to be considered calmly and thoughtfully. If you experience something like what I am describing, it is best to slow everything down, note the process, stay as present as possible, and return to the circumstances later, preferably in the presence of your therapist when you can work together to solve the mystery of being triggered. The outcome of noticing that you are being triggered is the discovery not only of data about trauma, but of ways that you can heal. Noticing how and when you are triggered, and identifying the experience as such, can help enormously in eliminating the unknown aspects of your experience as a trauma survivor. For example, I once felt horribly threatened when someone said, "You can trust me," until I realized that those were the exact words of a perpetrator of sexual abuse. Separating my previously unexpressed experience of terror in the past from the present circumstances helped me to behave more appropriately in my life and to protect and nurture the part of me that still needed to unravel her response from the past. This is how triggers are useful. Identifying the triggers as such is the first step in this process.

even when he or she is triggered or impacted by the present *as if* it were the past. Feelings and sensations experienced under these circumstances can be witnessed and noticed (they don't have to be stifled) without one's reaction intruding into the present. Careful work with an attentive and knowledgeable therapist who is alert to the dynamics of trauma is necessary to learn how to do this naturally and consistently. When trauma has occurred, this work must be done. It is our task and it is a loving and compassionate act we perform for ourselves with consistency and devotion. The benefits are cumulative. Leslie Ann did this work with me, and it had some interesting results.

Part of the therapeutic process for Leslie Ann was redefining her place in the world. As it became clearer and clearer that the demands, insults, and patronizing regard she received from her primarily male employers was exacerbating her trauma and impeding her progress, Leslie Ann developed an idea for self–employment. As her therapist, I supported her in this undertaking, realizing the risk that she was taking. What I wanted to emphasize was the courage it took to even consider such a plan. It was also obvious that until these issues of profession, finances, and security were resolved, her deeper therapeutic needs could not be addressed.

Survivors are, of necessity, outstandingly courageous people. And the cruel irony is that it takes a very long time for us to know that. Survivors are almost without exception filled with a sense of self–hatred, insecurity, and self–doubt. In fact, I have often thought that the greatest damage created by sexual abuse and early childhood trauma is that it evokes self–doubt of such enormous proportions that continual reassurance is necessary to overcome it. This self–doubt was entrenched in Leslie Ann's core, and yet I knew that with time and ongoing support, she could shift the self–doubt into deep self–love. Some of this work had to be done in the world, and so the arena of career was the perfect one for Leslie Ann at this juncture, when she had support from me and the group she had joined. Choosing to focus on career and professional development was, in fact, a decision that came from good pacing. This was the right time and place to put this part of Leslie Ann's life in order.

Leslie Ann was learning to listen to her body, and her body told her when she was not comfortable with the offhand, sexually harassing comments her employer was prone to making. She felt nauseous when he made these remarks, and then she felt furious. At last she came to know anger, the fiery serpent rising into her throat and eyes, longing for an outlet. When she discussed this experience with her therapist and with the other women in her group, she began to see the health of her response, and to fear it less. What would she have done if she hadn't had an opportunity to talk about these feelings? Probably shut them off again, she concluded. But that was not possible anymore. With the feelings rising and her support system in place, Leslie Ann was able to progress more and more into her life. Her feelings and her body's motility, in natural response to those impulses, would lead her to leave her job and to begin her own career, on her own, not under the domination of men. And in so doing, Leslie Ann was able to renegotiate some portion of her trauma. She took her power back when she defined her own future and made it happen. Each step she took towards ensuring that she would indeed be able to succeed in the world on her own terms, allowed her to have belief in herself, a commodity more difficult to come by than money.

The simultaneous evolution of her connection with her body and her reorientation towards work and career was a demonstration of the power of body–centered healing — a therapeutic approach that combines *every* aspect of the survivor's experience. Leslie Ann's life shifted as she came into wholeness and balance, and with every shift, of course, there also arose more information about the trauma she experienced. But with people around her on whom she could rely to give her the feedback that empowered her, Leslie Ann was able to meet every shift in her development as an opportunity for growth. Leslie Ann was slowly, carefully, and with great support, bringing herself into health.

It was because of the new, and sometimes unnerving, feeling of being supported that Leslie Ann decided she could take the risk of starting her own secretarial business. She formulated it well beforehand. She wanted to provide secretarial and administrative services for creative, free-lance people — therapists, writers, entrepreneurs, dancers, consultants. Circumstances began to conspire to encourage Leslie Ann to do this. It seemed there was a real need for these services. A friend offered office space at a low price. A computer became available, and soon it seemed as if Leslie Ann had no choice but to move ahead into her own life. This was not a sudden magic. This was the power of Leslie Ann's intention and clarity.

When she actually took the step of quitting her job and moving into her own space, actions she paced carefully, consulting me, the members of her group, and other friends, and tuning in profoundly to herself, Leslie Ann felt as if she were being born. Never before had she acted so thoroughly for and with herself. Never before had she taken a risk that implied such belief in her own capacities. To begin her own enterprise and to knowingly take on all that implied — the taxes, the purchases, the marketing, the exposure, taking the driver's seat, confronting people, etc., etc. — to do all this with eyes wide open — why, it was more exciting than a love affair! Leslie Ann discovered she had previously unrealized energy and capacity. Her excitement spilled over into her interactions with her children. She became playful and spontaneous. Life began to really happen for Leslie Ann, and she welcomed it. Some portion of her pleasure came from the fact that she had people with whom she could share her victory — her friends, her therapist, her children. And her joy bred more friendships, more contacts. A stream of events flowed; life bubbled forth; boredom and depression vanished. The image of being born kept recurring for her as her business took shape. And there were hands ready to greet her delivery with an embrace, and voices saying, "Welcome, Welcome, Welcome!"

Starting her own business did not by any means end Leslie Ann's therapeutic process. In fact, this shift allowed her process to begin. Because financial security and family stability were so crucial for Leslie Ann, you might say that her journey could not really commence until these were established securely, unshakably in place. Now the real work could begin. There were many issues yet to be addressed — issues of intimacy and sexuality, grief, anger, resentment, and creativity. But the adventure of acting for herself and succeeding (because Leslie Ann's business *did* succeed, and she then had to face the challenge of success, which was ominous for someone who had invested years of belief in self–doubt) gave Leslie Ann a foundation for self–worth. The steps she took and the resources she developed to support herself and make that success possible became a template for the ways in which she could face future issues whether they were relational, professional, or physical. Starting her own business and taking care of herself and her family financially taught Leslie Ann more about pacing than anything else in her whole life.

Knowing how to pace a healing journey is crucial wisdom. If you are a survivor who needs to build a foundation such as Leslie Ann's, find a therapist who can support you first on that level. Identifying your needs clearly and realistically and making them known can allow therapy to be much more useful. Leslie Ann's story is intended to encourage you to use therapy to build a foundation as well as to navigate the watery world of sexual abuse.

The question of whether group therapy, individual therapy, or both is appropriate is also a pacing decision. Leslie Ann needed *both* environments early on in her process to build her strength, and this was acknowledged in resonating agreement between us. For her, it felt right to do both. What is appropriate when? Take the time to be sensitive to these questions for yourself, and explore them in dialogue with others, especially your therapist. Learning how to pace yourself in order to heal effectively and thoroughly will reap ongoing rewards as your life unfolds.

There really aren't rules about this pacing because each person is unique, but pacing cannot be ignored. For someone like Leslie Ann, for whom depression was synonymous with daily life, for whom expression was horrifying, and who simultaneously was the head of her household with a family to support both emotionally and financially, building a foundation was clearly the first item on the agenda. There is a kind of common sense reasoning here, a first–things–first reasoning, that sometimes eludes survivors because of our old need to escape from the realities of abusive life. It was my job as a therapist (who, luckily for both of us, had also been a single-parent head-of-household and who also had to build a career in order to heal) to mirror the basics back to Leslie Ann. With someone else, I might have waited longer to recommend group therapy or I might have focused more on talking about family dynamics rather than trying to repattern them experientially in a group context. But when you have children to raise and for whom you have to be a model of health, sometimes you have to be active *and* thoughtful simultaneously. Children don't wait to develop until you have the maturity to guide them. Single parents have to become wise and mature even faster than other people! The chapter in this book on THE NEW FAMILY contains a section on single-parent survivors that will add even more dimension to Leslie Ann's story.

Here are some key points to consider when you evaluate pacing in your therapy:

1. Are my issues as a survivor of sexual abuse preventing me from functioning well in the world? If so, how can I rearrange those conditions so that I can both support myself and heal?

2. Do I have people in my life to whom I can speak who will help me problem–solve my concerns over work, financial security, family relationships, and balancing these with healing? If I don't have that kind of support system, how can I find it? Does group therapy seem like the kind of environment that would appropriately fill this need for feedback and community in my life at this time? If so, how can I find the group support that I need? Do I know therapists I can ask, or other survivors?

3. Are my issues as a survivor of sexual abuse interfering with my parenting? Can I resolve these questions amongst my friends and with my therapist, or do I need a community of single-parent survivors who can support me and help me find resources and solutions? Where can I find such a group? Do I need to start one or to ask my therapist to start one? Even raising this possibility with your therapist can be exciting and empowering. I have begun numerous groups, including the very first group for women survivors that I ever

convened, in response to the needs expressed by my clients. Being willing to generate what you need instead of merely noting the lack can change the dynamics of your life significantly and give you more information about pacing — if you're really ready for a group, the group will appear (build it and they will come).

4. The first and most important step to determine pacing for yourself is identifying your needs and seeing what you are willing to do to get them met. Once you know your needs and are clear about them, your next task is to brainstorm, network, explore all the ways you can meet your own needs. Start right now. Make a list of what you need and want to heal. Prioritize these needs. What comes first? Discuss this list with your therapist or friends. What can you do *right away* to get some of these needs met? Be realistic and strong and choose the three most important items on this list to address first. You have my support in getting your needs met and being creative in the process!

5. In the context of the message of this book, I have to underscore the role of Authentic Movement in Leslie Ann's process. While she had never before experienced movement as a therapeutic dynamic, it was a way into her body's truth, her body's story, and even though Leslie Ann was not conscious of needing her body's commentary, it was essential that she hear it. When you consider pacing, remember that you have a reliable guide — your own body. Use the tools offered in this book to listen to your body wisdom.

The Web of Trauma: Culture, Class, Religion and War

The Story of Zorah Lambowski

When we first name the trauma we knew as children and its impact on our lives, we feel grief, anger, rage, and a multitude of other feelings that gather to become a cascade of emotion. A long withheld flow springs forth for which we must make a space and a suitable container, so that we can come back into ourselves and find our way to a life we want to live, a life of our own making.

At this juncture of remaking ourselves, rebirthing into our true, unique, and creative beingness, we can, after the initial emotional maelstrom, look at how it all happened. We now have the opportunity to investigate the lives of our parents and their parents, and to consider how the family history created a lineage of abuse, which we are now halting through our intention to recover.

People abuse because they have been abused. But only the people who see and acknowledge this can stop the cycle of traumatic reenactment. If you are seeking resources for healing and using them, you are stopping the cycle. If you are using art to heal and you are acknowledging your own pain and suffering, you are stopping the cycle. This entire book is intended to stop the cycle of trauma and abuse. Knowing what happened in your parents' lives and in their parents' lives, in the lives of your aunts and uncles, cousins, and other relatives, can help put into perspective the events of your own life.

Sometimes getting accurate stories from family members about what happened is difficult and you will have to rely on yourself and your own intelligence to make sense of the information you gather. You may decide to pursue this course of data gathering extensively or you may be satisfied with getting an outline of the family history. In any case, *some* information about the family history as well as the socio–political–economic history that surrounded and affected your family (wars, depressions, inflations, recessions, political movements, cultural, and racial events, ethnic and gender–based conditions, class conditions, emigration, environmental conditions, etc.) is necessary for a thoroughgoing healing.

At some point in your process (and when this point occurs is up to you — this is an issue of pacing), you will probably want to get a perspective on what happened from this multidimensional view. You will want to explore this at a time when you can put the information to good use, when it will help you to see that not all of what happened to you was about you. We are human systems interacting with many other systems — environmental systems, economic systems, class systems, racial systems, cultural systems, biosystems, religious systems, social systems, etc. It is a relief to see these interactions and to integrate this holistic understanding.

As a result of a conversation with my husband, I realized that I lived in places in America at the height of their environmental toxicity at crucial turning points in my life. I was in New York during my earliest years, suffering from extraordinary abuse and abandonment, when New York had no controls over its ravaging pollution. I was in Los Angeles at times of extreme loneliness and pain, just when Los Angeles had its most severe and unregulated smog problems. I was in Pittsburgh, Pennsylvania struggling in an abusive marriage before Pittsburgh was cleaned up from the horrifying toxicity of the steel industry. Of course these environmental conditions did not *cause* my suffering directly, but they impacted it, they interacted with it, and they reduced my resources and gave me more to struggle against. This information, which was new for me, does not change substantially my understanding of my recovery from trauma, but it gives me greater compassion for myself and a broader view as I see how many coping skills I had to develop to survive. As a person who has always suffered from bronchial asthma, environmental pollutants weaken substantially my overall well–being. The dynamic interrelationship between environmental trauma and personal trauma adds more dimension to my understanding of my life. I see my own movement towards wholeness as parallel to the struggles of a suffering earth, plundered as I was, without protection from abuse.

The case of Zorah Lambowski is intended to illustrate the value of seeing some of the systems involved in trauma. It is also intended to cultivate and encourage the pursuit of a larger perspective on human process, and to point you in that direction when it is appropriate to go there.

The History

Zorah Lambowski was born in the Bronx, New York, in the mid–1940s to Ida and Leo Lambowski, first generation Americans, both the offspring of Russian peasant immigrants. Her parents were not well educated, nor were they especially intelligent. Her grandparents were poor but stalwart survivors of difficult times and brutalizing oppression.

Leo Lambowski had been traumatized by a head injury at the age of eight years, and that accident resulted in his distinctively belligerent behavior. He had frequent bouts of unpredictable anger and erratic emotional outbursts. As a result, he was never able to continue his education beyond grade school,* and he was always in some kind of trouble. Leo's brothers and sisters, on the other hand, were capable, competent, and normal, and, like most of their peers, upwardly mobile. They married, achieved professional status, and led regular lives. They began to shun their brother, whose odd behavior discredited their achievements in America. They urged their father not to deplete his resources by rescuing Leo.

The Lambowski family was Jewish. They brought to America not only their history of class struggle as peasants, but also a history of religious persecution replete with images of continual, ageless suffering. America was to be the promised land. Joe Lambowski, Leo's

---

*Leo's mother and father were Old World people, struggling with English and with American lifestyle. They were frightened by Leo's behavior, but they couldn't understand it. It never occurred to them that there was a relationship between Leo's accident and his erratic behavior. It never occurred to them that someone could help Leo. Increasingly, they became ashamed of their son, and both secretive and protective of him. They prayed for him, and they felt a tragic sense of grief, but they had no idea how to help themselves or Leo.

father, worked with martyr–like dedication to make a place for his family in New York. He was proud of what he accomplished and the way in which he succeeded in educating his children and providing a home for them.

Leo's disability, which was not named or known as such, was a horror to his father. Joe Lambowski would have done anything he could to change the course of his son's life, but he felt helpless. The tragedy of Leo's ongoing difficulties became so painful to Joe that out of desperation, he wanted only to block Leo out, to eliminate him from his picture of triumph over difficulty. Joe was a good Jew who obeyed the laws of his religion. Though not expressive or demonstrative, Joe was constant — he held to his goals. How else could he, a non–English–speaking immigrant with no money or connections, have established a business for himself as a kosher chicken butcher in a foreign land? Above all, Joe wanted to protect his wife, Sophie, a frail woman who had not survived her transplant to America well, from Leo's ever–worsening condition. From everyone's perspective, Leo was a blight on the family, and his ongoing acts of destruction (disappearances, inability to earn a living, emotional outbursts) were a source of aggravation and despair. The Lambowski family grew to feel that they *had* to deny the truth about Leo in order to continue their own lives.

Ida's family was Jewish, too. The Melmans struggled, as did the Lambowskis, to maintain Jewish tradition in the chaos of the multiracial, multicultural melting pot of New York's poorer neighborhoods, where they felt uncomfortable and wary. Even if they could not always completely keep the Orthodox rituals, at least they maintained the environment of Judaism, the climate of worship and family. All the children grew up knowing that they were Jewish and that their faith was honorable, even beautiful. Both the Lambowski family and the Melman family were loyal to their faith. No matter what else happened, the holidays were kept, the mezzuzah on the door was kissed, the children went to Hebrew School, the Sabbath was honored. They kept the practices, albeit amending them for American circumstances.

Ida grew up in the circus–like atmosphere of a large, poor family. The girls were warned to keep to their own kind. The surrounding neighborhoods were threatening, they said, containing all kinds of evil, and the possibility of abuse. Ida felt herself to be less than her sisters, not as pretty or outgoing, and certainly less than her neighbors, all of whom seemed to adapt much more easily to America. She felt herself to be less capable than the other girls at school, and her grades reflected her sense of inadequacy. She was ashamed of her parents' ignorance, yet she respected their struggles. They worked night and day to keep the family together, earning a living, maintaining the laws of their religion, holding the holidays, praying. Her father was kind; but her mother was harried, burdened by so many children, so many duties. Ida kept her thoughts to herself — when was there time for her, who was there to listen?

Ida's family struggled for survival. Her sisters aspired only for work, marriage, and family. The best they could hope for was marriage to a good Jewish man — as soon as possible. That was it. Ida met Leo at the onset of World War II and married him quickly. She was attracted to his swarthy, romantic good looks, and she was driven by her mother's concern that her daughters marry before the war progressed further, killing off the available men. With this compulsion and fear, Ida married a man she hardly knew, only to discover in the first weeks of their marriage that he was mysteriously violent, and utterly unpredictable. When Ida learned that she was pregnant, she tried desperately to abort. Life suddenly seemed a conspiracy to undermine her. It was all so hopeless, so desperate, she thought.

At that time, abortion was not only illegal, it was shameful. Not to want to have a baby when life was so dear and so much at risk was considered a sin. In fact, the entire subject was forbidden in her family, as was the subject of sex or childbirth. Ida had no hope of finding support from amongst her sisters or her mother. If she would have expressed her fears about her husband, the blame would have been put on her for making a bad choice and she would have been told to live with it. Or, she would have gotten sympathy, combined with fear, but no solutions. So, instead, she sought advice from her girlfriends, all of whom were as ignorant as she of these matters. They told her to try solutions of Clorox and water, and to use a coat hanger, thrust cruelly up her uterus. These experiences were not only agonizing, they were useless. Either Ida was utterly incompetent, or this child was determined to be born. Ida grew big against her will, though she sometimes enjoyed the dependency this allowed. Being pregnant eventually became a kind of relief from the insecurity of wartime and the chaos of marriage to a man who was a stranger to her.

Ida became an awkward mother, just as she was a reluctant mother –to–be. Her crying, sallow baby added misery to her predicament. She had felt better off when the child was inside her body than when she came out! Leo had abandoned his post in the service, and his whereabouts were unknown until he was returned dishonorably to his family against his will. At that time Zorah was six months old.

Leo despised even the sight of his daughter, who became the symbol of his bondage to unwanted family responsibility. As the child grew, Leo repeatedly abused her. Physical, and then sexual abuse were constants in Zorah's life. A son, named David, was born to the Lambowskis when Zorah was five and was welcomed as a distraction for the miserable triumvirate. While he witnessed his father's violence, David Lambowski was rarely the object of it. Zorah, however, could not escape her father's wrath. He found her ugly and useless, and a passive victim of his passions. Leo deserted the family regularly, could barely earn a living, and when he was at home, he was impossible to comprehend. Zorah lived in constant fear of her father's abuse and her mother's hysteria. When her father was gone, she lived in dread of his return, listening always for his footsteps on the stairs.

Zorah expressed her terror and unhappiness in physical illness — fatigue, asthma, eczema, stomach problems, refusal to eat, nervousness, and withdrawal. As she grew older, she found relief in books, writing poetry, and fantasy. The only thing that sustained her within the family were the Jewish customs and practices, and her relationship with her maternal grandfather. Zorah became devoted to going to synagogue, and, when she was little and her grandfather was alive, she was also devoted to him. Wherever she found refuge, there she became devoted.

There was communication between Zorah and her mother only at those moments when their fear gave them a bond. The child yearned for closeness with her mother but got it only when taking care of her mother's needs. Ida was tormented by fear and desperation, and Zorah found herself rewarded by her mother's smile when she offered Ida a respite from her suffering. Zorah would reassure her, cook for her, comfort her, entertain her. But, between Zorah and her father there was only alienation, never anything else. Zorah was left yearning for his love and affection just as she yearned for her mother's. When Zorah was 16, Leo Lambowski abandoned his family for the last time. There was no further news of him until, in her mid–40s, Zorah learned from a government agency that her father was dead.

During the sixteen years that Leo Lambowski tormented his family, Ida and Zorah in particular, no recourse was sought within the Jewish community, nor did the Jewish families who lived nearby, or any of the other families for that matter, intervene, despite the yelling and beating that was audible from the Lambowski apartment. Neither did Leo's family, or Ida's family, attempt to protect the children or Ida from the cruelty of the disabled Leo. All preferred to ignore the tragedy no matter how it damaged the children. To think of a Jewish man who was so perverted as to harm his own offspring was beyond the pale of possibility. This just did not happen in Jewish homes — at least that's what the old women who sat on the stoops said as they shook their heads back and forth and clucked their tongues whenever the Lambowskis walked by. If Ida walked by, they averted their eyes completely, for they had heard her pleading with her husband the night before to stop hurting Zorah.

In the summertime in the Bronx, everyone kept their windows wide open. People even slept on the fire escapes to avoid the humid heat that lay like wet blankets on them all. On the third floor, where the Lambowskis lived, the temperature was unbearably hot, even in the middle of the night. It was as if all the tenants of the building lived together, but no one mentioned what they heard and therefore knew, or at least suspected. The Lambowski family was a subject for secret conversations, not public ones. Everyone knew that Leo was disturbed, but no one said anything, no one did anything. It was better not to think about it; not to interfere. But "cluck, cluck, cluck" went the women's tongues, and "tsk, tsk, tsk" said the men, seeing Zorah going to school, her head bent, her face gray.

History Becomes Herstory: Stopping the Lineage of Abuse

When I met Zorah Lambowski, she was working as a writer and a teacher of writing. Our therapeutic focus was on relieving her self–negation, developing a healthy sense of self. Most specifically, we addressed her attitudes about sexuality and relationship, which were severely damaged. These subjects were highly charged, and so emotional release became an important consideration. We addressed this primarily by building a healthy, reliable, and supportive relationship with each other to allow honest communication. For the purposes of release, we used genuine movement process and energetic support systems such as Jin Shin Jyutsu, CranioSacral Therapy, and other appropriate, expressive, and integrating interventions.*

Zorah was a stately woman. Her body, like her spirit, was lush, and one would not suspect that a woman of her character and bearing would be so self–loathing. On the outside she was striking, unusual, perhaps even exotic. She had a penetrating way of being with other people. Her presence was strong, and those who met her remembered her. She was outspoken and direct. It was only when she became very tender and intimate that she revealed her distaste for herself and her longing to die. This longing was the persistent residue of her identification with the thoughts she had acquired from her mother and father. And because she had so desperately wanted to satisfy them, she believed she did, in fact, want to die. Then, as her life progressed, the trauma patterns established in her punitive and destructive home were so disruptive to her happiness and so persistent that death often seemed a good and likely choice.

Zorah and I began our interaction by laying bare the outline of her life. We recorded her history in writing, noting the nature and

---

*These tools are explained and discussed in the Resource section of this book.

frequency of trauma. The emblem of Zorah's ugliness and unworthiness, she felt, was her failure to establish a successful relationship with a man. She suffered, in fact, from a great deal of discomfort with men. In their company her pelvic floor would clench and tighten, her abdominal area becoming swollen and distended when there was the possibility of intimacy. The relationships she chose in her adult years were almost as abusive as the one with her father. Thus she had proven to herself time and again that she was unworthy of healthy, mature love. No matter what else she had in life — the admiration of others, physical comfort, even health — it didn't compensate for the loss of what she had always craved. . . to be loved by a man, to be accepted, and to be supported emotionally for who she was.

In actuality, Zorah had been raped many times, physically, psychically, financially, and emotionally by the men she had chosen. Despite her strength, she played the role of victim. The relationships all began similarly. Zorah felt an attraction to a man, and then she felt a need to aid him in his development or to help him in some way, often monetarily. In the same manner, she had given herself to countless projects which were frequently creative, artistic, or involved a social or political movement. Zorah was invariably a good servant to the endeavors of her lovers and to her chosen projects. Her intimate relationships, however, never endured. They ended one after the other, forcing Zorah to uncover in herself layer upon layer of perseverance, self–determination, intelligence, and commitment, just to survive. Despite these destructive relationships, Zorah was able to pursue the development of her skills and her education, and her devotion to these undertakings proved worthwhile. It may even have been true that the challenge of recovery fueled her creativity, causing her to become more and more involved in her work as a writer.

Zorah understood the cause of her failed relationships and her self–deprecation. Clearly the behavior of her father, and the inability of her mother to protect her, had led her to disbelieve her own worth. But despite understanding, her self–negation remained. She felt happiest in service to others and she didn't regret this need to serve. She only felt a longing to have joy carry over into her own life in such a way that she would not be forced to work unremittingly, as if paying for an old crime and never finalizing the debt. She felt she made her life unnecessarily difficult. And she longed for healthy relationships, particularly with men. While her relationships with women also bore the mark of the family's dysfunction, the more severe symptomology surfaced in her interactions with men. She had a few important women friends, and while some women had also betrayed her trust and devotion, several others saw Zorah for who she really was and respected her. She even had one or two women friends who could equal her with loyalty and creativity, and these relationships she could trust.

After hearing Zorah's history, I worked with her, using movement, sound, and writing as interventions. I sensed that she had a surpassing ability and was ready to allow emotion to surface and reveal itself and to learn from this revelation, so I used expressive forms in the hope of deepening her relationship to herself, and freeing her of the burden of her negative introjects.

Because of Zorah's intelligence and clear understanding and the years she had already spent in therapy before coming to work with me, verbal analysis seemed redundant and even depleting. I felt she would experience greater freedom and joy through other forms, and in gentle, albeit occasionally cathartic, release. She herself said she preferred these mediums at this juncture in her evolution, as they gave her not only a unique way to explore her own inner territory, but simultaneously awakened her to her own aliveness. Just talking had begun to have the opposite effect — it led her to feel trapped in the tragedy of her life, imprisoned by her story. This seemed reasonable, given her maturity and history in therapy.

In fact, there was also a great deal of power and strength, courage and fortitude in Zorah's lineage of survivors, and we had to find a way to access that genetic power as well as identifying the cruelty that had found its way into her father. The lineage of abuse had to stop with Zorah — that was a crucial component of our work together. Abuse breeds abuse, and survivors have the task of becoming conscious of their own violence, which is a response to the trauma they have experienced. All too often, victims of abuse victimize themselves the most severely. Zorah did this through her relationships with men and in her attitude toward herself. But there was a way in which she was perpetuating another lineage – the lineage of courage and strength, and we needed to identify that too, name it, underscore it, and let it, of its own course, balance out Zorah's suffering.

That lineage of strength was in her body, which had the structure of endurance, the ability to grow ever stronger and to respond mightily to recovery. Her lineage of strength and courage was also evident in Zorah's creativity, in her imagination, and her capacity to speak and write in vital, living images and to captivate others with her articulation. That was why she was not only a writer, but also a teacher of writing. In addition, Zorah carried on the kindness of her grandfather, which she had absorbed in the precious early years of her life, before he died, when he often cared for the little girl when her father was away. Even after her grandfather had died, Zorah felt his inspiring energy permeate her in her moments of despair.

Focusing on the endurance, perseverance, and creative power of her lineage was new for Zorah. I asked her to write about her grandfather, in particular, since he represented Zorah's only positive connection with a loving male figure who mirrored back to her worth, value, and respect. This is what she wrote:

WHEN GRANDPA HAD A STROKE
A Biographical Essay by Zorah Lambowski

It was in New York, around 1950, when it was almost summer, that it happened. On that important day, my brother must have been about a year and a half, and my mother was upstairs with him, in the hot, stuffy third floor apartment on our poor, busy street, where I was born and grew up. In this same neighborhood, within walking distance, lived all my relatives — aunts, uncles, and cousins. But my favorite was Grandpa. When he walked me to school it was the very best part of my day. He always wore a gray gabardine suit for the occasion, and a broad rimmed hat. He'd hold out his hand for me, which, despite Grandpa's angularity, was wide and open.

On the way to school, Grandpa would keep his eyes, peeled for lost objects of value — hangers, paper clips, bags, boxes, or cartons — cast off things that he could use to make into toys for his grandchildren. He'd construct his curious and playful objets d'art in his bedroom and store them under his high European bed, piled with comforters. Then, at special, magical moments, he'd put out one of his creations for the delight and surprise of the little boys and girls who came to visit, of whom I was probably the most frequent.

But on this near summer day, Grandpa didn't come to take me back from school. One of my aunts came instead, with a worried and distracted look on her face. I knew something was wrong. When I got home, at least four or five of Mama's sisters were there, with their children, and the air rippled with chaos. After taking me to school that morning, Grandpa had a stroke. That was the end of Grandpa for me. He never walked me to school again. I could never play with him as I used to, sitting on his knee in his bedroom, sucking sugar cubes soaked in tea from his samovar, wondering what surprises would appear from under his bed where his constructions of wire and paper were stored. His artistry and my curiosity had been perfectly matched. His was the only environment of sanctuary I knew, the singular place of safety in my life. Now, this was taken from me, all too swiftly, and without explanation.

A year later we left the Bronx, and a few years later, Grandpa died. So, now I see why illness has become so threatening to me, and why I invest myself so thoroughly in preventing it, and in transforming it, sometimes working too hard to make it something other than what it is. Illness took Grandpa from me. No one saw the special relationship I had with him. Everyone was too hysterical (they were ALWAYS too hysterical) to wonder what impact his stroke would have on *me*. No one thought I would want to know how he was or what he needed. Everyone assumed I would tire him, so they kept me from him, and they kept him from me.

Grandpa's stroke wrapped every corner of my life in darkness, where he had been the only light. Mystery and hysteria separated me from the one and only authentic, trustworthy connection I had. Illness became traumatically bonded to loss, and now perhaps I can look at that bond and unravel it; perhaps it is time to separate from that bond with illness, with being sick, and with needing help. A certain paralysis afflicts me now whenever I consider illness, though I have probably acquired more resources to deal with it than most other people.

What was the message of Grandpa's stroke? He was a failed man in a strange country, surrounded by women. His world consisted of his bedroom, the block, the stoop, walking his granddaughter to school, making toys. Gone were the fields of his Russian countryside, the villages of his homeland, and his comrades. His daughters surrounded him with their war-struck marriages, and I was the offspring of a horrible abandonment of all that Grandpa held worthy – loyalty, fidelity, fatherly love, honoring the children. A stroke, and the heart gives up, gives out, misses a beat, shivers. A stroke, a harbinger of death, the precedent is set, and a failed man is finally knocked to his knees, helpless, unable to rally any more courage or strength. Perhaps his illness was his spirit at work to muster up an awareness, to strike a chord between survival and truth, to strike a chord between the truth of the body and the truth of the soul.

I always gained so much from Grandpa. In reflecting on his stroke, I gain from him, though that event eventually took him from me. But in writing now, I get him back, in essence. Only this time, I pull the surprises out from under the high trundle bed — the bed of my intuition and my inquiry, which is as independent as he was, seeking in all the neglected places for a jewel.

Notice how in this writing Zorah begins to identify who she is in a positive way. While the strengths she points out about herself in this essay were obvious to me, and probably to many other people, they were hardly obvious to her before she wrote this. The evidence of this is that she never would have written in this vein if I hadn't oriented her in the direction of her lineage of courage, persever-ance, and devotion. Luckily, she was responsive to my suggestions. If she hadn't been, we would have had to deal with her resistance first, which could have been a long struggle, given Zorah's strength. But Zorah was open and responsive. She was ready to resonate with the spiritual support of her grandfather's memory, which carried with it the hereditary quality of people who, despite oppression, continue to live vital, artistic, imaginative, even humorous, lives. This is the energy of survival, and Zorah began to identify it, with all its laughter and tears, and to claim it, finally, as her own.

One of the most satisfying modalities for Zorah was movement. In my large studio I began to work with her to open, stretch, and express herself through her body, sometimes utilizing music but usually in silence. Music was so suggestive, and Zorah was so suggestible — I wanted all the creative space to be hers — I wanted her to focus on her own creative direction, rather than the influence of other artists. I wanted Zorah to realize what an important artist *she* was.

In response to my suggestions for movement, the stories came from her body easily. She was ready to tell them. She knew that the essential Zorah, the person who was joyous, the child spirit, was ripe to step out of the flesh that contained her. She trusted me because I made my compassion and my vision of who she was obvious. My belief in her inspired her to believe in herself. I named creativity as her essential nature. And it was to that creative, vital, victorious being that I spoke and beckoned. I kept my eye on this essential Zorah, and while I acknowledged her fear and its protective function, I did not indulge it. I believed thoroughly and unflinchingly in her courage. Zorah's therapeutic history indicated she was ready for this.

I allowed and guided Zorah through a slow process of dancing out her fear of her father, her rebellion against him, her anger, her identification with him, and her longing for his comfort. The need to dance was a mirror reflection of her passionate nature, which she had repressed, except in her devotion to others. I allowed Zorah to portray in movement her deep need for love and affection, and I allowed her to find from within herself the dignity of her own body through this expression. I also encouraged sound. I will never forget the session in which I asked Zorah to move spontaneously from the feeling of fear she had in regard to men. We had already worked together for three years and she was ready. It was an early morning session, and the light came through the windows softly onto the floor where Zorah moved by herself, without music.

She allowed her body to enter deeply into the moments of fear that she had experienced as a child, as the victim of her father's repeated abuse. She had described her father, Leo, to me as a large man, 6'2", 250 pounds, and Zorah had been a frail, small child. She'd had difficulty eating and digesting her food. The physical abuse had been constant from the time Leo returned from overseas. The sexual abuse began when Zorah was five years old, when David was born, and continued into her adolescence. Her father had remained seductive with her until the last time she saw him, which was on her sixteenth birthday.

Zorah's movement was accompanied by the sounds she had felt but never uttered. The movement consisted entirely of floor work. Zorah dragged and pulled herself on the floor, occasionally turning from side to side, keeping her eyes closed. She portrayed not only sexual abuse but the moments following rape, when she felt completely abandoned. Sound became a poignant rendering of Zorah's experience. The sounds she made cannot be translated into words. They told me more about what was within Zorah than any verbal communication could. As I listened to her lonely, deep cries and watched her express herself in pure, genuine movement and sound, I knew there was little I could *ever* say or do to heal her. Her movement and her sound, the release of long–withheld feeling, this was her healing path. My presence was of value as a compassionate and alert witness. Indeed, the witness is often necessary. Zorah had felt so thoroughly neglected by both her mother and her father, so thoroughly alone, that my presence, silent and nonintrusive, provided the sanctuary she needed to communicate, indirectly, her desire for connection, the knowledge that someone indeed saw and believed her story.

When Zorah was in the very center of her pain, she opened her eyes suddenly and looked at me. What I saw was an animal in the wild, a creature abandoned in the midst of attack. The terror that shot from her face marked itself indelibly on my heart. The only response I could make was a compassionate return, eye-to-eye. The only comfort I could offer was my constancy, the knowledge present in my eyes that I believed in her, that I knew that she had truly suffered. She understood all this from my eyes, and, perhaps even more importantly, our eye-to-eye contact gave the signal that the suffering was over. My presence, and our communication, was THE difference between past and present.

During the course of our work together, Zorah attempted three relationships with men, none of which succeeded, but all of which were, in comparison to her earlier relationships, less abusive. As a result of the impact of these relationships on her process, Zorah began to see more profoundly the need to nurture herself thoroughly and holistically. She wanted, finally, to work with her self–negation on her own and not feel that she demanded the presence of a man, supposedly to alleviate her self–doubt, though the relationships she chose ultimately reinforced her negative relationship to herself. It had been her earlier hope that the love of a man and a loving rela-tionship would erase from her mind and her heart the persistent belief she had in her worthlessness. But what was needed was that she herself eradicate this belief and that she herself connect with the essence within her that made many others feel so drawn to her. Then, perhaps, but certainly not before this, she could sustain a relationship of maturity and commitment.

One of our sessions underscored this transformation. For this ses-sion, we were working temporarily in a friend's dance studio, which was lined on one wall with mirrors. Zorah disliked the mirrors. In fact, her initial response was that she wouldn't be able to work here. Zorah's resistance was out! She stubbornly rebelled against the mir-rors, but I felt I knew something of the background to this reaction.

It was difficult for Zorah to feel that she was a beautiful woman. Her shapely, muscular body was not attractive to her. She was ma-ture and seductive but she hid from her own sexuality, despite her many relationships. This was very confusing to Zorah and the di-lemma, in terms of movement, was best solved, she felt, if she could just dance without having to see herself. On this occasion, how-ever, I used a risky intervention. I asked Zorah to stand and look at herself in the mirror. I asked her to focus on her own eyes. As she gazed into her eyes, she couldn't help but smile because there was so much vitality in the windows of her soul. She looked deeply into her own eyes and grinned back. I asked her to tell herself what she felt at that moment. The message was joyous. "You're terrific," she said, looking into her own eyes, "you're sparkling. Your spirit is beautiful." We both burst into laughter.

Following this interaction with her mirrored self, Zorah worked with movement to be able to discover her backbone, her spine. I wanted Zorah to move with awareness of the integrity she had structurally and emotionally. Her integrity, her backbone, and her ability to stand on her own were her victory. It was crucial that SHE become aware of this. The session included the release of an enormous amount of anger at the manner in which she had been mis-educated about this integrity. But it ended in triumph as she realized the power of creativity and compassion as her resources. At the end of this session, we returned again to the mirror, and I asked Zorah to look into her eyes and say what she felt in the moment. What she said to herself was, "I believe in you."

While this was not my last session with Zorah, it was a harbinger of the many fruits of our therapeutic interaction. Zorah did not complete therapy with *everything* she wanted — a successful relationship and complete and total freedom from her self–abusive thoughts. But, at the end of our work together, Zorah believed that she could stand well on her own. She had caught unforgettable glimpses, more than once, of her worthiness, her spirit, her indomitable courage, her deep–rooted desire to truly connect with others and to truly serve, and her remarkable, unique creativity. She had even acknowledged, at my behest, her spectacular willingness to heal. And above all, she had to acknowledge her commitment to being honest and constant with herself and her own experience. Zorah carried self–love as her reward for our ongoing sessions together. She could feel her uniqueness, and she knew that when she wanted support, she would be able to find it, without question. She knew exactly where to look.

Recapitulation:
Seeing Into the Web of Trauma

Zorah Lambowski's story is obviously not only the drama of incest and of a father–daughter relationship gone horribly awry. It is more multi–dimensional than that, and I believe all stories of sexual abuse have a similar multi-dimensionality. Within the striking tale of Zorah's healing, there are also many more stories, each of them as compelling and as multifaceted as Zorah's. Ida Lamb-owski's story, Leo Lambowski's story, David Lambowski's story, the stories of Ida's sisters, and the stories of the Melmans would be equally as fascinating and even as heroic as Zorah's. The economic and social dynamics in pre–war USA, the nature of relationships between family members in immigrant Jewish homes, the class structure in melting pot America, abortion politics, combat trauma, and the impact of wartime culture on sexual mores should all be considered as perspectives on Zorah Lambowski's story. The relationships between social systems, family systems, religious systems, class structure, and gender issues all are significant in gaining true understanding of what happened to Zorah and how she got better. There comes a time, I believe, in every survivor's evolution when these many aspects of an individual's journey could be considered with great benefit. The personal story surfaces as part of a complex tapestry, viewed on the wide screen of history and human development. Such wide-screen viewing provides detachment and we witness our own trauma and become interested in it, rather than being repeatedly re–victimized by the story of our own devastation. At the right moment, this broader perspective uplifts and enlightens us. In order to get to this vantage point for viewing the landscape, it might prove helpful to ask yourself the upcoming questions. If this doesn't feel appropriate to do now (if, for instance, you feel angry as you read what preceded this sentence), just skip this part and save it for later, when you may welcome the opportunity to look at your story anew. One of the keys to healing, as demonstrated in the chapter on pacing, is timing — knowing when you need what, and seeking it, putting the rest aside for the moment. But if this feels right and appropriate now, consider the following:

1. What do you know of the major national issues occurring at the time of your birth, and during your crucial developmental years? How can you find out the impact of these events on your family? Use libraries and literature for resources as well as making inquiries of the family members you can rely on, if there are any.

2. Do you have any information about the illnesses that have burdened your family? Has mental or physical illness played a role in the lives of significant family members? Seek this data from well informed sources, and use your own intelligence if the information you find is incomplete or questionable.

3. What is the immigration history of your family? What can you learn about the cultures and countries, the customs and environments, that have influenced your family history?

4. What were the dynamics of relational interaction like in the families of your parents? What can you learn about the trauma which might have occurred within the lives of your parents? Take your time gathering this significant information and weaving it together. You yourself may document the family's historical background from your own understanding. If you choose to do any of this, it could free you from the burden of personalizing the tragedies you know and have experienced.

5. What do you know or what can you discover about the strengths of your family? What power, courage, intelligence, resourcefulness, talent, and skill lies within the family story? Claim these as well as the knowledge you acquire of difficulty. Wherever there is difficulty, there is often just the right resource to balance it — gear your search for those resources and name them as yours, artfully carving the treasures from the mire. The effort will prove endlessly worthwhile.

6. Finally, in whatever way you can, seek out records of family history (letters, photo albums, journals) and view them from your perspective of understanding trauma. Then make your record, using your own writing and photos to document what *you* have learned. This way you become part of the story — you make your mark on your family's lineage, and, perhaps, change it — forever. Make your own story of courage and perseverance in a way that acknowledges who you are (journals, movies, dances, songs, etc.). Enter the stream of the family saga via your own voice. Don't let yourself be excluded by remaining silent.

When Zorah moved out of therapy on a week–to–week basis and into a relationship with me that allowed her to come to therapy sessions whenever she felt they were necessary, she was in a state of solid self–reliance and carried the power of self–trust. I feel certain that she will be fulfilled relationally and creatively because she is now prepared for that. What I respect enormously about Zorah is that she genuinely wants to share with others the quality of self–discovery and empowerment that she has gained for herself. This generosity of spirit is her greatest treasury. I am confident of her success in every regard. It is witnessing the triumph of self for people like Zorah that makes me feel certain of the value of this holistic, body–centered, multifaceted, and expressive approach to healing from trauma.

Sexual Abuse

in the

Name

of

Spirituality

What Happened at
Peaceful Valley Ashram?

This chapter is presented with the intention of demonstrating how individual experiences of trauma and abuse compound to allow collective abuse to occur. The events described in this chapter are all too common in a culture starving for spiritual direction. Peaceful Valley Ashram and Swami Amrita Bhajan reflect how this process occurs for Westerners attracted to Eastern spirituality, but this does not at all suggest that this is the only framework for this scenario. In fact, there are numerous examples, from Jimmy Swaggert to David Karesh, of Westerners who take advantage of the traumatic undercurrents that permeate our collective psyche with a poignant yearning for truth, spirit, direction, leadership, heroism, and meaning.

What I want to suggest is that while spiritual truth abounds in a variety of forms — Christianity, Judaism, Buddhism, Taoism, mysticism, Sufism, etc. — no spiritual practice or teacher should ever demand that you violate or sacrifice yourself or your feelings. I encourage all seekers, and particularly those who know they have been abused as children, to trust themselves first and foremost, and never to surrender their own truth, no matter what others say. Know Thyself and This Above All, To Thine Own Self Be True are the phrases I recommend as reference points for all action and choice. Read this story, which comes out of real and personal experience, with an eye to witnessing how trauma unfolds and how it can be masked and hidden. Pay attention to the undercurrents of vulnerability and denial and see how manipulation happens. This is an example from which I hope a great deal of learning and awareness will spring.

Peaceful Valley Ashram was built high in the Rocky Mountains on a stretch of land that would be treasured by any environmentalist. On all sides there were views of majestic peaks, the Himalayas of the West. From the heights of the ashram buildings, one looked down upon the valley below where people lived yearning for a higher truth. The master of the ashram, though physically a small man, was a giant in the minds of those devoted to him. Swami Amrita Bhajan called himself an emissary of truth and the words that he spoke were in many ways the same words that had been spoken for ages to the Hindu devout, and to all who had sought inspiration in Vedantic texts, the Mahabharata, the Ramayana, the teachings of Ramakrishna, and the wisdom and enthusiasm of Swami Vivikenanda. In fact, Swami Amrita Bhajan claimed all these antecedents as his spiritual lineage. Those who listened to Swami Amrita Bhajan were struck by his smile, his sense of humor, his deep, luminous eyes, his bearing, his authority (always a weak spot for Westerners), and by the way he exuded a certain charm that magnetically drew the loveless to him.

In California, Arizona, Colorado, and the Midwest, the Swami found there was a longing amongst needy people, young and old, for a passionate truth that might fill the culture's spiritual vacuum. Swami Amrita Bhajan offered what seemed to be a viable illusion for those on this quest and what he offered had enough substance to validate him, especially if one didn't inquire *too* deeply. Maybe if these needy ones did what the Swami said, they *might* get to this dangling, sparkling carrot sometimes called enlightenment. Maybe if, as he suggested, they sat and focused on him alone, day after day, night after night, and sang the songs that he told them to sing, maybe then something would change and they might step out of their landlocked suffering onto the boat of redemption. Maybe if they stopped thinking, or if they stopped analyzing, or if they stopped trying and gave up (the Swami called it "surrender"), and if they threw themselves at his feet, then maybe they would come out of this darkness of ignorance (that's what the Swami told them) and they might see a light of awareness, a place more vital than the common terrain. The Swami claimed to know such a brilliant state of being, and he said he could identify it in others, as well, or the lack of it. He said this, and everything else, with power and force. For those who felt spiritually stripped, it was worth a try. So much of what the Swami said sounded familiar, even traditional, albeit exotic. Maybe it *was* worth a try. And when they tried, they received *some* benefit, so they continued.

The seekers were sincere but they were also confused and the Swami knew that. From where he sat in his white robes (symboliz- ing his purity), he gazed down upon their confusion, and he gazed down especially upon the women. How needy they were and how needy was he. His life in India had been solitary. The intelligence and inspiration he felt were his were unrecognized or commonplace in his homeland. There he was just one of many claiming wisdom and awareness, part of a lineage that spanned ages. There he was nothing special. And while he came from a wealthy family and had suffered little in his life, nevertheless he had a taste for power. He told stories of a teacher but gave him no name. Who knew if he was given the title of Swami by anyone authorized to give such a title? And even if he was authentic, a true Swami, did that give him the right to bed with the women who wanted him above all else to be trustworthy, dependable, authentic? Did that give him the right to hide his acts of passion behind white robes of denial? Did that give him the right to use this power he had over needy, confused people to satisfy his lust for intimacy, control, recognition, sex, and power?

Swami Amrita Bhajan pretended to be pure, to satisfy the yearning for purity he perceived in his followers. It wasn't difficult. He ate, dressed, and spoke purely. He kept men and women apart and didn't allow a friendly, social, relaxed atmosphere at his gatherings. He rigidly controlled the relationships and activities of those who began to long for his attention. He appeared scrupulous. He recorded each and every donation. He kept records to the penny and he was immaculately clean. Everything was clean. The food was clean. The bathrooms were clean. How could he do anything wrong, a man who was so clean? Even while his devotees were being manipulated and controlled, his style was so smooth, so kind, so charming, that no one dared to notice.

And "Swamiji," as everyone called him, tenderly using the diminutive, Swamiji kept his intimate affairs quiet. He didn't try to bring large numbers into his halls. He kept things quiet so that nobody would pry into his bedroom: that cabin set off from the other quarters. "So humble a dwelling," the others said. But within it the Swami managed to create for himself nights of companionship, nights of the flesh, nights of being in control just enough to free himself, to feel the human love so long deprived him. He had worked hard to create a place in America where he could finally bring to his bed at night the soft Western lady white doves and say, breathlessly, "You mustn't tell anyone. Tell, and I'll never see you again. Tell, and no one will believe you. You will be shamed. Now, surrender yourself to me and feel your good fortune." His breath became rapid and forced, despite his supposed advanced knowledge of Pranayama, as he thrust his all–too–human self upon the acquiescent birds, each a hunter's delight.

It took at least 15 years before the story leaked out, but secrets like this cannot be kept indefinitely, no matter how neatly the binding is done. One woman who had given herself to him far too much finally burst. Two abortions, abandonment of her own child to be with the Swami, the destruction of her marriage, her sacrifice of hours and hours of her time, secrets, lies, humiliation, betrayal — it all came out in toxic waves of sadness, anger, and depression, striking the hearts of those who could hear her. All her self-negating (including secret and unwanted abortions) had been performed under the Swami's orders, and they had all been justified as "devotion to the Guru."

Under cover of suppression and silence, feelings ran strong at Peaceful Valley Ashram. If you looked into the eyes of those who meditated and chanted under the Swami's tutelage, you could see their burning intensity, their life's urgent need to break through to something real. But all those who swept and cleaned and packaged and listed and made phone calls at Peaceful Valley Ashram, cooking for the master, washing his laundry, buying and selling his books and tapes and records, all hoped with every ounce of strength they had that the truth existed in *someone*, and that if they couldn't find it in themselves, at least they could earn it, or pray for it, or find that someone who would bestow it upon them or tell them how to get to it. If they believed that the truth existed within themselves, and that it manifested as themselves in their uniqueness, they might view their quest differently. The responsibility and creativity such individuality implied made them feel helplessly inadequate and lonely. But to give the responsibility for truth to someone else, ah, *then* there was a system, there was meditation, there was chanting, there was reading of appropriate books, there was associating with appropriate people, there was abstinence from this or that, there was vegetarianism, there was a formula. And if one followed that formula, one could, maybe, someday, some lifetime, become enlightened, present, aware, and alive.

The students of Swami Amrita Bhajan hoped that enlightenment meant freedom from the suffering of their feelings of impotence and incompetence, their emotional confusion and their indecision. Their feelings of helplessness were sometimes so intense that they felt led to the brink of insanity. The faith the Swami evoked in them calmed them at such moments. When the stories began to spread about the Swami's indiscretions, this faith crumbled and panic ran apace throughout all the ashram's clean, calm domains. If Swami Amrita Bhajan was not pure, then what was there to live for? Certainly not their own individual purity, for what in the world could that ever mean given what the Swami had told them? And how could they ever get to the purity and clarity he inspired without a map, without a guide? A shockwave rumbled through the ashrams, affecting people differently. A few women were infuriated. Many men laughed to themselves, not at all surprised and not thinking it all that important. Some people upheld the purity of Swami Amrita Bhajan. After all, didn't the master work in mysterious ways? Wasn't truth known in ways that poor humans could not decipher? "Didn't you ever hear of crazy wisdom," they asked, "the way of knowing that is in chaos, in behavior beyond our comprehension?" Ah, surely this would be understood when enlightenment came.

But the women who had been coerced into sex with the Swami one by one began to come out of their trance like a community of opossums realizing that the sly fox is finally out of sight. They shook and quivered and cried as they realized what they had done and what had been done to them. And these women began to tell their truths, and, in speaking, they felt their simple, human power. They said that there had been nothing spiritual in the co–mingling with the Swami. They said that there had been nothing spiritual in their abandonment of their children, their husbands, their careers. They said that there had been nothing spiritual except what they were now learning in their speaking. And what they were learning had to do with finding their own voices, in naming their own unpolluted, simple truths. And they were strengthened by the sound of their voices telling their own stories.

"It was just another affair," said one of the women who was not yet awake, trying to downplay her own catastrophe, "just another affair." But this was not just another affair. For Swami Amrita Bhajan had presented himself as an embodiment of God, and the women were saying that God had a penis and that God had orgasms and that God needed someone to talk to and fondle when he was lonely, and that meant, that meant, that meant what?! That meant that when one achieved spiritual prowess, one remained human, and that spiritual development did not eliminate a craving for comfort and connection, and for affection. Swami Amrita Bhajan had been the exponent of desirelessness, so then, therefore, if he had desire, ego, how could he, by his own definition, be God? Swami Amrita Bhajan had carefully stated that God, or Enlightened Beings, were not human. Their actions were absolute, not relative. And if he were *not* God, but just a man with needs, and they were *not* devotees of a pure desireless Master, then what was left of faith and aspiration? What was left of their choice to abandon what they had been told were their egos? What was left if all they had were themselves?

Lily: A Case History

Lily was only 21 years old and just married when she met Swami Amrita Bhajan. She came from a Christian family of kind and simple people. All her relatives were decent folk, ethical and responsible — except for Uncle Dale. Uncle Dale was always a little unnerving — cracking sleazy jokes at the wrong time, eyeing the girls just at their most vulnerable transition into puberty, cornering them with questionable hugs, kisses too open–mouthed and wet to be comfortable. The others — the aunts, uncles, cousins — would glance at Dale's shenanigans and say, eyebrows raised, "Oh, Dale!" Nobody took his offenses seriously, and the pain in the young girls' eyes was pushed away by the matrons of the family, while the men smiled behind their occasional beers, making light, as they always did, of feminine distress.

Standing in the garden, waiting for "Swamiji" to appear, Lily surveyed the loveliness of the setting with wide–eyed wonder. She was surrounded by well–tended flowers, the air was soft, everything was peaceful, carefully arranged and expectant, rather like a wedding. Her long blonde hair framed her china–white face like sunstruck wheat, and her glistening blue orbs were radiant with innocence. When "Swamiji" walked into the room, he glanced at her in what appeared to be a cursory way, but he quickly gathered in her shapeliness and arranged his strategy. Then he shifted his attention to the others, nodding and speaking. Later, he invited her to a private interview in his room. Lily struggled against a nausea, as "Swamiji" kissed her and put his arms around her. She smelled, in rapid, unexpected flashbacks, too quick for her to really grasp, the scent of her Uncle Dale's aftershave. Why did that return to her now? Then, without explanation, she found herself bolting for the door, wordlessly escaping from the Master's grip that seemed a stranglehold, all the while feeling shame for rejecting this holy man whom her new husband so deeply respected. The battle within her was overwhelming. She tried to smile and to be respectful. She instantly took all responsibility for the incident, feeling it stemmed from her spiritual immaturity and resistance to God, phrases she had learned from the other "devotees." When she saw "Swamiji" the next day she was relieved that he smiled at her. "How kind he is," she thought, "to have forgiven my rudeness."

"I misunderstood his caress," she thought. "It just shows how low my mind is." "He was trying to be nurturing and I interpreted it as wanting sex. He is showing me my degraded mind." So Lily shoved this incident into the warehouse of her memory, where she kept all her concerns about Uncle Dale, and loyally accompanied her husband, with whom she was enraptured, on the path of devotion to the exotic and charming Indian holy man. She quickly learned how to interpret her doubts and concerns from the vantage point of the "spiritual seeker" who ultimately must "surrender to the Master, the Guru."

Lily had never felt special. She had never been acknowledged for her intelligence or her skill. She was pretty, but she looked rather like a little girl, the kind of good looks people called "sweet." And she was soft spoken, not asserting herself at all. Her shyness coupled with her childish looks made it difficult for others to take her seriously, and Lily felt protected by this way she could be ignored. People just assumed she was nice, and thought no more about her ideas or her life. Being with Swami Amrita Bhajan was the most exciting thing Lily had ever done, next to getting married. The Swami was such a break from her good Christian life, which was, truth be known, downright boring. There was often drama around the Swami — something unexpected, out of the ordinary and important could happen at any time. He lifted her life out of the uneventful pace she assumed was her destiny. The Swami made Lily's life interesting, and she didn't know how to do that herself.

When Lily was growing up, she was regarded as a perfect young girl, in the sense of being utterly unexceptional. As she grew older, she down–played her skill at sewing and designing dresses. It seemed so inferior to the achievements of the "smart kids." She liked being at home and baking with her mom and grandma. She liked the docile safety of the kitchen and the unchallenging companionship of her mother and sisters. She didn't like being noticed and she struggled with the way men looked at her. Her face, she knew, was pleasing to others. She could tell by the way people stared at her when she was talking to them, but she cringed so at this attractiveness that she became almost mute, and even the people who were drawn to her soon forgot about her and left her alone. This pattern had been Lily's story for as long as she could remember. She found sanctuary in dull, lonely hours, though she had to admit, she really *was* lonely and she had a passionate yearning for some kind of transcendence, some unnamable release from the boredom of her own repression, her addiction to safety. Both the safety and the transcendence were her primary preoccupations, forming a repetitive two–line track in her mind.

Though Lily identified her home as her favorite place to be and though she rarely went anywhere else, she nevertheless felt saddened by the limitations in the relationships she had at home. Her mother grew consistently less expressive, more distant. She gained weight and focused entirely on household things. And her father was just as distant. Sometimes Lily wondered if anyone at home thought or felt anything deeply, but she kept pushing that question away, and it was not that difficult for her to blend in, to be like the inarticulate, reluctant people around her.

Lily graduated from high school not sure of what to do next. She lived peacefully at home, spending most of her spare hours talking leisurely with her sisters and her mother about homemaking. She had a few friends, and once in a while she went out with a young man from high school, but no one really changed anything for her until she met Len. While he was shy too, he did some things that Lily found very exciting, like singing songs he made up, and playing the guitar. When Lily thought of what to do after high school, she thought of being with Len. She decided to go to a vocational school and become a dressmaker. She got a job doing clothing repairs at the biggest department store in town, and she waited for Len to call. He did. Life soon seemed perfect for Lily, because Len was interested in her. She was both thrilled and reassured. She felt safe with Len, and safety, in some way, was her passion. That was why she hated to go to family gatherings when Uncle Dale was there. Just the sight of him or the mention of his name filled Lily with dread.

When Lily was five years old, Uncle Dale had been her babysitter while Lily's mother was in the hospital having a difficult time delivering Candace, Lily's younger sister. Whenever Lily thought of that time, she was overcome with anxiety and she didn't know why. Once or twice she had wanted to ask her mother if she had any ideas about why she might have felt that way about Dale and why she remembered that weekend of Candace's birth with such fear and trepidation. Any mention of it made her palms sweat and gave her a horrible headache. Lily did everything she could to stay away from the memory and to stay away from Dale, but complete avoidance was impossible. Her family was the kind that included all members at all events, and if someone didn't appear, everyone wanted to know why. It was a relief when Lily and Len became sweethearts and Len accompanied Lily to all the family dinners. Dale didn't taunt Lily about her eyes or her hair or her beauty half so much when Len was around. When Lily was nineteen, Len proposed. They were married in a simple wedding held at Lily's family's home, just 50 miles from where Peaceful Valley Ashram was being built.

Len and Lily rented a one–bedroom apartment, and life proceeded as before, except that Lily had a home of her own. She gained some independence and privacy, but she lost the almost constant companionship of her sisters and the reassuring closeness of her mother, always a source of security and relief to Lily. They spoke on the phone daily, Lily's mother giving her dependable guidance on recipes and things to make for the home, like curtains and bedspreads. She graduated from her two–year program and got a job with a dressmaker in town. Lily found it inspiring to merge color and shape and to put fabric together in a way that pleased others. Len found a group of musicians to practice with, and they were the ones who told him about Swami Amrita Bhajan and the Peaceful Valley Ashram.

Len visited Peaceful Valley Ashram the first time without Lily. When he came home that night, he was smiling radiantly, and, bright–eyed, told Lily about the subdued atmosphere, and the singing. There were people there who sang songs in English and in another language that sounded absolutely heavenly to Len. He had never experienced anything like this. He wanted Lily to come. The following Sunday, she did, though with a great deal of fear about this very new experience. She heard the songs, she felt the quiet, and she listened to the Swami talking. He smiled brightly and was firm about certain truths and the necessity of doing certain things; he was so delightful, making jokes occasionally, and he carried all the power and authority that Lily remembered of the ministers in the churches she had gone to occasionally with her family. But he was much warmer than those ministers, and much more humorous. What was most important to Lily was that Len was transfixed by the Swami. It was as if a light had come into his life. Len had lost his mother when he was young in a disastrous car crash. His father had been driving, and while Len's dad survived, he never recovered emotionally. Len's home had been devastated by the loss of the mother and the ongoing depression and guilt of the father, which incapacitated him as a parent. Len had lived his life trying to make things better for his dad, and being a surrogate adult to his younger siblings. Lily had brought so much femininity and nurturance into his life, he didn't think he could ask for anything more, but the Swami was more. The Swami wanted to hear Len sing his songs and the Swami offered more home than Lily could offer — he offered new words, new ideas, new visions, new music. He offered an ideal that was not commonplace and a way of being that organized feeling and gave it a relative value in the spiritual hierarchy. Len acted as if he were in love with the Swami, and Lily's security in her marriage catapulted. She decided she had to go along with Len in this attraction to the Swami, holding onto his shirtsleeves like a little girl following daddy at the carnival. She was desperate. Insecurity moved in on her and didn't leave.

It was two years later that Lily found herself in the garden at a retreat with Swami Amrita Bhajan. She and Len had been meditating daily since they decided the Swami was their "teacher." Lily's family had been shocked at this break from their mundane Christianity, and Lily now had nothing left in life but her husband, her sewing, and the path described by the Swami, a path very different from anything Lily had ever known.

Lily gave up her relationships with her mother and sisters for the Swami and for Len. Her choice to meditate, to call God by other names, to become a vegetarian, and to have a Guru was beyond their comprehension. While everyone remained superficially friendly, there was no doubt that their interactions were radically different. Whenever Lily sat at her mother's table or talked to her over the phone, it was as if a silent condemning ghost had joined them. Lily comforted herself by remembering the Swami's smile, his bright eyes, and the cleanliness of everything, the politeness of the other people, and the quiet, which was her sanctuary. But she was secretly panicked, almost constantly distressed. And even worse, she had to hide this distress from Len because any fear or concern Lily had, she knew, would be labeled as "resistance" or "negativity" or "doubt." She would be accused of being jealous of how much attention the Swami gave Len. She knew this because she had seen it happen to other couples at the ashram. Lily *couldn't* lose Len, therefore she *had* to believe in the Swami, the meditation, the ashram, and all the behaviors that went along with it. She had to accept all of this as "karma," though a melancholy descended when she thought this. But the truth was, she did believe in some of what the Swami said and in her meditation practice and experience, which was frequently uplifting, serene, soul–stirring; and she was well–liked at the ashram. Her gifts at sewing were appreciated, and her sweetness and angelic face made the others smile. When Swami Amrita Bhajan talked about the universality of God and the peaceful way, of being quiet and unobtrusive, humble and meek, she felt as if she had made the right choices, she felt like she fit in. But when she saw him criticize the others in the name of making them humble (the "grace of the Guru's anger," he called it), when she felt the strictness and rigidity of the separation of men and women, and the lack of socializing (it was criticized as a stupidity, a common weakness), she felt uncomfortable, fearful. This was what she was afraid to mention to Len. And then there was the incident after the retreat, which was repeated from time to time. On each occasion Lily bolted, and each rejection of the Swami's advances were followed by a loss in recognition for Lily. She would then not be invited to the special dinners the Swami hosted for those in his favor. She would not be asked to do work at the ashram, a privilege for the fortunate few deemed by the Swami worthy to come closer to him by cleaning the toilets or cooking the meals. The *really* fortunate "ladies" (as he called them) got to clean *his* toilet and cook *his* meals.

Lily went along with the whole thing. Even when Len asked her for a divorce because he wanted to go into the ashram, become a renunciate, even then Lily went along with it. She stayed loyal to the ashram, because now she had no other family. She hoped maybe some day she could go into the ashram too, become a nun just as Len was a monk, and thereby retain her closeness to him. But when the news came out that Swami Amrita Bhajan had been promiscuous and that he had ordered the abortions of several of his unborn children, then Lily felt huge waves of loathing and dismay, despair and fury, well up inside of her, and in her small apartment where she lived alone now, she sobbed and shook, inundated with a sense of betrayal and abandonment. There was no one to turn to. She was utterly alone, and she felt herself punished by this isolation, justifiably banished from human companionship.

The first disclosure of Swami Amrita Bhajan's indiscretions was made by one of Lily's most valued friends from the ashram, a woman Lily respected for her devotion and calm. Shocked at what the sweet Claire told her, Lily found herself sinking deeper and deeper into a horrible, lonely sadness. There was no one with whom she could share the disastrous sense of hopelessness she felt now about the world and about her life. She had never known such grief. If she had only remained true to the simple life her mother had modeled for her, she thought, this would never have happened. How could she live her life now, earn her living making patterns for other people's dresses, their celebrations, while her life was re–formed as a morbid lie? She felt like a sleepwalker, going through the routines which had once secured her to a sense of familiarity, but this familiarity no longer was comforting. On the contrary, it became a torture. Her loneliness escalated to the point of unbearable anxiety. She felt tortured by her own thoughts, which were more and more self–flagellation. And then, to make matters worse, into this life of confusion and distress, Lily began to have unpredictable and incredibly ugly memories that emerged from her body and that suggested the possibility that her Uncle Dale had played with her genitals during the weekend he cared for her when her sister Candace was being born. These memories were coming to her mostly at night, but sometimes when she worked; and their horror was intensified by the way Uncle Dale, in these flashes of visual memory, sometimes resembled Swami Amrita Bhajan.

In this state of despair and desperation, Lily went into therapy, humiliated that she even needed to, but not knowing where else to turn. She saw my name in a directory, and with great timidity she presented her situation, which, once spoken of, began to resemble a mystery or a puzzle. How did the events at the ashram connect with Uncle Dale and with this beautiful, talented women's sense of overriding inadequacy? Who would have guessed that from this blend of circumstances and eruptive emotional states would emerge Lily's strength, and her very first experiences of self and empowerment? In this regard, these betrayals and abandonments ultimately liberated Lily from the life of static repression she thought she desired above all else. By putting together the trauma puzzle pieces, Lily found that she was not at all what she appeared to be, and that her angelic face was actually the face of deep feeling, deep sensitivity. Slowly she discovered that she was a much more expressive, much more articulate person than her life had ever permitted her to be. It was not so much that all her previous behavior had been a lie — it was that Lily never knew she had options other than the options of docility, passivity, implosion, and repression. Indeed, Lily slowly discovered (primarily by simply speaking her own truth from deeper and deeper levels of authenticity) that her real self had been under cover, in hiding, for almost her entire life!

What surfaced first for Lily was a physical experience of nausea that invaded her life, but especially her nights. Luckily she had mastered the masking of feeling, so she could perform her responsibilities at the sewing machine and earn her living. No one really attempted to get below the surface of her behavior, and no one suspected this queasiness, this detoxification from untruth. So, for a while, Lily's life consisted of work and therapy. She came to see me twice a week and phoned me daily for six months, while she tried to discover who she was and what she was doing. Like the pieces of paper she cut and shaped to pattern beautiful dresses, Lily cut and pasted together the pieces of her life, with me as a reliable and dependable witness. It turned out that it was not such a far distance from the emotional repression of her home life, the modeling of resistance and denial that her parents offered her, to the unspoken story of being violated by her Uncle Dale at the age of five. And the distance from there to the discovery of the sexual abuse perpetrated in the name of spirituality by Swami Amrita Bhajan upon her and others was but another short walk, once the map could be surveyed with clarity and equanimity. In order for Lily to trust me enough to view the trauma map of her life with her, we had to establish an extremely safe relationship, one of mutual respect — a boundaried friendship. For a while, I played a very important role in Lily's life — I was the mirror of her health.

The connections between the parts of Lily's life were made primarily through a slow, carefully titrated process of talking with me and with hardly anyone else. The isolation, self- imposed by Lily out of her fear of others, was not my preference, but hers. Eventually, once she had learned to trust me and herself enough to be open about her feelings, other relationships became possible — first with women, then with men. But Lily had to do this alone for a while — perhaps because loneliness was her greatest fear. She had to immerse herself in it now, feel that she could manage when no one accepted or validated her. The temptation was too great to get support by being falsely accommodating. She had done this all her life. Only when she could go out into the world with the mask off her face, only then did she feel the possibility of making friends. And that time most certainly came, and when it did, I no longer had to play such a key role in Lily's process. I was a bridge, a hand she could grasp *en route* to herself.

The betrayal of Swami Amrita Bhajan and the loss of her husband had devastated Lily. Once the mask was off, she could acknowledge the magnitude of her loss. She realized that she felt as if she had nothing left. And when she saw that her ex–husband would stay with the Swami despite the sexual violations, and even when those violations were proven beyond a shadow of a doubt, then Lily knew that there was nothing left for her but change. There was no going back. The transcendence she had secretly conceptualized as an impossible experience, originating, if it ever occurred, outside of her, became one she had to create for herself by courageously remaking the pattern of her entire life. This was an awesome undertaking.

Lily's discussions with me became punctuated more and more by tears, as the grieving was admitted. Sometimes she could do almost nothing but cry. She keened as if she had lost her entire family, her community, her world. The losses accumulated when she began to recognize more of them — the loss of her childhood sense of fun and play, the loss of the ability simply to talk, to share true emotion, stolen by the horrible violations of her uncle and the environment of denial her family created that prohibited her from mentioning the abuse. She realized and re-experienced over a long period of time the loss of her adolescence, the time of flirtation and sexual play. And she acknowledged the profound loss of trust, which was replaced by a lifestyle that demanded she win love and acceptance by always being cooperative. One of the cruelest losses of all, she felt, was the loss of her relationship with Len, whom she deeply loved, her sweetheart. His artistry, his creativity, his playful singing — all of these had delighted Lily and brought, in the early days of her marriage, a joy she had never known before.

She revisited this time with unbearable melancholy, affirming the innocence of these two young lovers, a sweetness forever lost. She deserved the space for this justifiable mourning. She adored Len the musician, the maker of songs. His voice and even his bearing represented for Lily all she had ever wanted in a partner. He had been her playmate, her soulmate, her only real companion. For the first time, she acknowledged that she never wanted to lose him. Lily truly grieved the loss of Len, her husband. She felt herself to be a widow. Even worse, she felt that part of her was dying. Who was she without her companion in life? Why had she given him up so easily? She thought she would never recover from the grief. Where would she ever find trust, safety, friendship, closeness again? She could not, at this point, even fathom the possibility that all those qualities of charm, playfulness, sensuality, and musicality existed within her, and that she would find them there and give them completely to herself. And even more remote to her was the possibility that others would want to be with her, to know her, to share life with her. No one had suggested these possibilities to her previously, so when I raised them she was quizzical, unsure, even shocked. Eventually, however, my belief in her beauty would find a resonance in Lily.

One of the most challenging tasks of a therapist is allowing someone all the space they need for the organic evolution of feeling. In order to do that, to not rush feeling into resolution, there must exist an inordinate, almost a religious, faith in process, in the human capacity to heal, unhindered but supported. Such trust only emerges from a personal experience of it, and it was because I myself had accompanied my own process with such devotion that I could be devoted to Lily's process, and though all evidence revealed that she was too meek, too passive, to survive such an earthquake as the loss of her family, her husband, and her spiritual beliefs as well as her spiritual community, I could sense underneath the tremors, the power and endurance of a strong woman. Living within the confidence and humility of my own survivor's space, I held, in my vision, a real hope for Lily. This was not difficult for me to do. I simply remained constant in my belief in her, just as I was constant in my belief in myself, and I could meet her fears with my faith as naturally and as effortlessly as water flows over rocks.

The sustenance I provided, of course, was always intended to function as a model or a mirror, not as dependency. I supported Lily's process to return Lily to herself. My contract was to give her the vibratory reflection that spelled survival, transmutation of pain, awareness and awakening to self as well as Self. Having journeyed emotionally where Lily was journeying, I could do that. Someone had to — to keep her spirit alive — and I was the one Lily chose. It was as simple as that.

My role was to hold the space, to witness the scope of the pain, while Lily stepped, flagstone by flagstone, on the path of her own chosen journey. She had to see how her mother's demeanor was actually named depression, and how that depression left Lily feeling completely abandoned, utterly unsafe. Who would have guessed? Her tired, good cook mother? Depressed? But how else to understand the lack of feeling, the unexpressiveness, the insistence on always returning the conversation to the mundane, and it was because of this feminine abandonment, so unacknowledged, that Lily could not, from the age of five years, speak to her mother about what really mattered. Knowing that breaking the silence of denial was a taboo, Lily had struggled to be as mundane and faceless as those around her at the expense of her aliveness.

And who would have called her father an alcoholic when he only had two or three beers a night and then fell into a snoring sleep in front of the television, completely unavailable for anything, completely without a spark of interest in the lives of his children? Who would have named this as abandonment except someone who knew well enough the true needs of a child, and could acknowledge when they were not being met?

Being so abandoned, how could Lily tell them of a violation like Uncle Dale's violation of her? Even at the age of five, she had to protect them from things like that; she had to protect them because they could not protect her. And so the pain and disgust she felt traveled inward, having nowhere else to go. The emotion that was not allowed expression became energy seeking a target, a home, and Lily offered herself, feeling there was no other choice.

The hatred Lily felt for herself was coupled with an incredible longing to be free of pain, to be liberated, as if by magic, from the bonds of ugliness and degradation that Lily introjected into herself. She would express this by repeating a desire to "get rid" of what she called "these yucky feelings." The longing for transmutation, for transcendence, was born along with the violation, along with the wounding. Lily's childhood died the weekend Uncle Dale gave into his wretched little fantasies, his immature cravings, and his awful abuse of power. And at that same exact moment, Lily gave birth to a secret passion for transformation, her life of fantasy was born in the form of a naiveté so self–diminishing that she was a ready receptacle for Swami Amrita Bhajan's spiritual ploys. Interestingly, though, Lily's rage burst through her body in her rejection of the Swami's advances, and thereby she saved herself the additional pain of having sex with him. This, though Lily tended not to credit it, was a potent statement about her personal process. Because her revulsion at the Swami's advances came specifically from her body, it revealed that on an important motoric level, Lily was ready to individuate from her trauma pattern and history. Curiously, this act of rejecting the Swami physically spoke little to her, but strongly to me, as the harbinger of her future empowerment. For this very reason, an alert, knowledgeable therapist was essential to allow Lily to see what she would not and could not see alone — her strength, her beauty, her future empowerment, her ability to cope, and all that she was hiding under cover of passivity.

My work with Lily became not only the piecing together of the jigsaw puzzle of her life, but the creation of a structure for action, the means by which she could express the violations she felt, not only to Uncle Dale but also to Swami Amrita Bhajan. This was a long process because it required that Lily strengthen herself and feel her strength in a variety of ways — spiritually, physically, emotionally, socially; that is, completely. In order to tell her story to completion, Lily had to complete herself as a person, as a woman; she had to birth herself and rebuild the spirit that had been so wounded and devastated. She had the capacity to do this. Her instincts, once they were supported, guided her way. Keeping her needs and her intuition always in the forefront and allowing her to pace the entire process from her internal sense of timing, I was able to support Lily in declaring her separation from her abusers and from the pattern of abuse.

Together we constructed a possibility for Lily to talk to her family about Uncle Dale. And together, once that was done, we constructed a series of steps that made it possible for Lily to tell Swami Amrita Bhajan and Len (in writing) about her experience of betrayal and abandonment, and, very importantly, Lily could then express in a public as well as a private way her sense of outrage about the abuse of power demonstrated by Swami Amrita Bhajan. Because she had built her own internal resources, she had little difficulty in holding her ground when the Swami attempted to use fear to silence her. By the time these confrontations occurred, Lily had friends to support her, numerous outlets for her emotions (especially writing and exercise), and she had built a strong relationship with a loving man who respected Lily for her courage and stood by her side throughout the confrontations.

By harmonizing the imbalances within herself, Lily, for the first time in her life, began to feel that her words had power, her expression had value, her feelings had substance, and she felt, deeply, within her body, an energetic shift that led to a sense of profound aliveness. Her anger fueled her to an expression that was coherent, even brilliant. The angelic quality of her face took on another meaning, a meaning she didn't know was possible. Sweetness began to look like the radiance of energetic resurgence, and her politeness became respect for others, *as well as herself*. Lily dared to take the journey through herself. Lily dared to peel herself off the false picture of vacancy she had been raised to call life and to find beneath it the original masterpiece of vitality and selfhood.

As the process, which was the purpose of our relationship, was coming to closure, when Lily had reclaimed herself, she designed a red dress to wear — a dress that flowed with the lines of her body, a dress that danced her spirit, and the redness made her blonde hair even more blonde, golden, electric with self–love, self–appreciation. I admired her in the red dress and sent her confidently on her way, to live her life with the honesty and enthusiasm that were inherent to her nature.

Lily stepped out of my office into a life she navigated from her center. Swami Amrita Bhajan left for India and would never return to America because of the publicity Lily had generated. Lily's strength came not only from having stopped the Swami from further abuse, it came from her reclamation of her natural self. The defiant, willful, strong–minded, creative and intelligent person she was born to be was now free to do her work in the world and to live the vital, human life that was always her birthright.

How Does Abuse Happen in the Name of Spirituality?

Look carefully at Lily's story. Do the details of her family seem in any way familiar to you? Do you recognize the dynamics of passivity and denial, avoidance and silence as forms of betrayal? These are the accepted modes of interaction that conspire subtly to make the collective abuse that Swami Amrita Bhajan and others like him perpetrate possible. And remember, he too is acting out of his own history of trauma, which, ultimately, he will have to explore.

From this perspective, Swami Amrita Bhajan is not the only culprit. Responsibility for abuse is always multifaceted. The solution is not in punishment or blame (though that energetic process may have to occur to enter deeper layers of resolution), but in awareness, awakening to the truth of who we are, understanding the dynamics of childhood and development, and finding healthy resolution. This is *all* possible, but it takes the kind of diligent effort outlined in Lily's experience to make this transformation occur. The word behind abuse is always abuse. Trauma perpetuates trauma.

If you are attracted to a group that requires commitment of any kind, and you are a survivor of trauma, don't commit yourself too readily. Here are some questions to consider as you evaluate your participation. *Take your time answering them!*

1. Does this group have a hierarchical or authoritative structure? Where would you be in that hierarchy if you joined? Is that position similar to your role in your family? How do you feel about revisiting that role? Do hierarchies seem fair or reasonable to you in a spiritual context?

2. What do you really need from this group? What do you have to do within the group to get those needs met? Can you get your needs met elsewhere? Why haven't you gotten those needs met before?

3. Does this group have a leader or person in charge who dominates with his or her personality? Does this leader represent or resemble something or someone significant to you? The father you never had? The lover you always wanted? The friend you've been seeking? Hope? Excitement? Trust? In Lily's story, for instance, Swami Amrita Bhajan gave her life the vitality she felt cut off from in herself. Once she reclaimed her own life, she didn't need the Swami at all.

4. Can you be fully yourself and fully comfortable in this group, asking all your questions, expressing all your needs? If not, why? Look carefully at what you don't like in this group. Take your time. Don't push aside your objections. Raise them. Discuss them. And then see what happens. Are you perhaps afraid of what you don't like in this group?

5. Is it okay to take your time committing to this group? If there is any pressure, be wary. Above all else, *go slowly!*

Sexual Abuse

and

Family Dynamics

The Theory of the
New Family

How could it be otherwise? All of a survivor's relationships, including family of origin relationships and current family relationships are profoundly impacted by the discovery and admission of trauma and abuse. Whether that abuse be physical incest, emotional incest, or any other form of abuse or trauma (verbal abuse, physical abuse, witnessing and hearing the abuse of others), it is impossible to maintain a relational status quo once the story is told. The chaos and concern, the confusion and guilt, the fear and the panic which ensue should all be allowed to occur, unfolding until the dust settles, and the deepest implications of the situation are felt.

The NEW FAMILY is a term I have coined. It reflects a goal, perhaps an ideal, perhaps a hope. the New Family is a conscious family. It incorporates conscience and conscientiousness into the family system — a willingness to pay attention and to honor truth. In the New Family, for instance, if the mother or the father should discover that they are in the process of healing from sexual abuse, they would have the opportunity of being supported in that process by their partner and their family members. the New Family includes an openness to the many facets of healing and personal development, of human evolution and of holism. Do such families exist? My answer would be that such families are in the making. We are making them. People who are healing form families in which healing has a high priority, and people who are healing *include* their families in that experience, whenever they can. Families are essential and primary sources of comfort in healing from any trauma. Unfortunately, sometimes they become the opposite. When that's the case, new families of the spirit must be found and created to support ongoing healing. Healing is always a collective experience, just as abuse is always a collective experience. Tragically, our culture has become more skilled at collective trauma than it is at collective healing. It is up to us, you and I, to change that pattern.

The New Family includes an understanding that trauma happens, that suffering occurs, and is, unfortunately, commonplace. There is no denial or avoidance in the New Family. The New Family is aware that sexual abuse occurs. With public knowledge rising of the increasing cruelty to children, including abductions, rapes and other horrifying events, we must find a way to listen to the fears our children have. We must believe them when they say that Uncle or Aunt so and so makes them feel "yucky," or when they say they don't like a teacher or a baby sitter. Children have an innate ability to read people, and in our ignorance, we often do not hear what our own children are telling us. Now, we *must* listen and make space for what our children say about people, and validate them when they share those feelings with us. Children who are respected like this are very unlikely to become victims.

The New Family is not a family that relies upon escapism and addiction for protection. The New Family relies upon honesty. It does not fall prey to the cultural mania for pornography and infantalized appearances. It is not a victim of media. It makes way for open discussion, and notices when anyone is expressing distress. It asks not who is to blame, but what can be done to heal.

The New Family realizes that it contains amongst its members and within its structure enormous healing capacity and potential. The New Family is devoted to realizing the individuated human possibilities of each of the members of the family and of the family as a collective force. Each person contains within themselves unique gifts, qualities of self and being which are healing radiances. Just as Dr. Edward Bach*, (the innovative English physician who discovered the specific and unique healing properties of each flower) used the flower essences to balance psychological moods, so can we use our individual capacities for insight, humor, playfulness, calm, stimulation and transmutation to heal ourselves, simply and gently.

A family is a microcosm of the macrocosm. It is a hologram of the larger system. Look at the members of your family now, whether these members be your family of origin or your chosen family of the spirit. See, for instance, your daughter's gift of liveliness or your son's gift for whimsy. See the meditative calm of your sister or the vigor of your brother, and realize how all these elements of self can be blended and balanced for healing. See how you could draw out and amplify those gifts, focus on them, and see how you can make

---

*See the Resources section of this book for more information on Dr. Edward Bach and the Bach Flower Remedies.

your own contribution to family well–being. In recovery from trauma, these are the simple human elements, the innate gifts, which make healing possible. When trauma occurs or is recalled, the New Family brings forth its gifts. All of us have the capacity to give affection and comfort — to prepare a meal for someone, or to take over duties to allow someone else space to heal. What holds us back from offering these simple gifts that can make such a difference? In the New Family we don't hesitate. We give readily, generously, with an open and trusting heart.

Sexual abuse is cultural, it tells us about our communities, and about our relationships. It makes sense, therefore, that the healing of sexual abuse and related traumas requires a cultural awareness, a community awareness, and a relational awareness. Holism is not only about the integration within each individual, it is also about the integration within and amongst systems, particularly family systems. It is about the relationship of the parts to the whole, and that relationship is intimate, unbreakable, intricate and irrefutable. I believe that, in fact, the long–term perspective on healing from sexual abuse demands a healing within the world, a healing amongst and between heretofore alienated systems, a redefining of one's connection with family, with families everywhere, and eventually with the whole world.

This perspective on the true meaning of healing from sexual abuse should encourage us to be patient and to see the New Family, which we as individuals have to create, as the seed from which this larger healing process can be born. Sexual abuse in American culture is a horribly bloody and torn flag, waving unavoidably in front of us, saying our larger community, our society and our culture is deeply troubled and deeply in need of healing. As reports of abuse continue to rise, we lose the capacity to ignore this bloody flag. Whenever we see it waving on the front pages of our newspapers, our hearts clutch and our stomachs twist. The answer to this fear is to find what heals, not to increase the false shelter of denial. And *we* are what heals. The New Family is a healing system. As you read this book, think about all the ways you can create your own New Family, your own healing system. Then put those thoughts into action.

What follows are explorations into how abuse and trauma afflict family process and development at every juncture. I begin this with a journal excerpt, offered by a survivor who was pregnant with her second child. More and more women are discovering while they are pregnant that they were sexually abused. The process of pregnancy organically and hormonally awakens an awareness of any sexual violations. It would be enormously helpful if health care providers who work with pregnant women could be aware of the role of trauma during this cycle. The journal writing of a pregnant survivor helps set the pace for this awakening.

From there these explorations cover couple dynamics, parenting, and the single parent family, all from the perspective of the impact of sexual abuse and trauma on these systems which create the foundation of our society. If our families are dysfunctional, and our young people are without resources for their honest expression and experience, then our world will topple and fall into its own materialistic escape, leaving nothing of value. On the walls of the cliffs and caves where the Anasazi lived in Colorado and Utah, you will find the handprints of the people , each one suggesting "I Am" or "This Is Me," or "I Was Here." These simple pictographs are the imprint of selfhood, bespeaking the value of life. If unique selfhood is erased with spiritual emptiness and a valueless philosophy, what will we leave? Just the waste of materialistic debris. Does that speak for you?

Pregnancy, Childbirth and Sexual Abuse
The First-Hand Account of a Survivor Pregnant with her Second Child

I. High Risk Pregnancy

Perhaps the most damaging wound of incest is self–doubt. Despite numerous achievements, I live with the pervasive suspicion that I have done something wrong. This suspicion haunts me like an omnipotent ruler, closing one by one the doors to my happiness.

For me, the affliction is made more complex by its contrast to my daring. After many years of therapeutic introspection, I have discovered a basic conflict within me: my healthy inner child is creative, a mischievous risk–taker, while my wounded inner child is frightened and hesitant; she works hard to become invisible. What a curious and difficult internal battle. While the bold one inside me is outspoken, the meek child is embarrassed, often shamed by the bold one's actions. This makes for long, ferocious internal warfare.

In my daring, I chose not to marry, but nonetheless to bear my first two children. The reluctant part of me suffered from this exposure. As I grew bigger with child, I noticed each time someone looked at my naked ring finger, I cringed with humiliation and then felt even more guilty when I admitted that I had brought it on myself. Thus, I spawned, as was my wont, another mini–scenario embodying the victim's thought pattern. The challenge was to disentangle the threads of abuse. For me, the unwinding into health consists of making my relationships and my motherhood successful by my own standards.

All the emotional vicissitudes of pregnancy seem to me to be underscored by sexual abuse issues, and this, I am afraid, is virtually unavoidable for the survivor mother–to–be. Because of this, I felt isolated in my pregnancies. My doctors, my midwives, even my 17–year–old daughter who was with me for the latter stages of my second pregnancy, were not privy to this aspect of my experience.

Childbirth is an exaltation of the feminine. By claiming and owning this experience through natural home delivery, I make my statement about my belief in myself and in the power of femininity. It is a courageous statement, but not so much because of the physical risk. For me, the mental and emotional risk is much greater. Because I am defying the false beliefs which run rampant in my mind and which I confront daily, it is my own monsters I face by taking center stage in birth, by not surrendering authority to others.

My daring consists of being more focused on self–trust than on self–doubt. Being "at risk" to the doctors meant being 45 years old and pregnant. To me, "at risk" means trusting myself to go yet another step into my personal process, and repeatedly returning to the belief that I can succeed. In so doing, I overcome the hypnosis of victimization.

2. Weight

In my ninth month, I had the distinct feeling that my pregnant body was trapped within massive weight, and that my arms and legs were helpless limbs. Then I remembered: my father was a large man, well over six feet tall, and over 200 pounds. His weight held me down in a literal way, and his psychological demand that I do his bidding and be available for him held me down emotionally. My body needed information in order to discriminate between the negative experience of my father's weight and the positive weight of pregnancy.

Similarly, any passivity, even receptivity, implied abuse. Activity, on the other hand, spelled freedom, power, and vitality. To refrain from action while still retaining self-esteem and a sense of safety was extremely difficult for me. It required constant emotional reorganization to keep myself clear to reinterpret containment and inactivity. I had to explore my emotional experience of feeling threatened by passivity, particularly in the context of carrying the burden of weight. Since none of my care-givers considered sexual abuse issues relevant to pregnancy, my responses to gaining weight confused them. They, including my partner, wanted to reassure me that it was okay for me to be big. Their reassurance, however, confused me further. I began to blame myself for not allowing the baby to be completely nourished when I didn't gain sufficient weight. The job again was one of unraveling, separating the threads, and acknowledging the abuse. This was a time–consuming but necessary process. I did it best alone, and this writing is my opportunity to describe my discoveries.

3. Pain

The contractions that precede, initiate and endure through labor are an intensely demanding physical trial. One night a few weeks before my due date, I was plagued by an onslaught of contractions. They brought me a memory of physical and sexual abuse associated with my womb and my pelvis. A child's voice inside my head pleaded, "Mommy, there's something bad inside me that hurts. Please help me. Please take it out."

I felt my child self spreading through my mind, and I gave her the space she needed. She said that since no one came to relieve or explain her pain, she believed it was her fault and of her making; the pain was her responsibility by virtue of the fact that no one else took responsibility for it. At the moment of hearing my inner child's declaration, I was overwhelmed with anger at my mother for abandoning me. Why was I left alone to endure insufferable pain? Simultaneously, I knew that I must make a separation between the pain of abuse and the pains of pregnancy and childbirth. The latter are healthy pains leading to flowering and abundance, and I did not want the child inside my womb to feel that her urge for freedom was negative. Therefore, I felt challenged at that moment to simultaneously direct a positive and encouraging thought pattern to the infant growing in my womb, to relax myself in the midst of pain, and to heal myself by comforting and loving my courageous essence. It seemed a lot to do at once!

As I continued to experience waves of deep, cramping contractions, I sorted through the cacophony inside my head. First, it was clear that my compulsive over-responsibility came from the moment of being abandoned in my pain as a child victim. This was a major awareness, and in itself would have made the sleepless night worthwhile.

Next, my partner, lying in bed beside me, agreed to send a message to our child to encourage her to let her movement be free. We allowed ourselves time to focus completely on informing our child that her movement was welcome.

The hardest task I faced was to separate myself from responsibility for others and to believe that my unfinished tasks would be accomplished appropriately and in due time. As it turned out, I did not go into full-fledged labor then, but dozed on and off through the remainder of the night, and awoke somewhat refreshed to write about a night spent being a witness to pain. I was gratified to peer into the mystery of birth, the extraordinary and irreversible opening into the feminine labyrinth of surrender and power. I felt honored to be permitted further foray into the realms of my own myth and ecstasy, and above all I longed to hold my healthy and vibrant child.

4. Mother-Daughter

From the beginning of my second pregnancy, I was aware of a longing for contact with my mother - or more accurately, for contact with a mother. From one perspective, my second pregnancy was marked by the "mother theme" - or, the "absence of the mother" theme. Recently, I wrote to my mother and expressed my sadness that she had not phoned me throughout the pregnancy to inquire about my health and well-being. Her response was to be offended and to judge me as cruel. This supports my fear that in fact I cannot be open and honest with my mother. I cannot share my real feelings or any aspect of my authentic process with her.

It is natural, perhaps even instinctual, for a pregnant woman (no matter what her age) to seek deep feminine communion, and to want to go to her mother for that communion. The drive is deep. If the vital and abundant issue of pregnancy could not be broached, how then could I discuss incest? So, I retreated into a mute internal place, a silence active with unspoken language. This was unbearably familiar — it was the territory of my entire childhood.

My mother's abandonment of me was acutely painful during my pregnancy. For any survivor who is pregnant and who has been actively addressing the pain of incest, I believe this poignant place is unavoidable during these crucial nine months. The primary solace I found for myself during two pregnancies was the acknowledgement that healing was a living possibility and that I *could* have a healthy and joyous birth. The pain I experienced about the impact of incest on pregnancy and childbirth may have, in an odd way, augmented the ecstasy I felt in both experiences of the utterly triumphant, gloriously healthy, completely natural deliveries of my two daughters.

Even as I write on this subject and recognize my clarity about it, I experience myself distancing emotionally. This writing becomes a good (and healthy) way to put space between me and an abyss of loneliness and isolation. Yet, I am glad to have these words. The raw emotion, without art as a salve, is too much for me. In the midst of the vulnerability of pregnancy, writing becomes a loving mother for the healing survivor.

5. Labor and Birth

Both my daughters were born at home. For the second birth, I went into true labor on the night of a full moon lunar eclipse, and delivered the following morning at 2:48 a.m.

The contractions were fast and furious, with barely a pause between them. As they increased in intensity, I found myself again in the state I described earlier, in which a pelvic agony connected with birth became confused with the pelvic agony of incest.

In the room where I was laboring, however, I didn't feel I could openly speak about these flashbacks. For one thing, my 17-year-old daughter was present, and while she knew about the incest, she had repeatedly told me that she found any discussion of it upsetting. The midwives were really not attuned to the issue in me, and, finally, even my partner did not do well with the subject. So, in this situation, I did (you might say) give in to the needs of others, in order to protect myself, I suppose. I nevertheless did work with clarifying the two kinds of pain on my own, internally.

About midway in the labor, an image came to me. I saw a delicate, old fashioned scale. On one side were my "transgressions" — starting with the incest. The other side showed the slow process of paying off my sinful debt. This side of the scale would never equal the other. First of all, in order to even merit a point on this latter side, I had to complete my tasks perfectly, and since I so rarely did this, I rarely gained points — or the required weight to tip the scales.

The last phase of labor, the pushing phase, proved to be the most demanding for me, emotionally, in both birth experiences. In the second delivery, I completely lost faith in myself. I had worked so diligently to handle the contractions, but pushing seemed beyond my capabilities. For the first time I found myself giving up. I had no choice, obviously, but to push, but where would I find the strength and belief in myself so that I could do this job? I called for God, my birth attendants offered bouquets of encouragement, but still I felt inadequate. Why was I abandoning myself when completion and success were so close? This was familiar. My pattern was to deny myself the victory, the reward. Despite all this, I did push. I made high pitched sounds, deep growling sounds; and I pushed. For the observers, I was doing incredibly well, even great, they said. But for myself, I was already a failure. I had failed to meet the requirements of the challenge before me. I had not met the test with dignity and refinement. Quite the contrary, I was reduced to a state of begging and groveling, and so with the last of my fading energy, I pushed the baby out.

Now, with a child to tend to, I still feel the warnings of failure like echoes in my mind, though they are fading as I enjoy her more. I see my opportunities to mother as opportunities to heal. The process, I accept, is an exceedingly long one, having to do with erasing tapes that have been deeply etched with false beliefs. I keep at the task with perseverance. It is an act of selfless love I perform for myself.

How Healing Happens in the New Family
The Couples: Heterosexual and Homosexual

These case histories represent dynamics that can occur when trauma and sexual abuse impacts partnership.

Kate and Lydia

Kate and Lydia have been living together for well over a year. They struggled with identifying themselves to others as a lesbian couple, because this defied the entire social structure in which they lived and worked. The pressure of being different, of having different needs and different goals was a persistent stress on their relationship, but when Kate confessed that she felt increasingly disturbed by unavoidable body memories* of having been sexually abused by her father, experiences she had been forcing herself to hide and disbelieve, the relationship experienced yet another stress that threatened to break it in two.

Kate was ashamed of these memories, ashamed of the lack of in-

---

*Body Memories: These are memories which emerge not so much as visual experiences, but as physical experiences which erupt unexpectedly and produce a variety of somatic possibilities. For instance, while making love an experience of terror totally disconnected from the pleasure of lovemaking can emerge, causing the individual to break into a cold sweat and to feel paralyzed. No pictures may come with this somatic experience, or there may be some vague visual experience, such as the sense of seeing a large figure appear in the doorway. Other body memories which have been described to me and/or which I have experienced myself are feelings of suffocating, feelings of the mouth being full to the point of choking, shaking, and spontaneous screaming. Body memories may interrupt sexual activity, but they may also interfere at other times. For instance, if one's employer resembles a family member who was an abuser, body memories may interfere at work. Body memories may also occur when an individual is in a position of getting a lot of attention, while giving a public talk, for instance, or doing a dance performance. Body memories can easily be evoked by interventions such as massage therapy, Rolfing, or other situations in which the individual is lying on a table and the practitioner is standing above or nearby, especially if the

formation she had to substantiate them, afraid of how vague and yet persistent the body memories were, afraid of how they interfered with her sexuality, afraid of how they would erupt suddenly, displace everything that was presently occurring, and leave her feeling intolerably vulnerable and confused. It was a relief to her that Lydia could comfort her and accept unconditionally Kate's process, and offer to support her no matter what. But Lydia could not be the therapist for Kate. Lydia herself was confused about her own past history. She didn't know why she felt compelled to drink, to lie, and to hide her feelings of attraction to men. But she knew that each time she confessed these feelings to Kate, Kate remained loving and understanding, and that was Lydia's model for being available to her partner and her friend.

Kate's sense of being troubled about herself was hardly new. She had been suffering from deep feelings of inadequacy for so long, she didn't know where they started. She was a beautiful woman, with a bright gleam in her eye, a whimsical smile and great curiosity about the world, but she could not enjoy these qualities in herself. She tended to doubt her own sensation, to discount her perceptions and to detach herself from her emotional life until it erupted in an outbreak of fury or grief.

Kate had already been in therapy for two years. But therapy had been frustrating until this identification of the possibility of incest. While facing this possibility was hardly a relief, nevertheless it made so much of what Kate had been experiencing understandable that, as a diagnosis, it brought order out of chaos. As Kate's therapist, I was not eager to declare that sexual abuse indeed had occurred and that it was incest, but I did participate with Kate in exploring that

---

recipient is naked or just covered by a sheet, as occurs in massage therapy, and other bodywork systems. Meditative experiences, sitting eyes closed in front of someone to do a visualization or intense breathing therapies such as Holotropic Breathwork all may evoke body memories. Reading this book may trigger body memories, though it is my intention to diminish that possibility as much as I can. *It is most important that the individual who is having the body memory slow things down as the memory emerges and find a safe way to identify the experience and not activate it further without therapeutic support that is dependable and conscious of the trauma surrounding the body memory itself. As soon as possible, that quality of support should be accessed.*

explanation of her low self–esteem, her panic attacks, her incredibly distressing body memories, and her extremely frightening recurrences of a desire to commit suicide.

It was while reading a book about sexual abuse and incest that Kate began to wonder if her father had abused her in this way. Her father's undependable behavior, with its cutting edge of brutality, had already been identified by Kate as a source of trauma in her life. His history of drug use was known by all the family members, and Kate herself had been the victim of his frequent and compulsive daring adventures in cars, during which he put the lives of his wife and children at risk. Despite her father's mania and unquestionably neurotic behavior, Kate loved him and wanted more than anything else for there to be peace between them. She remembered fondly her father's care in instructing her how to fix cars, how to build with wood, how to sail and how to swim. He had been a friend and companion during his sane moments, and a resource for her in many ways. Incorporating her awareness of his cruelty with her awareness of his kindness was a difficult task for Kate. She had grown up believing it had to be one or the other — he had to be either good or bad. Now she was admitting he was both, and that admission had the resonance of truth in it. She could tell because when I suggested that to her — that her father combined great heartfulness with great distress — she calmed down, she relaxed, she felt clearer about her dilemma.

So, in this odd way, considering the possibility of her father's abuse and feeling supported by the people around her, provided some relief for Kate from the ongoing anxiety she had been feeling about herself and her life. By letting the support in, by feeling the nurturance itself, she began to shift, to become more peaceful and simultaneously more energized — and maybe, it occurred to her — maybe that was really what this was all about, feeling support for her uniqueness, feeling support for her ideas and her perceptions, feeling that it was okay for her to be who she was, noticing what SHE was noticing, and making choices that originated from her feelings, and not from some pressure outside of her. Just these awarenesses began to have a powerful impact on Kate, and she found herself experiencing a sense of wholeness, a sense of security in herself and a sense of being at home in her own body. Nothing in her family life had ever given her this feeling. The newness of feeling that she really was accepted was a keynote for Kate, though she asked herself, "WHY WAS THIS SO NEW?"

The unconditional support which Kate received from her partner was crucial to her ongoing process. I might even say that without it, Kate would have found it difficult to continue working on herself at the juncture at which she was flooded with body memories. Eventually Kate lost her job because of these body memories and the absenteeism they produced, and Lydia supported her through that transition as well. Lydia's support had not even a touch of sacrifice to it — it was done very naturally, out of her commitment to Kate. And it was the energy of this support which functioned as a profound healing resource for Kate (and probably for Lydia as well) and which made it possible for her to continue her healing journey. As Kate's family proceeded to deny any possibility of trauma within the family of origin structure, not to mention incest, Kate and Lydia were forced temporarily into forming the New Family for themselves. They found friends who could support and identify with this healing process, and these friends became a true community, a kind of extended family consistently increasing their awareness and understanding of each other and their capacities in supporting one another.

This is the very quality of support, caring and trust which is inevitably required in the process of healing from sexual abuse in the context of a relationship or partnership. It is not always necessary for the partner to know all there is to know about sexual abuse or even about healing, but the unconditional quality of the support seems to be basic. You can't put a time limit on healing; in fact, healing is an ongoing lifetime process, but that process has within it growth and movement, change and transformation, and a sensitive partner will be aware of that. This quality of support is not a one–way street. The healing partner provides it for the supporting partner, as well as the other way around. In fact, these two roles are always interchangeable and reciprocal. In the New Family, support is a healing dance of its own within the context of recovery from trauma. In fact, support is one of the major themes in recovery — what it is, and how one finds it. Having a partner who can embody support for you and for whom you can embody support is a developmental leap.

How important was it that Kate prove that her father had sexually abused her? From my point of view, that was not the most significant aspect of our work together. There was a larger context in which Kate had been denied her individuality within her family dynamic, and it was my challenge to help her build a viable sense of self *now*. Her father's addictive behavior, her mother's negligence, depression and narcissism, and her sister's unwillingness to decline being the favored and most helpful daughter despite what she witnessed, created an environment of abuse in which all the family members were damaged. Kate's sense of self was beaten down by these circumstances, and she hid from early childhood sensations of terror and loneliness. The sexual manifestations, through her somatic experiences, of the trauma she experienced as a child led to the implication of sexual violation, and Kate's increasingly more visual memories of her father's abusive interludes when he was alone with her, led to a strong possibility of incest. But what is most destructive here is the entire family milieu, the place that was created of denial and devastation, of hiding and violence, all draped with a cloth of all–rightness, the lie children suffer to maintain.

Eventually, Kate's father went into a recovery program because his second marriage could not withstand his substance abuse. It took years before he had sobered enough to tell the truth — that indeed he had terrorized his family, and that his substance–induced fantasies created sexually violating behavior. You might say that at that time, years later, Kate (who had in the interval created a new career for herself and built an enduring and loving relationship with Lydia) was vindicated, but vindication was not her only feeling. She felt both relieved and hopeful and through the magnitude of her healing process she remained available (after years of using expressive mediums to release her rage and grief) to build a new and healthier relationship with her father.

In our work together, particularly after the possibility of incest was identified, Kate tapped into an energetic warehouse of rage which she had been keeping under lock and key for her entire life. The rage was not only toward her family, but toward the surrounding social fabric that enabled the fantasy of the nice family with the nice house, despite her father's clearly manic behavior and the sexual escapades of both mother and father in the community. No one noticed the family's disintegration and no resources were sought that would imply the need for help. The damage had to be multiplied and multiplied again before the truth could be told, and this was both infuriating and tragic. Kate carried these big, unexpressed feelings in her body, secretly, but once the secret had been whispered, albeit to me alone, the heretofore repressed energy bubbled out of her and all her somatic symptoms shifted. Fatigue was replaced by a kind of hyperactivity as repressed feelings sought to rearrange their function in her body. It was at this juncture that art became an indispensable tool for Kate. What a surprise! Kate had always seen herself as a rather contained person. Suddenly she found she was a very expressive person, with enormous feeling — almost too much feeling, but that too found its balance eventually.

At this juncture Kate and I began to discuss creative and expressive options for the embodiment of her feeling. We had spent two years identifying feeling, becoming aware of it, and now that it was known, it sought an avenue of outlet. Kate felt drawn to doing things with her hands, to building and carving with wood, and eventually to wood sculpture. Underneath the mask of staunch non–expression lived an artist, a woman who knew instinctively how to build something from nothing, a woman with a knife in her hands determined to shape something from the undefined emptiness of a material whose life she could feel. Kate discovered she had a strong relationship to wood, to its texture and its essence, to the various resonances of different kinds of wood, and she found great joy in letting beauty emerge from the interaction of her hands, her tools and wood. Her life force surfaced and found a loving and powerful function, and new directions began to develop for Kate, directions she allowed as more and more, she put her mind to rest and let her feelings speak.

When our relationship had served its function for Kate and she felt strong enough to walk away from our weekly meetings, she gave me a gift which I will always hold dear. It was a wood carving, small enough to hold in the palm of my hand, of a woman holding within her being the image of a child. The comfort of placing this smooth, dark, wooden shape in my hand remains a treasure to me, a reminder of how the long hours of honest and genuine communication between two people builds a future, and that this has great, enduring value, and always will.

Roberto and James

Roberto and James met on a sunny morning at a ski lodge in the Colorado Rockies. As they connected over steaming cups of hot chocolate, they felt like they were living in a movie, with the script composed by a new Hollywood writer, a gay man writing about contemporary homosexual relationships. The sun warmed their skin, relaxing them despite their almost unendurable excitement.

The combination of companionship and sensuality which pulsated more strongly the longer they talked, could hardly be contained. They skied together that afternoon, had dinner together that night, and then stayed up talking, getting closer, and finally making love. Their relationship survived this early romantic interlude of a ski winter punctuated by sunshine and dramatic feats of daring on the slopes. They were young and strong, and love made them unbearably attractive. After such a long time pretending they were heterosexual, it thrilled them to fall in love the way they had always wanted to and to actually experience the closeness they had secretly feared they would never discover. In the passion and heartfulness of their first months of coming to know one another, they deliberately avoided any discussion of AIDS. But the tragedy of AIDS lurked everywhere now and without saying a word they each secretly knew that they were finding a tainted comfort in avoiding the subject.

Roberto was an established and successful lawyer; James a social worker. Both were respected for their consistent and responsible performances on the job and both were compelled to continue to do well. To stabilize their lives, they quickly moved in together, and made a home. They were ecstatic. In the cosmopolitan world of ski towns and progressive communities, they were okay, they could make it, they would not be shunned. They might even become the token gay couple at some of the best parties. They had been living together for over a year when Roberto discovered he had AIDS. He had been suspicious for months before he had the test, but he had withheld his suspicions from James.

Roberto came from a middle class Chicano family, an anomaly in itself, so he grew up feeling he was different even before he admitted he was gay. His father was a school teacher and his mother was a school administrator, so Roberto and his sister had grown up more like white children with absentee parents than Chicanos with a close, extended family. He had always had a secret longing to get to know his *real* people, and he tried to find them on his underground forays into the gay bars of the Mission District of San Francisco, where he grew up. There he met some of the wildest Chicano men he had ever seen — men with long curly hair wearing ornate crosses around their necks and bright, tight (very tight) pants. They spoke a Spanish which was interrupted only occasionally with English, and they pursed their lips and batted their eyelashes and swaggered, their hips moving brilliantly to the beat of fast–paced music with incomprehensible lyrics pulsing all around them. Roberto reached for them like a little boy reaches for his father when he has been away far too long. He stroked their hair and breathed in their secret scents, and he listened, enraptured, to their rapid fire Spanish, the only language they would speak. But eventually he became a lawyer, and he did well, and his parents never knew. When Roberto got a job as an assistant district attorney in Colorado, he escaped not only from the confines of his family's conservatism, he escaped from the lie of being heterosexual. Without his parents' watchful eyes he was free, and gliding down the slopes with James by his side, he felt he had finally come home.

James and Roberto became supporters of the campaign to educate people about AIDS. It was at a conference they attended together, a conference that was happening in part because of their support, that Roberto began to suspect that he had AIDS. One of the workshops was about the symptoms that surround the AIDS diagnosis, and as Roberto listened to them, his heart sank and panic filled his mind and his gut. Maybe that rash on his leg that wouldn't go away was not to be ignored. Maybe the fact that he had had a sore throat and a slight cough for two months now, on and off, was not just because of the "weird flu" that everybody said was "going around." And the fatigue — that had been the hardest for him to wish away. He had been hoping it was from overwork, but he just ran out of steam so fast now. When the conference was over, Roberto, unbeknownst to James, went to his doctor, who ordered the test. Three weeks later it came back HIV positive. His T–cell count was in the low 300's — he might still have time.

Before Roberto told James, he spent a long time thinking, trying to discover when he could have gotten AIDS. And then he remembered, and the memory filled him not only with loathing, but with a feeling of incredible anxiety, the very feeling he'd had when it happened, when he had been raped. It could have been called acquaintance rape. Roberto was so young — so very young. He'd been going to one gay bar regularly. On Friday nights he'd make up some story to get away from his family, and then he'd go to a gas station, slip into his tight–fitting jeans and ragged T–shirt, and strut down to the gay bar he liked the best, the place where the wild Chicano men came. One of them really liked him, and brightened noticeably whenever Roberto appeared. He bought him not only beer, but whiskey. Roberto got incredibly drunk, and a friend of the man who liked Roberto, Jesus was his name, got the hots for him. It was ugly and fast, and happened in one of the back rooms of the bar, but the important point was that Roberto really didn't want to have sex with *that* man. He was drawn to the other man, not to Jesus, but he did it anyway. He did it because he didn't know how to say no; he did it because he felt so ashamed for being there, this seemed just a part of that shame; and he did it because he thought it was expected of him, and because he was drunk. Somewhere in his young mind he may have hoped that this would attract the man he really wanted, the man it seemed he couldn't have but for whom he longed.

Roberto didn't go home that night. He called his parents when he was somewhat sobered and told them he was spending the night with a friend. It worked. They believed him. He was a good boy. But that night stayed etched forever in Roberto's mind. Something terrible had happened then. He always knew it. He could feel the tragedy in his soul, long before he got the diagnosis.

When Roberto finally told James the news, the room filled with a tragic darkness. The two men fell into each other's arms like doves shot by a hunter's bullet. They encircled each other and they rocked, they rocked and rocked, and their home, which they had made together with such love, held them like a cradle. They knew they would fight like the warriors they were, they would fight together, and at the same time they knew that Roberto would die of AIDS. On that day, just a little over a year from their first meeting, death moved into their liberated home, and stayed.

Roberto came to see me when his T–cell count dropped below 100. He wanted not only to work with the material of his life and to free himself of the remnants of resentment and anger that tormented him about his family, but he also wanted to know about some healing alternatives, and he had heard that I had information about that too. I did, and I was glad to share that material with Roberto, and to offer him options for living and dying with dignity and health, with a strong sense of self and of having made a real contribution with his life. Little did I know the powerful gift Roberto was bringing me when he became my client.

It was three years before Roberto died of AIDS, and in that time, his life flowered, and the flowering, I am certain, is not over, despite the cremation of his flesh and bones. Roberto really came out of the closet in those three years — out of the closet of his family's lie of success, out of the closet of the rape, out of the closet of *all* of his pretenses, into the open, flowering field of himself. And I was the fortunate one to witness the flowering, and to see the honor and beauty of the loving kindness that evolved between Roberto and James, who I began to think of as the Twins, Castor and Pollux, as the dancers of brotherly love.

What Roberto and I traced together was not only the emotional and psychological ramifications of the rape that may or may not have been responsible for Roberto's infection with AIDS, but also the way his family's ignorance of who he really was and their deep narcissistic pressure to make him into what they needed him to be, paved the way for Roberto to succumb, as he tended to do, to the needs of others. And that behavior, the helpless behavior which is the mark of trauma, was precisely what began to shift for him, so that by the time he died, he was making all his own choices, purely and completely for himself.

What was of particular significance in Roberto's story was the way in which American materialism had robbed him of his rich, sensual, emotive culture, the culture of his people. By giving in to the demands of fitting in and making it in America, his parents had stolen from their children a spirit and a fire which was their birthright, and which the children sensed was missing, though they would not have been able to articulate this absence. It was no accident that Roberto's sister too struggled desperately, despite appearing successful. This was the way in which Roberto's family had modeled life — repress the passion; look and live Anglo. Roberto's sister also had a secret life — she was addicted to food. She sacrificed her beauty and her sexuality to food, which no one saw her eat, but functioned magnificently as the administrator of senior centers in Northern California. No one talked about Celia's food addiction, though the results were obvious, just as no one talked about Roberto's homosexuality, or later, AIDS.

Roberto's attraction, as a young man seeking his identity, to the wild and colorful Chicano gays in San Francisco, was his way of exploring his longing for his homeland, his music, and his sexuality. But even if his parents *had* shared their culture with their children, Roberto would still have been gay. His sexual choice felt natural to him. However, if there had been more openness in his family, less pressure to hide whatever made his parents uncomfortable, less repression of sensuality, less emphasis on living a white, homophobic life, then perhaps Roberto might not have been so secretive about his life. Roberto felt horribly betrayed by his family, because they had never allowed him space to be who he truly was. And this sense of betrayal battled against his admiration for what his parents had achieved, and the sacrifices Roberto knew they had made to educate their children, to give them what they felt they never had.

The fact that he felt his parents would be ashamed of him, de-

spite his success as a lawyer, tormented Roberto. He wanted to tell
them the whole story — about the Chicano bars and his many, many
experiences with these men who celebrated with daring and vivac-
ity who and what they were. As Roberto traveled back in time to
those years when he lived a double life, he was filled with a sense of
celebration and joy that these men were able to dance the way they
danced, sing the way they sang, and he realized how much hope
they had given him to continue to live *his* own truth. This joy at
remembering was interlaced with tears as he realized how many of
these glorious men had and would die of AIDS, and how their deaths
were not the result of their promiscuity nor of their homosexuality
alone. Rather, their deaths would be the result of the rigid mores
that condemned them to live secretive lives, to hide their passions.
Named unnatural, they became unnatural; forbidden their health,
they became their disease. These men were sacrificial lambs — they
were all called Jesus, and in the solitude and inactivity of his pro-
gressing illness, Roberto mourned them; he made mantras of their
names, Jesus, Jose, Umberto, Eduardo, Carlos, Pedro, Xavier, and
he thanked them for the terror and disgrace they leaped over in
order to dance and sway to the music of their hearts.

When he shared this with me, I encouraged Roberto to write a
tribute to those years of his life and to the people he loved. I asked
him to reclaim those innocent teenage eyes of his which saw with
such clarity, and to make portraits of his brothers and his lovers,
both the ones who treated him tenderly and the rapist. All these
men suffered from the same abandonment, the same loss. All these
men whom he adored and cherished, who he chased like a thirsty
man chases water, had lost their homes and their fathers, their cultures and their families. In one way or another they were all deserted and abandoned and forced to make their own passionate,
separate communities, and to die within them, in American territory, on American land. I encouraged Roberto to sing their praises
and to mourn their beauty and their foolishness, their lust and their
courage. They, like he, were creatures swimming in waters too tur-
bulent to sustain them. The inability of the moral environment to
support their difference had deepened the need for escapism and
radical behavior. But at the moment of death all this becomes irrel-

evant. Death is the Great Equalizer. And Roberto was moving stead-ily towards death.

I gave Roberto the opportunity, which was quite new to him, to express his anger toward his parents. He was brought up to believe it was close to a sin to criticize his family in any way whatsoever. But he found that it unburdened his heart to speak the words of anger which he had so long held back, and once said, the anger was quickly gone — in part because Roberto's nature was deeply for-giving, and in part because he knew he would die soon and death works a molten magic on the hardness of the heart. What was much more difficult was for Roberto to write to his parents, once the hard core of the anger had been released, and tell them of his process and to invite them to be with him. He told them he had AIDS, and he expected never to hear from them again. But Al and Betina Hernandez appeared on the doorstep of Roberto and James' home unannounced, their arms open. The love that filled them whenever they thought of their son transcended their condemnation, and their tears mingled with his before Roberto died. No one should be de-nied the dignity of these fulfilling farewells.

What was significant was not whether or not Roberto had con-tracted AIDS that night when he was raped, but that he had learned somehow by the environment in which he was raised to discount himself, to discredit himself, and to be ashamed of what he wanted and needed. What was also primary was that he had learned by age sixteen that he couldn't express his needs at home, that he had to go elsewhere, secretly, to get his needs met. There was no one at home with whom it was safe to talk. Death was Roberto's greatest teacher. It taught him to love himself and to value his life. How ironic. And James too became more whole, more integrated as a result of the loss of the only person he had ever known to be truly loving. The home that meant everything to James was decimated by Roberto's death. Loneliness engulfed James like a shroud, and he died per-haps the more ugly death, though he lived AIDS–free. But James too came to love himself as he walked every step alongside his lover. The two men quickly bowed out of the circles of false smiles, the social life which had preoccupied them before they knew that death was their housemate. Together they entered the quietude of truth and they abided there, with some very sensitive friends, to see not only the dying of one of them, but the unfolding of Roberto's spirit.

A crucial part of my work with Roberto involved returning to the moment of the rape, and allowing the young man part of him to say no to the man who forced himself on him. This incomplete part of his history needed release as much as Roberto's anger at his parents. Like that anger, this was an unfinished motoric experience, a muted voice waiting for permission to speak. It was a serene awakening for Roberto to realize that he could have said no, and for him to realize that he might have been able to talk to his parents about his needs, if only he had had a stronger sense of self. And even though death was just around the corner, it was not too late to build a stronger sense of self. We did that. James, Roberto and I colluded in that construction, and we were successful.

The interlocking traumas that bound James and Roberto and the way in which those traumas were mutually unraveled is another significant aspect of this story and of the function of the New Family. The adults in the New Family come to realize the way in which they have indeed been brought together to heal each other, and to evolve their human potential. They actively seek to find the ways in which their past suffering and pain, or any aspect of who they are, calls out to be healed in their interactions. The dynamics with other family members are promising healing scenarios. In the atmosphere of family love, with kindness and respect, members of the New Family make a space to do that healing. This process is not usually easy. Frequently the ways in which we discover our interpersonal trauma patterns is through difficulty. But the members of the New Family look for that undercurrent of healing, the place where the growing can occur, the place where some more of the true self can appear from the wound. And that's exactly what James and Roberto did together, conscientiously, daily, and with great humor and compassion.

James had always been the little boy part of Roberto. His shyness and insecurity mirrored the hidden part of his lover, the part that was frightened and vulnerable and felt intimidated by the fast pace of the lawyer's life, the dramatic moments of exhibitionism and the cutthroat politics that ruled the life of success. James functioned in a much less dramatic way, and he did his work well by dint of his quietness, the hesitancy which allowed him to listen more to others than to himself. Roberto had been the strong arm in the relationship, making the decisions, being aggressive, managing the money and the time the two spent together. But as the AIDS symptoms accelerated, this shadow play could no longer continue, and James was forced to look into how his story interlocked with Roberto's, and to find the way in which their love for one another transcended their stories and made those stories comprehensible and resolvable. Love gave these two men more and more healing resources.

I remember sitting with James and Roberto several months before Roberto died. They were talking easily together, reminiscing about their lives, and I was witnessing their interaction. Roberto was talking about a woman friend they both knew who had visited them once, and who Roberto wanted to cultivate a relationship with because she was involved in so many things that interested him. James, however, was very much against the relationship. He didn't feel safe noticing Roberto's unusually strong interest in the woman. It threatened him, though he couldn't say that directly — he just hemmed and hawed, and avoided plans for specific meetings with her. The two men were just wondering whatever happened to that woman, and because the approach of death evoked a greater level of honesty than would be cultivated otherwise, Roberto was sensitive to James' insecurity about her. He asked him about it.

James was a slight man, sandy-haired, and shy. He down-played himself always, avoiding any discussion that drew attention to him. Now he looked at Roberto, whose dark eyes had grown more luminous as his face thinned, and the quiet became inundated with a sadness that seemed to darken the room. Was it suddenly twilight, I wondered? Why was everything softening, darkening? I took a deep breath, acknowledging a certain magic that occurs when death is so present. "I was afraid she would take you from me," James whispered, and he began to shake.

James was going to lose Roberto soon, there was little doubt about that, but not before James faced his fear of abandonment. I couldn't believe the shout that came from Roberto's tired voice in response.

"Don't you know what you mean to me," he yelled. "You are my soul mate. No one could take me from you, no one, and no thing, not even death. I will always love you, and my love will always nourish you. Don't *ever* doubt that. You deserve this kind of love. You deserve this kind of love."

All this was said with such power, I thought saying it would kill Roberto! But it didn't. James looked up at his lover wide–eyed, and slowly took in what he had said. In the transformative environment of death's magic, I could feel the cells of James' being rearranging themselves as he absorbed Roberto's message. This was it. This was the love he had been waiting for, the love that could make him whole. James soaked in every word. Nothing was lost. He heard Roberto's message, and he accepted it.

It was a sunstruck winter day, much like the one on which James and Roberto had first encountered each other, that Roberto died. He sat upright on his bed at home, wasted and weak, mute and blind, but extremely alert and present. In his hands he held the prayer beads I had given him when we decided together to add a meditation practice to the process of preparing for death. James, Roberto and I regularly meditated together, visualizing Roberto's healing death, and to allow Roberto's spirit to leave his body at its highest level of development, at the peak of his consciousness, so that his life could be completed as an offering. By the time he died, Roberto had forgiven, thoroughly and without pretense, not only his parents but the man who had raped him, and most importantly, he had forgiven himself. He felt complete with his life. When he left, a soft breeze, from quite a different clime than a Rocky Mountain winter day, swept through the room and everyone present was uplifted and inspired by the sweet softness of the wind.

Estelle and Ed

Estelle and Ed had been together over 20 years when Estelle began having panic attacks and night sweats. After consulting with her physician and eliminating menopause as the cause, Estelle concluded that these nocturnal episodes were probably connected with recurring memories she had been having of trauma in her childhood. Estelle had been the daughter of wealthy parents who had hired numerous nannies to tend to their three children. Estelle's mother had been an active socialite, with several volunteer functions and charity assignments, and Estelle's father had been a surgeon who was very much in demand. The children created their own world, and the nannies supervised them. But sometimes the nannies were sadistically unkind, and there was one, Estelle had found out just recently from her sister (whose memories were sometimes more substantial) who did extremely cruel things to the children, and to Estelle in particular.

Estelle also had long suspected that she had been inappropriately fondled by an older, visiting cousin who had shared the nursery with the other children for over a month, when his mother was hospitalized. But when Estelle's sister added the news about the abusive nanny, Estelle felt devastated. She felt as if she couldn't integrate all this horrible history, and she found herself sobbing unexpectedly and for long periods of time, longing always to be held and comforted, wanting her head stroked, wanting a dependable closeness that was consistent, unwavering.

Ed didn't get it at all. He couldn't comprehend why, after 20 years of marriage, when he felt so secure with his family and his relationship, that this demand should be made of him. He hated being awakened in the night, and he detested the incomprehensible quality of his wife's needs. Talk as much as you might, Ed could not understand why this was at all necessary. But finally, he gave up trying to understand and just gave in to being there for his wife. The singular motivation behind this transformation was love. Ed loved Estelle. He had loved her thoroughly from the first day he had met her, and he loved her thoroughly now. He could not fathom her extremely emotional nature, but he loved her nevertheless, and from this place of love he held her, even when he was tired from being awakened in the middle of a peaceful sleep, he held her and stroked her hair, and was comforting, and while Estelle knew that he was not able to give her deep understanding or even insight, she also knew that she could count on him, and so, with a deep sigh, she let him comfort her, and so allowed herself (and he with her) to fall asleep.

Estelle lived in a world that was defined by her emotional reality, and this made her a strange, exotic and sometimes threatening creature in Ed's eyes. He watched her mercurial changeability with all her expressive needs, and he wondered how she could sustain what appeared to be chaos amidst the insecurity of her spontaneous feeling states. Because of this strength he observed in her to flow with her own authentic variability, he had come to respect Estelle. He, on the other hand, found safety in the invisibility of his seeming similarity to everyone else. And Ed felt good protecting his wife, giving her the shelter she so clearly needed in his arms, and in his dependability. He also found that by watching her and abiding with her, he was, little by little, feeling more himself, though most of what he felt he thought was for Estelle, and for her powerful process which magnetized him, and made him stand in awe, much as one regards a waterfall.

So, it was shocking to Ed, in his 68th year, to find himself, as he was comforting his sobbing wife, thinking of his own childhood and reliving the month when he was alone with his mother, while his father was away, helping grandpa with a business and financial crisis. Ed was just six years old and his mother was quite distracted with the job of tending to him and the baby, his sister Joan, born just before dad left. The family was not poor, and they did have help, but Ed's mother was not used to being alone and being so much in charge of so many parts of life. At night, exhausted from juggling family responsibilities, the care of two children, and the business details she had to complete, she would ask Ed to sleep with her, and snuggling up against him she would relax and fall asleep.

Ed's father had met and married his wife after they had had a business relationship, and he had respected her enormously for her business acumen and management skills. But trying to be mother, housewife and business manager was more than anyone could handle and it was a cruel burden to leave her with so much responsibility. Caring for two children without a co–parent is virtually impossible, but somehow complaining or asking her husband to return was out of the question. Rather than that, his mother leaned on Ed. When her temper was short, she took it out on Ed. When she needed comfort, she asked it of Ed. And his father made it worse. "Be a little man," he had said when he left, and then again each time he phoned, "Take care of your mother for me."

It was no accident that this memory came back to Ed as he held his distraught wife in a gentle embrace. Maturity kept him from confusing the two experiences, but he hoped the anger coursing through his body would not interfere with his wife's sadness about the loss of her childhood, the neglect of her parents and the cruelty of her caretakers. He had enormous compassion for Estelle's suffering, and he was just thinking that perhaps this compassion he felt for her was also, in some way, his own compassion for himself.

Ed looked out the window. It was about 3:00 a.m., and the light that came in through the window was from the full moon and the bright stars, crystal clear in the cloudless, cold winter sky. At the age of 68, Ed felt himself to be a healthy man. Years of exercise had kept him slender, and had helped him to maintain a youthful appearance. He liked feeling alert, mentally and physically, and he was willing to cultivate his endurance in that regard. He looked down at his wife's bent head. He was proud of her. She had made a strong statement about life and living — she still danced and kept vigorously at her work as a therapist. She avoided nothing, and was completely honest about her feelings. She was nothing like his mother. In fact, Estelle was responsible for keeping them both emotionally current and spiritually young. Yet, here he was again, tending to a disconsolate woman, giving her comfort in the night, finding a secure identity in his nurturing and comforting capacity. A quaking sigh released itself in slow shudders from his body, and tears trickled down his face. Why? The memory of that month alone with his mother had faded. Estelle was asleep. Carefully he placed her head on the pillow beside him, and he also lay down, very tired. Within a few moments, he too was asleep.

This moment of interface between the traumas of these two people represents how the dynamics of the New Family can occur. All that is needed now is the transformative awareness, the consciousness, to see how these separate histories become catalysts for awakening to the function of recalling personal history in a healing process. Because Estelle and Ed have a good relationship, they will talk about this interface with each other, and they will discuss the subtle intricacies of the way in which Estelle's crisis is triggering Ed's awareness, and they will anticipate and create the reversal of that linkage, in which Ed's insight will cultivate Estelle's growth. Ed lacks some language and some knowledge of process, but Estelle can provide that if he will tell her his memory and listen well to her response. And Estelle lacks some confidence to bear the accumulation of trauma which is her history, but she is willing to ask for help, and Ed will help her, so the support and resources she needs will be found. Thus, these two people, with patience and commitment, can encourage a process of personal discovery for each other despite the necessary pain involved. They have the resources to do this together. Estelle's perseverance and dedication, not to mention her vital body, will create the orientation that will lead to increasing her confidence and expanding her capacities. And Ed will find the dynamic that explains his compulsive nurturing. He will become freer to make choices about nurturing, because he is willing to soften and attune to the wisdom of his wife, and, most importantly, he is learning to pay attention to his own internal guidance.

I was fortunate enough to work with both of these strong, honest people. They chose me to honor their relationship by seeking counsel, and they chose me because I was schooled in the dynamics of trauma, since that's what both of them brought to the counseling table.

Ed's first barrier to breaking through this point in his development had to do with his resistance — the belief that this shouldn't be happening to him now. A combination of pride and fear made him cling to the thought that this was all "touchy–feely–woman" stuff, that men of his years must not fall prey to emotionality, and that he had other objectives for his near retirement years, tasks he had been anxious to tackle. Hadn't he given up most of his own creative inspiration to serve the needs of his mother, his wife, his children? After working all his life, hadn't he finally earned the right to do what pleased him, to sleep when he needed to sleep, to read what he wanted to read, and to volunteer for the environmental groups he so strongly supported? Ed was an environmentalist and a naturalist and he wanted to offer his skills to these groups now that his family was out in the world. Was Estelle's process holding him back, or did it beckon to a dark part of him he had left unattended? Ed was in a great confusion about this, thinking he had to make a choice. He could not forget that his wife had always awakened him to significant, even life changing experiences. It was not easy for Ed to ignore Estelle's experience. In a way that he simultaneously felt frightened of and adored, Ed was fascinated with his wife. He had never spoken of the profound impact his wife had made upon his thinking and his decision–making. Looking at other women her age, he knew Estelle was unusual and rather spectacular in her ability to never compromise her reality for what was culturally demanded of her. Ed was much less successful at this individuality, though it probably appeared that Estelle was less confident than he.

Ed was able to work less now because of his achievements in the computer world, his ability to adapt computer technology in meaningful ways, and his ability to manage financial matters efficiently, with a combination of conservatism and courage. He felt proud of his place in the world, why did he now have to attend to the hidden part of himself, what was the need? Wasn't this his time for fun, as he defined it? Dealing openly with these resistances in a therapeutic setting allowed Ed eventually to surrender to what was actually happening (which could not be prevented anyway), and to accept it.

Estelle, on the other hand, had not completed her work in the world. The raising of three children and the way in which she had chosen to support Ed by caring for the basics at home, since he could bring in the bigger salary, had limited her involvement. Her practice as a therapist had been curtailed by these choices she had made, and she was clear about that, but as a result she still lacked a certain belief in herself. It was hard for her to take Ed's time. Letting herself be the healthy, deep–feeling, emotional being she was, without guilt, was our therapeutic goal. Estelle's difficulty in "taking" time for her needs resembled many other of my women clients who struggled against a desire to speak at length or to be the center of attention for very long.

Estelle's sister's revelation of further abuse in the family system had thrown Estelle into a nonstop emotional whirlpool. Having cultivated an adherence to her feelings and a respect for them, she could not now hide the panic attacks, the crushing need for comfort, the fury and the enormous grief she had at this juncture in her life about the pain she had been forced to squelch during her early years. That pain was uncontrollable now. What could she do? She suspected that this eruption, like a destructive, uncontainable volcano, would damage her marriage, but what could she do? She sought help amongst her valiant women friends, many of whom were younger than she, who supported her commitment to herself, and she sought energetic healing resources.

Despite their many resources, when Estelle and Ed came for therapy, both were at the end of their ropes. I asked them first to honor all the ways in which they had survived and kept their relationship alive. I asked them to make, either mentally, visually or actually, an altar to the sacred vessel of their relationship which had endured vitally through hardship, and which had brought them to this vibrant point of development. I was awed by their living tribute to loyalty and constancy in an age when divorce was matter-of-fact. Resting, even if temporarily, in the resources of their devotion gave them space to calm their nervous systems which were rattled from sleeplessness and fear. Sleeplessness and fear were in themselves triggers for both since they were throwbacks to early childhood trauma, when each of them had lain awake worried for their futures. Noticing this and separating the past from the present, both of them were able to acknowledge how far they had come from those early years of nocturnal distress, night after night of sleeplessness and panic.

I would alternately work with Ed and Estelle, letting the other person witness in silence the deep internal shifts, allowing the other person to see the unique qualities of their partner's struggle. Thus deep compassion was awakened, and a significant individuation was experienced, as each realized how independently they were wending their way through their histories, and how their occasional but dramatic points of meeting were interlocking possibilities for transmutation.

This individuation and compassion, this simultaneous evolution of detachment and commitment, allowed them to support each other in a much more mature way than they had ever known before. They stepped into a new level of relational awareness. they saw both the distance between them — that they had come from very different points of origin — and the similarities — that they were still struggling to overcome some early trauma patterns. They were humbled and enlightened by these discoveries.

Relational maturation is crucial in the New Family. It is the foundation upon which the whole concept of genuine support rests. There is a spiritual quality to this support. It is a microcosm of the holistic way that we can support others without martyrdom and with clarity. When Estelle and Ed began to feel this place of relationship, a renegotiation took place in terms of their understanding of the function of their support for one another. They felt simultaneously more secure with each other, less frightened by the other's process, and more independent of each other, freer to do their own personal work. And they felt appreciative rather than angry at the way their interlocking processes awakened them to deeper awarenesses of their evolutionary work. This personal work, and the ongoing, continuous nature of it, requires profound surrender and acceptance. It is spiritual understanding, knowing that this is the purpose of our lives — to develop and evolve, and that suffering, release and renegotiation are aspects of this development.

Because of their capacity to grow, Estelle and Ed supported one another through this challenge to their relationship. Estelle went on to discover even more resources for soothing and balancing her nervous system and Ed was able to develop creatively in the areas of his passionate interest. These movements forward enhanced their relationship profoundly. Ed and Estelle continued together into the rich, fecund territory of their maturity, coupling aging with wisdom and love. I felt honored to bear witness to this beauty.

The Impact of Sexual Abuse on Parenting

Teresa grew up in a home where abuse was a daily occurrence. Her father's chronic alcoholism, coupled with her mother's addiction to control (perhaps to compensate for her husband's utter lack of it) made Teresa's life a living hell. Her father was a military man, and her mother came from high society, so a great deal of attention was given to making sure the horror of their family life did not show. There was never any room for Teresa, or her sisters, to express their nightly terror and panic when their father went on his regular violent rampages, threatening to kill them all, including himself. And, eventually, he did kill himself. One Sunday morning, gunshots echoed through this tortured home. The children huddled in their rooms, listening, just as they listened each evening to the screaming. In fact, screaming was synonymous with Teresa's memory of her home. Screaming and gunshots. She didn't need to watch television to learn about violence.

After a brief career as an aggressive businesswoman, Teresa married Wade and bore three children. She still reflects quizzically on the mirroring — that she grew up in a family of three girls, and now she is the mother in a family of three girls. But there the similarity ends, for Teresa's home is a loving and friendly home, full of the activities of learning and relationship. She chose to home school her children, and she keeps just as busy at this task as she would at any other. She is an active and vital woman, devoted to doing whatever she does thoroughly, and with unbridled enthusiasm and commitment. Her ability to question, her challenging mind, and her awareness of her own feminine power and resources impressed and moved me.

Teresa's personal interests are eclectic and multifaceted. Adept at yoga and athletically inclined, she keeps herself physically present and healthy. Deeply concerned about education and Christian spirituality, she nurtures her involvement in activities which allow her to keep learning as she keeps mothering. She is dedicated to keeping alive and current not only her relationships with her children, but also her relationship with her husband, and her friendships with other women. She seemed to me to be incredibly healthy, a wonderful model of what survivorship really can mean. She acknowledged her own capacities and celebrated her ability to be herself. Why had she come to me?

The unresolved trauma of Teresa's life would erupt in sudden explosions of anger toward her children that came tumbling out unexpectedly and unpredictably. She would find herself screaming at one of the girls, usually the eldest. The screams would shatter the relaxed comfort of their home–school day, and the children would stare at their mother with terror on their faces, paralyzed, just as Teresa had stared at her mother as a child.

And then there would be retreats, apologies, discussions — all the healthy things that Teresa knew were necessary to repair the damage of the outbursts, but the outbursts themselves didn't stop. And sometimes the outbursts would be aimed at Teresa's husband, a friendly but often passive man, somewhat aghast at the chaos that a three–child family inevitably creates, and simultaneously challenged and overwhelmed by the financial responsibility he carried. With a wife at home and three girls to clothe (one of whom was almost a teenager), and home schooling supplies to be purchased, he felt impelled to take every money–earning opportunity that came his way, and that frequently meant long trips away from home, only to return to an overburdened wife who needed him to take the children for a while so that she could tap into her well–stocked warehouse of resources and get back to herself.

Having been solely responsible for the three girls while her husband was away, Teresa's pent–up tension would erupt at Wade, the only adult she had seen in weeks with whom she felt safe. In some ways you might say the outbursts were understandable, but Wade always *did* take the children whenever he could, and he really cared about all of them. He was successful at meeting the financial challenge and he was committed to understanding Teresa. He was acutely aware of her trauma history, and he knew he had one too, though it was quite different from Teresa's. Wade was really trying hard, pushing his limits, and usually finding himself feeling good that he could meet his responsibilities. So, why the outbursts, he wondered.

Life was full for Teresa and Wade, and mostly it was good — except for the screaming and the difficulty in repairing the traumatized environment that stayed shattered from the out–of–nowhere explosions which, when they happened, felt like bullets rippling through the house, destroying for what seemed like forever, the comfort of being at home. And there was real difficulty for Teresa and Wade in establishing and maintaining intimacy, given their erratic schedule and the intrusive trauma that kept interfering in their sincere efforts to be healthy. Teresa was filled with shame and confusion about her volcanic eruptions, but she was not afraid to talk about them. Her guilt tormented her and prevented her from seeing into the pain she felt she had so successfully handled. Almost free of body memories, outspoken, confident, Teresa thought she was just about done with healing, but her children denied her this belief, as they kept mirroring back to her the wide–eyed look of trauma trapped in a body too small to integrate its meaning, and too overwhelmed to move or protest.

The other telling piece of information that revealed the magnitude of what remained unresolved for Teresa was the difficulty she had in letting Wade into her life in a truly intimate and complete way. She bridled at his insensitivity, though he tried to bridge it. She found herself attracted to other men and fantasizing different lifestyles, more exciting than the mother–of–three home school teacher lifestyle she found herself in. Accepting Wade as her committed partner was something Teresa rebelled against, even avoided. She complained about him, but she also depended upon him. She was caught in a bind, and it made her nervous, even furious.

From the very beginning there was an easy trust between Teresa and me. As women of almost the same age and as mothers of daughters, our similarities bonded us. Both of us were dedicated to healing, proud of our womanhood, physically alert and active, resilient, strong. But Teresa still carried within her body and within her nervous system in particular the experience of terror and immobility, the paralyzing and frozen sense of helplessness that was activated immediately whenever she felt overwhelmed by anything at all — noises, responsibilities, media, danger, even love, even pleasure, even fulfillment. There was always this territory of paralysis and confusion that interfered with her healthy responses. She was burdened with interludes of impossibility which appeared apparently out of nowhere, like a road she hadn't anticipated, when passivity might expand or hysteria explode. The helplessness triggered or led to the outbursts, and in both affects there was an image of Teresa the child, the traumatized little one. Thus her life confused and trapped her, leaving her dissatisfied. She was incredibly articulate about this despair, and quick to recover her health, but the pattern continued nonetheless.

These remnants of breakdown defined the region of unresolved trauma, the deeply ingrained destruction that resided within the delicate structure of Teresa's history — all the wounds waiting to be healed. The first step was to acknowledge the situation as such. Teresa's first task, from my perspective, was to identify herself as the wonderful, caring, loving and resourceful mother she unquestionably was and individuate from the abusive parents which she knew as her mother and father. Her parents had both screamed and erupted just as Teresa screamed and erupted. This appeared, on the surface, to be a similarity between them. But there were also significant differences. We had to identify each of the differences carefully, thoughtfully, consistently and repeatedly. It took a while for Teresa to admit that there really was a significant difference between her and her parents, that yelling at her children didn't automatically make her like them. This individuation was extremely important, and it had to be undertaken and given its time. The differences between Teresa and her abusive parents had to sink into her awareness, into her body, into her nervous system. The differences were far, far greater than any similarities.

Once this individuation was done, once Teresa knew that indeed she was not an abusive parent, that she was distinct and separate from her parents, and that she parented in the present, with a part-

ner who was truly caring, and that she parented three girls who
were *not* a replica of her family of origin, then Teresa and I could
proceed to tackle the next aspect of this dilemma which had to do
with embracing her anger, identifying it for what it was, naming it
as her own, and finding a workable outlet for it. This, like the previous task, had to take its time and was not so easily done.

You could call these tasks routes to empowerment. Identifying
them, embracing them, and meeting them face to face become steps
on the path to self–hood. The dynamics of abuse and trauma rob us
of self–hood and set into motion the need for discovering these tasks
at all. Thus, our wounds become transformative, and in their transformative power they become sacred. And so it was for Teresa. A
woman always eager for a challenge and a test, she took on each
one with that spirit of eagerness which was her hallmark.

But the rage Teresa discovered she felt was enormous, more ominous and dark, more foreboding and destructive, more murderous
than she could have imagined. Her rage was against everything —
her mother, her father, her sisters, the church to which her parents
were superficially faithful, the country club society which seemed
to have more power over her family than the needs of the children,
the patriarchal structure in which she lived and which denied her
her outrage — everything. And what we discovered in our joyous
and demanding work together was that this rage was so big that it
had spilled recklessly wherever it could, and particularly where it
didn't belong because it didn't have anywhere else to go. It was up
to Teresa and me to guide this energy elsewhere.

Teresa could and would eventually model for her children the
health of feeling and the capacity of women to not deny instinctual
power and to live in a healthy and sane way with big feeling. In our
culture, emotional women and expressive women carry the identity of hysterics or madwomen. The women who have not been
able to integrate and contain the enormity of their feeling are generally women who have not had the resources and the guidance to
do so. It takes incredible focus and devotion to self to manage the
magnitude of feeling which survivors are privy to. For women, the
beings who can bear and bring forth children, there is an opening

to feeling and a sensitivity which appears simultaneously as a gift and a burden. Men too *can* carry this gift and when they honor it, they, like women, have the task of carrying to maturity the meaning of sensitivity.

It was through her body that Teresa found the route to both release *and* contain the rage which marked her life. It was a curious discovery for her. Teresa had identified herself as the comedian in her family of origin. Whenever too much pain was present, whenever the situation looked hopeless, Teresa could be counted upon to make it easier with a joke or a comedic routine. Her cute face and trim form added to her capacity to be a successful diversion from pain. And this gift of hers — truly a delight — was also an obstacle, for it kept her from being able to be with a natural uprising of feeling.

Teresa had lived a childhood of unmitigated horror and terror. No one should be asked to repress the expression of feelings from such a background. Those natural feelings which had not been resolved were leaking out into Teresa's parenting and into her most important, most intimate relationships. Whenever she recognized, even unconsciously, any of the passivity which marked her response to trauma as a child, she lashed out against it. The very sight of such passivity, in her children or in her husband, filled her with explosive rage. Whenever she saw a response which was anything less than enthusiastic, aggressive, humorous, resourceful and athletic, she smashed it. There was no room for what she identified as weakness, no time or space to accommodate fear, unresponsiveness. These possibilities were horribly threatening. She would damn them, squelch them before they could even be named. The fury of her fear was all–encompassing and instantaneous. It unfurled from her compact body like the flames from out a dragon's mouth. This was the masked trauma she exposed to her children. The renegotiation of this murderous rage was Teresa's work with me.

This rage could not be met or resolved by talk alone, so I offered Authentic Movement as a container. Authentic Movement is a vehicle for self discovery and expression and an unfolding of process which includes the body but does not train it or make it adhere to any of the rules of structure of dance or performance. Rather, it is a way of moving that allows the body to be authentic to its own motivation, to find its own motoric initiation, and to move only in response to that. It is a way of hearing the body's story of wisdom, truth and pain, without judging, evaluating or defining, by simply letting the body unfold into organic movement. It is a way to let the body talk without interference. Time limits and conditions of space create natural boundaries to shape this process and allow it to be useful rather than pushing movement in the direction of emotional flooding. I offered Teresa Authentic Movement in the context of our sessions together as a way to discover, identify and transmute the enormous rage she had the right to feel as a result of her history of abuse and trauma. (See the Resource section of this book for more information on Authentic Movement and related expressive modalities.)

Within the context of our therapeutic meetings, Teresa was the one who moved and I was the witness to her movement. As the witness, I held the calm and quiet of the containing space; I created the boundary which made the expression of Teresa's body safe and secure. With me as witness, and with our aftermath discussions as grounding mechanisms, she could safely unfold, in measured increments, going to the edge of overwhelm and retreating from that edge, only to return later, when the feeling process had been well integrated. And knowing that she had a place where her rage was welcome, permissible, acceptable and most importantly, completely harmless, completely non–damaging, boundaried and witnessed, lessened her physical need for the explosion of this energy in her home. The physiological impulse to be rageful had a healthy and appropriate structure, so the inappropriate expression became unnecessary.

Rage that is engendered in the home will seek its outlet in the home. There is something about abuse and trauma and repetition compulsion that makes some very specific rhythmic demands about time and place, and the nervous system of the survivor needs to be carefully and consciously educated into other possibilities, new options to configure and express experience other than by repeating it verbatim, other than by mirroring the qualities of the original trauma exactly. Unconscious obsessive repetition is not doomed to hold to its pattern if awareness enters upon the scene. THERE ARE OTHER OPTIONS, but it takes work, consciousness, focus, and a lot of dedication to discover those other options and take them, make them happen, physically, emotionally and spiritually. Teresa could do this, even after she discovered that the task was harder than she thought.

Using the tool of Authentic Movement, Teresa unveiled her desire to destroy the people who had tried (unsuccessfully) to destroy her sense of self, and she allowed that feeling to move through her body, little by little, until she found the feeling wasn't there anymore. That did not happen quickly. It took several years for this unraveling and during those years Teresa had to augment her Authentic Movement experiences with writing. The writing, along with the witnessing I did and the discussions we had together following our Authentic Movement experiences, allowed the physical expression to find a balance in cognition.

Teresa began to know in her body that her anger was natural, an organic response to the inability she was sentenced to as a child to express her enormous experience of fear. Her rage at how little space she was given to be who she was, to have the feelings that anyone would expect her to have under the circumstances, was too big to even name. It was rage that expanded beyond the level of Authentic Movement or writing, and that is why we had to allow its expression in titrated increments and not in explosions.

Explosions were common in Teresa's life. Her father had died from an explosion, in more ways than one. She had been subjected to explosions almost every night of her childhood. Her relationship with her mother was an explosive relationship, a power struggle that threatened to explode, all the time. Even Teresa's relationships with her sisters, both of whom were in denial about the extremity of abuse in their homes, were also explosive, and Teresa was justifiably enraged at them for continuing to squelch the truth, for pretending.

I have not yet mentioned Teresa's history of having been sexually abused by her father. Within the context of the environment I have described, the environment in which Teresa grew up, the environment in which her foundation for living was built, the sexual

abuse was a significant component of *overall* trauma, part and parcel of a stream of ongoing events and circumstances which were
altogether unhealthy, altogether destructive, and that entire environment had to be considered as a therapeutic whole. All the rivu-
lets that fed the stream of trauma lava had to be acknowledged to
face the ember burning at the core of the volcano, which could be
said to be the sexual abuse. As a therapist, I felt directed to calm the
exterior regions, the envelope you might call it, the larger fabric
that surrounded the place where the fabric was most horribly torn.
And, of course, the greatest degree of rage existed at that rent volcanic core, but when we got there so much rage had already been
emitted in our expressive work and our dialogue that that rage,
that justifiable, honest and righteous rage, came out like a wave of
a beautiful red chiffon scarf, moving easily from a body that will-
ingly surrendered its truth. Her fury at the incest was enormous,
but when we got to it, Teresa could express and contain it.

Energetically releasing the truth of Teresa's rage was a victory for
both of us. This process did not in any way deplete Teresa. In fact, it
had the opposite effect — it energized her because it relieved her of
a great and old burden of congested feeling and created opportunity for fresh experience, fresh insight, fresh perspective, and fresh
response.

In the interim, however, before we had come to this place of relative clearing, Teresa had to have a way of dealing with her impulse
to explode, especially vis–à–vis her children and her husband. We
had to identify what the explosive triggers were. This involved a
careful, almost meditative process in which Teresa allowed herself
to put the slow motion on her memory experience, by going back to
the moments of explosion and backtracking, slowly, slowly, and
naming her sensation as it built to the point of explosion. Carefully,
ever so slowly, we tracked her sensation as it evolved, identifying
each moment of panic and redirecting the responsive possibilities
at each interval. Thus, we began to find other options for Teresa.
Each moment, of necessity, that we identified as a triggering moment had to be slowed down and, similarly in the actual activating
experience, Teresa had to slow things down. She had to not be so

ready to react; *she had to wait.* She had to back off from her reactions once she could identify that indeed they were occurring. This is the careful, focused work of uncoupling feeling from reaction, and we had to do it many, many times. But it was quite successful.

Now, when Teresa could identify that she was triggered (by the sight of her daughter's passive, paralyzed eyes, for instance), she just stopped, she backed off, she slowed down, SHE DIDN'T ACT. And then she didn't explode, and having not exploded, she freed herself of guilt, and having freed herself of guilt, she was able to go deeper, to see what REALLY triggered her. Her greatest reward was the look of relief on her daughter's face when she didn't yell at her.

Teresa had, in fact, identified herself as a screamer, as a yeller and as a tumultuous person. Was this really true? Or, was she carrying a label she actually thought belonged to her mother or her father? To research the question thoroughly, we tried eliminating from Teresa's diet those things that activated her nervous system, like coffee. Coffee doesn't necessarily activate everyone's nervous system, but we experimented with whether it was a nervous system stimulant for Teresa. And we found that it was. By eliminating coffee, Teresa found that she was less responsive to being triggered. She went through a period of fatigue and irritability, but because of her healthy diet and her yoga practice, that period passed quickly and Teresa was happy to be less reactive. The rage was still there, but each time we lessened her reactivity we shifted the cycle of activation, explosion and guilt, and the less guilt the more space we had to work with what was actually underneath the reaction to begin with. In this way, we proceeded, and made enormous progress.

It turned out that the characterization of Teresa as explosive and over–reactive was not accurate. After the expressive work, after the Authentic Movement had done its job, and the writing was happening as a regular part of her life, after the coffee was eliminated, we discovered that Teresa was a calm person. She had a serenity that was a treasure hidden under the many blankets of trauma that had covered the true Teresa.

Teresa's family was very supportive of her process of discovery. They came close to being a living embodiment of the New Family I have been trying to describe. Because of the family system that Teresa and Wade had created, each outburst of Teresa's as well as what she was learning about these outbursts could be discussed in family meetings. For instance, Teresa's explosive reactions to Wade's returns from two or three–week business trips were clearly due to the difficulty of bearing so much responsibility while he was gone. In family discussions, and sometimes in consultation with me, alternatives could be found to allowing this tension to build so consistently. I encouraged Teresa to find new supports for herself, such as people who could come and relieve her of the daily responsibilities while Wade was gone, such as the car driving, and the meal preparation. And the children could be given more information about these periods in which they were single parented, so that they could brainstorm with their parents and participate in the problem solving. By looking at the dynamics of the situation and reconfiguring strategies before the explosive moment came, Teresa's nervous system was saved yet another opportunity to be over–adrenalized, its weakness from childhood, and thus a renegotiation on a family systems level was possible. *The whole family could support the possibility of preventing trauma.*

It was with enormous gratitude and appreciation that I worked with Teresa and her family. Their responsiveness to my suggestions and their willingness to look at their interlocking traumas and to find new options for themselves as individuals and as a family system was incredibly gratifying, and made my work satisfying. It is rare to find a group of people so willing to go into the fiery territory of trauma renegotiation together and to combine their efforts to be helpful.

If you have been abused as a child, if you have been yelled at or struck, you can expect that some of the influence of that experience will come through your body and your interactions with your children if you become a parent. Furthermore, if you become aware of the trauma or abuse you experienced as a child while you are a parent, your interactions with your children are bound to be impacted. It is important to pay close attention to how remnants of abuse experience find their way into your relationship with your children, even when you believe you are so much better at parenting than your parents were. What is required is the kind of honesty and fearlessness that Teresa demonstrated. She was willing to admit that her behavior was not appropriate — it didn't feel good to her and she wasn't going to deny that. That allowed the possibility for healing to occur.

In alcoholic families in particular, but in many dysfunctional families, screaming, sudden outbursts and flare–up tantrums are common occurrences. It is a shock for a mother or father who want terribly not to expose their children to the kind of trauma their alcoholic parents inflicted on them to suddenly find themselves yelling at their children. All such events can be remedied by apology and loving discussion and have an entirely different course when acknowledged and addressed. But the cause of the outburst has to be tracked and traced, and the parent freed of the burden of guilt and compulsive repetition. These patterns of abuse don't have to continue generation after generation. They don't have to be acted out in private nor do they have to be acted out in public, as they are, increasingly, much to our horror. These patterns can be stopped but it requires attention and conscientious awareness and a great commitment to healing with patience for this shift to happen. But these qualities *can* stop the lineage of abuse. I have seen this happen and I have experienced this myself.

In my idea of the New Family, it is entirely possible to find a healthy way to understand how to become aware of the lineage of abuse as it plays out in parent–child dynamics, and to begin to shift those dynamics away from trauma into healthy responses. In the New Family, the emphasis is on honesty, expressing remorse when necessary and appropriate, and not on denial or saving face. So, if a mother yells at a child, the mother can apologize and the child can forgive. If the father yells at the mother, the children can witness the father apologizing and the mother forgiving. Guilt is not calculated as part of a healthy process. Events that have occurred and have been resolved are complete, and they are released. There is resolution. Of course, outbursts that involve violence are another matter and must be stopped at all costs, but I believe that if you can feel safe enough to trace trauma dynamics to their source, violence will not occur.

Teresa continues to work with me in group situations and on an as–per–needed basis, when issues arise in her life and her home. It is always a delight to see her. I can tell from her glowing smile that violent outbursts don't happen in her home and that conflicts are resolved lovingly and successfully. She is happy to be at home with her children and her life is rich and creative. The trauma she experienced as a child will never be completely forgotten, but it is not in the forefront of her consciousness. She still struggles to create a healthy relationship with her husband and sexual issues surface for both of them as they face the demands of raising three children and the interference of past trauma into current interactions. But these issues are known, ahead of time, to have a multiplicity of healing possibilities, and so there is not an experience of threat or despair because they occur. This healthy state of balance is one I am glad to have instigated.

Stories of healing such as these must be told when they genuinely occur, for how else are we to find the faith and support we need to work with these demanding issues? Resolution IS possible. Healing IS possible. Transformation IS possible. *Not only possible, but probable.* This is not only a theory. This is a reality. Healing has already happened and healing will continue to happen as long as we are ready to participate in transformation and to open ourselves to the multi–leveled process of renegotiation and awakening.

Sexual Abuse and the Single Parent Family

When sexual abuse issues surface, the single parent is heavily burdened, and needs to recognize the vulnerability implicit in his or her situation. For that single parent, whether it be a father or a mother, the survivor's key is to find support systems, resources, and friends who can function dependably as allies. A natural extended family is a wonderful asset if it exists. Unfortunately, for the survivor of sexual abuse, the family of origin is sometimes threatened by the very mention of sexual abuse issues or they are in denial about the abuse completely, or perhaps they are even aggressively rejecting the survivor as a way to discount and avoid their suffering.

This is terribly painful, and frequently stirs up even more rage than the issue of the abuse itself Since sexual abuse never happens in a vacuum, and the family dynamics are always part and parcel of the entire phenomena of abuse and betrayal, it is not unusual to find the family vigorously and thoroughly pushing the survivor away, even abandoning him or her. There have been times, however, when this is not the case and the family rallies strongly and lovingly to the support of the single parent survivor.

It is also true, sadly, that it is possible that the family of origin cannot generate this spaciousness, and the single parent survivor finds himself or herself emotionally overwhelmed and isolated, with children to care for. If this occurs it is crucial that the survivor access available networks of support. The task of dealing with emotional issues and parenting is too great to undertake alone, and the single parent family depends on, and demands, the participation of others to enhance and expand the definition and experience of support. Isolation is not really feasible under these circumstances.

In discussing this theme, I speak from my own experience. I raised my first child as a single parent from the time she was two years old, and in the course of our life together the issue of recovering from sexual abuse was a main event in my life. As issues surfaced, primarily during the time when I was in graduate school and my daughter was entering the full throes of adolescence, I found myself very confused about how to parent when feeling emotionally overwhelmed. For the most part, I determined it was better to keep my emotional process separate from my relationship with my daughter, and to not mention incest or abuse until she was older and more mature. I first discussed the fact that incest was part of my history when my daughter was much older, and while she was deeply shocked and quite compassionate, she also felt that this was not something she wanted to go into deeply with me — she didn't want this to be a big deal in our relationship. This made me feel that my original choice not to discuss this with her earlier, when she was even less mature, was correct. I had very few people to consult during this time. For one thing, I was deeply involved in a spiritual practice that emphasized silence, introspection and self reflection rather than relationship. I wonder now what this time would have been like for myself and my daughter if I had had more people to talk to who were sensitive to this subject.

When my daughter began high school the conflicts which had been submerged during our primarily compatible years together erupted. Vital and strong in her independence, she confronted me with all the heretofore unspoken differences between us. Most of my friends minimized the painful struggle that ensued. My spiritual comrades asked me to "trust your Guru and know that it's not your will but God's will." My colleagues in graduate school either didn't have children or were overwhelmed with their doctoral program and unable to talk about anything else. I desperately sought understanding within myself, in my meditation and prayers, and in my faith in the basic core of love my daughter and I had for each other. Her father was glad we were having differences, thinking this his vindication at last, and, two thousand miles away, he counseled her against me and what he defined as my "bourgeois lifestyle," beckoning her into his more bohemian way of life.

I felt desperate and often spent night after night sleepless with longing for the delightful years of camaraderie between my little girl and myself and simultaneously tormented by my inadequacy in addressing the crisis of alienation and rebellion in which we were embroiled. When I finally did seek professional help, the person I selected was inadequate to finding creative solutions, ignorant about the role of my own sexual abuse issues, and dogmatic in her parenting suggestions. I had selected her, in part, because of her low fees and felt so poorly about myself that I was unable to terminate with her even when I realized she was doing neither my daughter nor me any good. I felt compelled to try to succeed at what she was suggesting and continued paying her for what proved to be utterly worthless sessions, while I struggled in the fashion I was familiar with, against great odds, expecting failure, plodding on, ruthlessly self-critical. Unbeknownst to me, because I was still so early in my recovery, I was simply repeating the patterns of dysfunction, abuse, and self-depreciation that were endemic to my history. The therapist, a social worker without children herself, mimicking the rules and regulations she'd learned in some training program somewhere, had no insight into the uniqueness of our particular situation, and no therapeutic skills of her own. But from my point of view, this well-dressed, slender young woman in private practice had to be more intelligent than I, a mere bumbling graduate student, struggling with little money against severe obstacles, to become professional. I was pulling myself up by my bootstraps. Surely someone in heels and nylons, with even white teeth and a stylish flair, knew better than I how to survive in the world.

It wasn't until much later that I discovered, that rebellion of this magnitude was common for this stage of individuation. She and I were finally able to talk about it in retrospect, but that period remains marked in my heart as a time of failure, when I couldn't meet her needs. I couldn't find a way to communicate the incredible hope I had for the two of us to continue our bond of friendship. I feel that this failure weakened me in some way from which I have not yet regained my strength. The terrain of adolescence, which I myself had walked in such an odd way, and the demands of parenting during this time, are still mysterious to me, though I believe I have learned a great deal from my daughter.

The sexual abuse issues that were becoming clear to me during this period were part of the tide that worked against resolution for my daughter and me during her adolescent years. Encountering contained emotion in an onslaught of awakening means that feelings preoccupy you, distract you from the mundane functioning that makes life work. It takes support, strength, creativity, and great awareness to allow the memories or flashbacks their space and still parent, clean house, earn money, go to school, drive a car, do the laundry, etc. I was confused with this multifaceted array of crises and grasped constantly at whatever straws came my way to keep afloat. On the surface, I did very well. I completed my doctoral work, my daughter graduated high school, I got healthier, and eventually so did she — and our relationship continues to thrive. But having flailed through this time alone, I feel more lucky than wise, more fortunate than skilled at having survived intact.

In addition to my own personal experiences, there are many similar stories I can relate from my work with survivors of sexual abuse. In my practice, I see primarily female heads of households (though men's stories will also be told here) who are frustrated with the need to develop themselves and supervise as well as participate in the development of their children. Often the family is suffering from a recent divorce or separation, and the memories of parental fights, sometimes violence, and the echo of cruelty and hurt adds to the emotional turmoil. Enormous courage is needed, and it will carry you through even if it's all you have. *Courage plus resources*, however, can actually make this interlude of life a vital struggle rather than a depleting one.

One client, let's call her Marie, was in the middle of a graduate program she'd longed to complete when her family started exploding with the ramifications of separation and divorce from a husband and father who had become suddenly irresponsible and financially incompetent. Graduate school studies, especially in the field of psychology, tend to bring up for the student all the unresolved feelings from the past. And they should — how can anyone work in the field of psychology and human services without being aware of their own problems? Many people do, but they cause more damage than good. Survivors tend to be rather impeccable, when they become conscious of their own issues, in addressing resolution for themselves before they demand it of others.

The biggest dilemma Marie faced once she became a single mom was that the family's expanding demands on her ate up all the time she needed to process her own feelings. The space that was essential to being calm and clear enough to answer her children's needs, at which she was very good, was devoured by the many things she had to do — taking the children to classes, arranging for therapies for them, meetings with teachers and school counselors, meetings with lawyers, house cleaning, making money. There was nothing left for her, not even enough funds for her own therapy. I suggested several things, such as:

1. Get big brothers for the boys, and big sisters for the girls.

2. Ask other family members to make contributions to the family — like paying for special classes and inviting individual children for overnight visits and vacations.

3. Call friends together to brainstorm and provide support.

4. I advised her to get into a women's group, one with survivors, preferably also with women who were parenting and whose issues paralleled hers.

5. Get lots of exercise, with or without the children.

6. Write — keep a journal, share writing with others who are sympathetic.

7. Be expressive — sing, dance, let the arts support you.

8. Don't expect yourself to be supermom, be honest with the children, talk about your struggles without bad-mouthing the other parent. If the latter is unavoidable, give the children the opportunity to vent their feelings about both parents.

9. Even though it seems impossible, make space for feelings. Trying to squelch feelings, minimize them, or repress them has the opposite effect — it makes the repressed feeling bigger in reaction to being held down.

10. While it seems imperative to take care of business before addressing feeling, the reverse order can be more efficient. Feeling can interfere with clear thinking, but thinking can become not only more focused but also more creative, more resourceful, when feelings are released. Journal writing on coffee breaks, Authentic Movement in the bedroom before sleep, or singing in the car can make the present moment a more living reality. The fog of unresolved feeling can blur the obvious. See the Resource section of this book for more information on using these tools.

If the survivor single parent attempts to avoid the sexual abuse issues that surface during the difficult years of recovery, the result is usually that the feeling comes out in negativity, anger, and sometimes even violence or screaming at the children. It is far, far better to allow room for the feelings, to accept the sexual abuse flashbacks, memories, or sensations and find an appropriate time and space to address them. Denying, repressing, or pretending that these issues are not there tends to backfire, causing great harm.

This said, such juggling is near to impossible all the time. It takes enormous courage and fortitude to organize a healthy life for an entire family while confronting the pain of traumatic recollection. Solitude is oftentimes an ally during this difficulty. I often took long walks, alone or with my daughter when she would go, and found strength in silence and nature.

Spiritual resources can be lifesavers, whether they be meditation, prayer, chanting, or practices of any kind that attune you to a larger perspective, a way of knowing that you are not alone in your often agonizing movement toward wholeness. But as much as this strength can be mobilized on an invisible, visionary, or spiritual level, nothing can replace human companionship, friends and kindred spirits with whom the single parent survivor can talk, share, embrace, connect, cry, sigh, and laugh. Finding people who can affirm that we are here to help each other, not just to hurt one another, can be the key during times of confusion and crisis, not to mention during the daily struggle of meal time, off to school time, Friday nights, weekends, and holidays.

Community resources as well as personal resources must be researched as thoroughly as possible. Some agencies may be helpful, others may be damaging. Check them out carefully. Parenting centers in some communities have networks, classes, child care, and materials. Recreation centers often have good baby-sitting, inexpensive classes for all ages, and family exercise times. Colleges and universities often have child-care services and listings of student baby sitters. Explore all avenues of help with eyes wide open. The time you invest could make a huge difference in your life. If you do have family members you can trust, bring them into your life. Once when I was feeling on the brink of hysteria, I asked my brother to come and visit us for his vacation. I told him up front that I needed help. He provided not only child care (which really meant he got valuable quality time with his nieces), but help around the house, mealtime companionship, someone to brainstorm with and get feedback from about life strategies and philosophies for change. This was hardly an imposition. Rather, it was a time for genuine contact, reunification, recommitment to caring, and, perhaps most importantly, it was a time when brother and sister could get to know who the other one really was, aside from the superficiality of long distance phone calls on birthdays.

Similarly, when my client Lisa left her husband because his anger toward her began to resemble too often her childhood of verbal abuse from her father, she moved in with her brother, a bachelor in Colorado. Her family of two daughters and a son brought vitality into her brother's life, which was marked by his sad and withdrawn demeanor, his own way of responding to the abuse in their home of origin. Late at night, when the children were asleep, Lisa and her brother, Donald, talked over the impact of their sad family structure. Their shared insights made it possible for them to offer a much more balanced way of living to the children. They supported each other in therapeutic involvement, and in the subtle shift from traumatic re–enactment to healing patterns. It wasn't easy for brother and sister to be together, and they knew it wouldn't last forever, but during the period of transition when Lisa was getting her feet on the ground, Donald was an anchor, and being so helpful to this sister and her family made Donald believe in himself and made him think about having more people around him more often, and that maybe he had something to offer.

Allen, a survivor of physical abuse, violence, and terror in his family home, took care of his two daughters most of the time. He tried to start a men's group to get support but found there weren't enough other men in his small town who were in a situation resembling his. After searching for community connection in the local coffee house, the recreation centers, and the PTA, all to no avail, he found himself doing something he thought he would never do — he joined his local Jewish Community Center, though he felt anger at his Jewish roots, which had been watered by the seeds of suffering in his early life. But the Center proved to be a place where he could go with his daughters to family programs without feeling strange — they were all Jewish and therefore completely accepted, even welcomed. Camping trips, outings, sports activities all became communal rather than just Allen trying to get everything together by himself, the girls straggling along, not sure they wanted to go on any of dad's family trips. With a whole community of men, women, and children, these events took on quite another flavor, and surprisingly Allen and the girls even found it interesting to rediscover the holidays, the culture, the songs, and the foods of their lineage. And there was even decent counseling available through the Center, financial support, parenting materials, and classes. Discovering resources he didn't know he had was a bright light for Allen during a dark time and he didn't have to convert to being a full time Jew (he'd become a curious seeker, interested in many spiritual paths) in order to tap into the community of friends his heritage offered.

These thumbnail sketches are not intended to be complete case histories, proving that it can all work out. For all these people — Marie, Lisa, Allen, and myself — the help we found sustained us at difficult times, but the struggle remained intense, demanding, challenging, and sometimes all consuming. Our resources provided relief, innovative strategies, helping hands, shoulders to cry on; but it was still up to us to weave all the threads into a whole piece.

One more description, I think, will help to bring into bold relief some of the actual daily details of what it means to struggle as a single parent when sexual abuse issues add their own peculiar dimension and coloration to the portraits of family life. I am going to take this opportunity to tell the story of another man's struggle, and I'd like to share with you my reasoning in making this choice. Women's stories are told primarily when the subject of sexual abuse and incest is raised, and while the statistics reveal that it is overwhelmingly women who are abused, I believe it is, in part, because women are so frequently portrayed that men are restricted in recognizing the ways in which they have been abused.

It is my belief that men and women equally have been damaged by a culture materialistically driven to stereotype sexuality, to infantalize women, and to limit the opportunities for expression. I am opposed, personally, to seeing the emphasis so strongly on gender in terms of trauma since I feel men and women have been undermined equally and that our struggles are interlaced. Having been severely betrayed by masculine figures of authority in my life (my father, my spiritual teacher), I am painfully aware of how abuse hurts women. But I feel the turnaround, in terms of ending trauma, can occur when men too identify, articulate, express, and find real help for their suffering. It is because my father and my spiritual teacher refused to identify their own pain that they felt compulsively driven to inflict pain on others, and specifically on women. I adhere to the belief, based on my personal life experience, that hope comes through healthy communication and expression, so I am choosing to tell men's stories here as well as women's. I want men to find models for the unexpressed parts of themselves in these pages, and therefore lessen a compulsion to hurt others. The survivors I work with are wonderful parents and I believe they have learned their parenting and even their relationship skills by expressing themselves openly in safe, creative environments that do not limit who they are. I encourage men as well as women to explore these possibilities and dare to be true to their own instincts for healing.

David

When David married Sue, he felt he had mated for life. Though Sue's life had been extremely difficult and she was subject to harrowing emotional bouts as a result, David felt such overwhelming love for her that he knew he could commit himself to being with her, without a shadow of a doubt. Sue had been adopted into a family that was hardly a sanctuary. Her adopted father was an alcoholic, and her adopted mother, who struggled to make up for her husband's outbursts, was worn and weary from a lifetime of compensation. In her early twenties, Sue had decided to search for her birth mother. The result of her quest was not a joyful reunification. She found that her mother had been incested by an uncle, and Sue was the result of that violent, unwanted co–mingling. Her birth mother had no desire to build a relationship with Sue. Quite the contrary. She never wanted to see or hear from her again. Sue was devastated, and while David's arms remained open to her, her wounding drove her deeper and deeper into herself, into feelings she felt incapable of communicating. Valiantly, she struggled to mother their three sons, to be cheerful and to strengthen herself, but as time progressed, the thrust of the abandonment and rejection that had been aimed at her took a toll that demanded bigger and bigger payments. Sue's wound festered, and one day she would have to devote herself totally to her healing.

David had always been the good son, the good brother, the good husband, the good father. His manner was soft and sweet. He wasn't aggressive. As a child he had been in a severe car accident and his entire left side had been weakened so that he couldn't participate with his peers in the roughhousing activities and daredevil fun that often marked a boy's maturation. Instead, he cultivated reading and thinking. He had ideas, visions, and dreams, which preoccupied him. He wrote, fabricating stories that he experienced not as novels but as films, as living dramas. In his withdrawal, however, David was never bitter or resentful. Quite the contrary. He was exceedingly kind, and while his mannerisms reflected his meekness, he never hesitated to speak when anyone questioned him about himself, and if someone showed an interest in his thoughts, he gladly shared them. David performed extremely well at school and was soon recognized for his intelligence, both in mathematics and in creative writing. When he learned about computers, he found he had discovered electronic friends. Indeed, he eventually made a successful career from his bonding with computers, though writing screenplays in his spare time continued to engage him deeply. Even his dreams became plays and films, as did his relationship with Sue, and their three sons, all of whom he adored.

David was a happy man, though he had few friends. Love was the center of his life, and having a loving family meant everything to him. He protected his family by providing for them, and for Sue he was the ultimate soul mate, talking her out of her depressions, holding her through the long nights of her fear and panic, reassuring her that while she was rejected before, she was fully accepted now. Sue told David everything. She never hid from him her distress, her insecurities, which were extraordinary, her deep fear that she could not fulfill her responsibilities. Her sense of inadequacy bred jealousies, fantasies about losing her husband. The abandonment that marked her entry into the world seemed to haunt her mercilessly.

The loneliness that Sue carried with her wherever she went evoked such powerful empathy from David that he felt he lived his life to sustain Sue. Comforting her, giving her some will to live her life from day to day, convincing her of her own beauty and brilliance, of the beauty of her soul, was David's passion, and he devoted himself to his wife gladly. He was happy when she was happy and deeply concerned when her depression overcame her and made her incapable of connecting with her family. David encouraged Sue to paint, to create, to write, so that she might have an objective experience of her own capacities.

In David's home of origin, he had certainly been the odd man out. But that was not such a bad thing, he thought. Quiet, internalized, David didn't feel he suffered from his parents' disinterest in him. They were certainly caring parents. They attended all his school programs and praised him for his good grades. It was just that they never wondered what preoccupied him, never engaged in long conversations, inviting David to share his visions. They were pleased with their son as the intelligent one in the family.

David's brother and sister were much more outgoing. It was easy enough for the family to get along without David's overt participation. The only time he was special was when Mom was lonely. Then David would be the one she talked to, the one she snuggled up with on the couch, sometimes she would even put her head on David's shoulder, when he got older. David's father was a very successful businessman, and when he was home he was robust, jocular, engaging — but he wasn't home very much. Business trips grew longer and more global. Dad's success reaped huge financial rewards. The family was certainly secure. The scene was tediously typical. It was happening in every other house on the block. All of the four bedroom homes in their neighborhood were occupied by lonely women who didn't know what to do with themselves, and children who were either frighteningly isolated or compelled to hyperactivity and achievement. But David kept to himself in the midst of the world's tedium and obsession. He comforted his mother. He did well in school. And he found another world for himself inside his mind, which he found to be spacious, inventive, compassionate, involved, and quietly active.

After fifteen years of marriage, Sue determined that the only hope for her was to break away from the family. She didn't have the energy or the resources to take care of the children, so she left them with David. David accepted this without condemning Sue, but with great personal pain. Sue had suffered so much all her life, and David genuinely wanted her to find relief.

But now life took on an entirely new rhythm, one David had never experienced before. He woke at 5:00 a.m. to get ready for work. He needed not only to get showered, dressed, and his papers ready, he also had to get his nine year–old son to school (this included making sure his clothes were clean and his lunch packed, not to mention checking that his homework was done).

The hardest part, however, involved the teenagers, both of whom were in tremendous rebellion and excitement over Mom's departure. David had to be sure they were actually going to school, and that they would stay there. David's job was an hour away. He had bought a comfortable rural home for the family, but business wasn't done there — David had to drive into the city to earn the living that sustained this family, now a family of men. And David was overcome with grief. As accepting as he was of Sue's needs, he was broken with sadness, with a longing for his wife. He was like an addict without his fix. There was no one to comfort in the night, and much to his surprise, David felt that he was the one who had lost the comforting. Ever strong, ever moving forward, never stopping in his fulfillment of his obligations, David cried unshed tears as he reached out at night to reassure someone who wasn't there. David was excruciatingly lonely. And there was no time to make friends. After work there was the nine-year–old's homework, and tracking down the teenagers, and trying to create an environment in which studies could be accomplished, not to mention the work David had to bring home with him every night since there was no way he could ever stay later at work now. Cooking, dinner, cleanup — time had to be found for these crucial family commitments. And there really wasn't enough money, it seemed. Despite his decent income, the house payments, the car payments, the private schools, the therapists for the children — it was all gone very quickly.

In his exhaustion, David stopped creating fictional families and dramas and started instead to remember his own. And what he remembered most was the way his mother leaned on him, the way she enveloped him in her need, the way she transmitted her loneliness to him, and the way he could successfully reassure her that she was loved, loved by him, needed by him, appreciated, unabandoned.

Remembering, David filled with rage. He wanted to run away, to go outside, to race through the neighborhood, which now, in a sudden, awful way, resembled his childhood home, and scream into all the houses, "Lies, lies, lies!" But of course, he couldn't do this. The boys needed his supervision. Each day carried an endless list of things to do, and those lists got added to the next day's list, so that David was always in a doing debt. David was aghast. Always so calm, so competent, so capable, always available — suddenly David discovered a furious energy inside of him, an energy that wanted to get out, to get away, to be free, to run and scream and yell, to play, to fall down, and to be picked up, to be held, to be reassured, to be treasured and healed from his hurts. He felt like a little boy, a little boy he didn't really recognize. But these feelings were his, and he had to stifle them — he had three boys to take care of, and he had to earn money. He was trapped.

How would David get out of the trap? Was blaming Sue the answer? Was finding another wife the answer? Was abandoning it all, sending the boys away, the answer? Interestingly, compellingly, David found, the answer lay in being more thoroughly with the situation, in opening more completely to the dilemma he found himself in. How and why did David do this?

Working with David was always a challenge for me. He was steeped in the pragmatism of the business world, and I marveled incredulously at his capacity to martyr himself, apparently without too much damage to his spirit, though his body took a terrible toll as it acquired more and more exhaustion and loneliness. But David taught me a powerful lesson when he himself turned the corner in his situation of unrelenting pressure. I wondered how he could survive a life in which every moment of his waking day was spent taking care of something or someone, and not a moment was left for himself, for his creativity or his rejuvenation. Quite honestly, I wasn't sure he could survive!

There were two periods in his day when David could take in something for himself — the time he spent driving to and from work. These two hours could be used to listen to tapes that could inspire, encourage, or educate him, or perhaps even entertain him, thereby giving David something to go on, some energy to stimulate his own creativity. And David used this time conscientiously. One tape he particularly liked talked about how working on ourselves instead of worrying about conditions gives us the power to influence the conditions of our lives. This made sense to David since he was rapidly learning that agonizing over his situation got him nowhere.

Expansion into himself became David's route of transformation in what anyone would have regarded as an overwhelming, near impossible, life of duty, responsibility, and difficulty. We have all read a story or two that tells of the agonies and transcendence of a survivor of torture, holocaust, misery, or oppression. Each of us, at one time or another, has encountered a tale of incredible abuse that becomes incredible breakthrough, wherein much good flows out of much suffering. But scattered throughout America, there are countless vignettes of people struggling as single parents, with the hint of abuse everywhere in their consciousness, in their environment, struggling against great odds simply to have a pleasant meal time, simply to be able to attend a child's recital with a peaceful attitude, simply to help a child through school without frustration and distraction. Thousands, probably many thousands, of individuals are working to get their children off to school and themselves off to work without screaming, without losing their focus, without giving up in tears the remarkable effort it takes to survive abuse, trauma, abandonment, and desperation. These are heroic songs that are rarely sung.

David found his solution in the awareness that resulted from his expansion into himself. He decided to embrace more deeply his own story, and to see how his story brought him to where he was, a lonely, single parent, the ex–spouse of a dearly loved wife who was severely abused, a conscientious parent and a hard-working man, who went to sleep each night with tears streaming down his face.

David's therapy sessions were on Saturday mornings. For a few hours the older boys could watch the younger one, who was mostly busy at early morning cartoons, and David could meet with me and then spend a little time reflecting on our session. Instead of inquiring into who was responsible for his dilemma, he decided to ask how he got to where he was, and to see what he had to do to make his life more closely resemble a satisfying experience for himself. This research, intended from the outset to make him stronger and happier, revealed the labyrinth of intricate and abusive ties that David maintained silently to his mother's need for him. Bound to a sense of being needed as his only identity, David had found it somewhat natural to sacrifice repeatedly what he wanted almost before he knew what that was in order to survive.

Never sexual, nevertheless, his mother's touch told David that she needed him and only him. His particular way of passively being present with her and allowing her to touch him in ways that made him uncomfortable, in ways that made him feel trapped and restricted, in ways that gave him the impression he had no freedom at all, that very touch which repelled and paralyzed him also told him how special and needed he was, how wanted and treasured he was — and all for his silence, his availability, his dutiful acquiescence. David, the child, allowed himself to soothe his lonely mother, forcing out of consciousness his own desire to move out of her world and into his own.

Was this sexual abuse? Could it ever be categorized as such? It was so subtle, so invisible, yet David remembered it well, and with repulsion. He remembered the sensation as if it were happening in the present, a kind of tingling in the flesh that was filled with excitement and dread. No, it wasn't sexual abuse by any classical definition, but it was abuse by intention, or abuse by unconscious manipulation. And David knew this within himself, though he had always been afraid to speak of it. Who would understand? Wouldn't he be ridiculed for this apparent fabrication, these invisible experiences, all based on sensation, all buried within the deep sensory memory of an exceptionally sensitive child, a very bright child, a child who was available to be used in the hope of being loved?

David's expansion into himself during the time he had available resulted in the retrieval of this experience of being touched by his mother in this particular way, and David was surprised to rediscover it. Though he remembered this all very well, he also had always assumed it was not important. And why was it now important? Why did this recollection of experience stand out now as being at the core of his present predicament? He didn't know the answer to that, but he knew that when he recalled this particular and repeated sensation from his past, it made him brighten now and say, almost out loud to himself, "Oh, that's *it*." This was not a logical experience, but somewhere inside of him it made sense. He had to trust it.

David felt an incredible sadness and compassion for that little boy who wanted so much to be loved and needed. And that sense of compassion and love that David experienced for that little boy felt EXACTLY like what David felt for his ex–wife, Sue, and what David felt for his own abandoned sons, struggling with their motherless lives. David cried with recognition when all these feelings wove themselves together as he spoke to me, he cried realizing how much he had given up of himself, of his own voice, his own expression, in order to feel wanted.

The first thing David wanted to do was to say to his mother that he didn't want to be touched like that, but he wanted to have her attention, and he wanted to have it for himself, not indirectly, via the satisfaction of HER needs. Saying this, slowly, carefully, and letting the saying create a reorganization of sensation within his body freed David. He felt like he occupied more of himself after he had spoken these words. And these words were not so much spoken to his mother as they were to the way that he had kept his mother alive inside of him, the way that he had preserved this belief about himself through the image of his mother, from whom he could now separate as a result of accepting this awareness and acting on it, verbalizing it. It took a while for this reorganization to really complete itself and for David to integrate how he felt now that he was free of this obligation to be in passive relationship to his mother's needs. And then what happened?

The result of this discovery of David's was very important for him and his whole family. David began to be more proactive about himself and about his life. He began to talk more openly with his sons about his own needs, and he provided a space for all of the boys to express their feelings about their mother's abandonment. David allowed himself to voice more of who he was — to his children, to his friends, and to himself. As a result, people became more aware of David's needs and moved more in the direction of being involved in David's life. The families he knew began to offer to take the boys and thereby to allow David some free time. Other fathers offered suggestions for the dilemmas the boys found themselves in. A greater community of responsiveness grew around David because he could let go of his passivity.

As a result of his open admission of his own needs and his availability for voicing them, new options were created for David and his family. This may seem simple, perhaps even too simple to report. But this shift resulted in a big change in David's life and in his identity. He became more available for all kinds of relationships that were interactive, dynamic, and these relationships nourished David in a human way that he always thought happened to other people, but never to him. With more people involved and helping, David had time to write again. Eventually he even had time to submit his screen treatments, and last I heard one was being considered for a movie. David is a very talented man, but he had to clear away the rubble of his outmoded passivity in order to step into his life. No one could do this for him. It was his job. Identifying the trauma he had experienced as a child, subtle as it was, was the crucial first step to David's increased vitality. Being believed and supported, being understood, being heard — this too was crucial. I KNEW what David was talking about as soon as he shyly began to describe his mother's touch. And he knew that I knew. He could feel it. I didn't pretend it was bigger than it was — in and of itself it was sufficient abuse to have made him suffer, and I could see that and reflect that back to him. Mirrored by my understanding and support and by his own impulse to heal, David learned more about himself and thus became more available as a parent to his children while simultaneously becoming more available to himself. This was all done in the time David had available to him. Surprisingly, it turned out to be just the right amount of time!

The
Later Healing
Stages

Intimacy, Maturity and Resolution:
Sustaining the Healing

Intimacy is one of the most compelling frontiers for the survivor of sexual abuse. Relational life carries the largest risks and evokes the greatest fears. Survivors often find themselves confronted with the challenge of intimacy when a foundation of personal healing has been secured. In this section I describe the issues that arise in the later stages of healing, by describing therapy in a group setting for mature survivors.

I brought together a group of women precisely to explore the questions of intimacy and the role of trust in resolving abuse and sustaining healing. A community environment is necessary to explore the possibility of transforming family issues. Yet, the very environment that replicates family is mined with after–images of the past. Courageous and open, determined to grow but vulnerable to the pain that arises when entering the arena of relationship and intimacy, these women of stature grappled to uncord their enmeshment with trauma.

Trauma thrives in confusion and hysteria. Healing often occurs in silence. The group I organized for women who had already been hard at the task of recovery for many years afforded space and the quiet removal from jobs and families to address intricate relational dynamics and to examine them carefully under the microscope of sensitivity. For each woman the group was a gift to self — a laboratory in which to experiment with connection, renegotiation, and relational equilibrium, not to mention the great hope for relational satisfaction.

Jane, Teri, Frieda, Susan, Melanie, and Kathy were, in my view, a holographic assemblage of mature women survivors. The group represented a cross–section of female survivors who, as the years of recovery accumulate, eye the question of intimacy with a calm, honest, and steady eye.

Though for each member of the group the experience of abuse was radically different, all felt betrayed by the mothers who had, sometimes of necessity, abandoned their children to their pain, and often that pain was similarly ignored by other female family members, sisters, aunts, and cousins, who tended, in order to protect themselves, to descry the abuse as insignificant or fabricated. Feeling unseen and unheard, these women struggled to support each other through the crises of recovery, which were often monumental, though they were smaller expeditions when compared to the already successful and mammoth achievement of the initial survival from sexual abuse.

Jane

Still intensely dreading closeness, Jane entered the group with trepidation. Though her primary abuser was her brother, it seemed her mother haunted her the most when it came to issues of intimacy and friendship. Revealing herself genuinely to another woman seemed impossible. Speaking her truth, opening her vulnerable and wounded heart to friendship, reminded Jane only of the terror of her childhood and her fear–impacted early years when no one rescued her from the horror of nightly torment and daily abandonment. She found security alone, by controlling her environment, by walling herself off, making things clean and orderly, and denying the emotional lava spill of relationship, which she felt would certainly burn her to death. This fear needed space and respect to be both tolerated and considered, much less healed. The group would have to continue for a substantial duration before Jane could face and shed these fears. Our initial task was to identify the relational issues, articulate them, sort them through, and separate them from each other. Doing that in the company of others would be a major achievement for Jane, but she was ready to undertake the task.

Boundaries! What to say; what not to say? When to open; when to remain contained? When to reach out? When to come forth? When to retreat? When to comfort? When to allow? All of the options for relational exchange were mysteries to Jane, and having to solve these mysteries in the moment, in a group context, made her feel profoundly insecure, even paralyzed, as she had been as a child. Each time she recommitted herself to the group rather than retreat and isolate herself, she wondered why. Throughout the group's duration, she was inundated with onslaughts of low self–esteem, sleeplessness, self–doubt, but at this juncture of her development, she knew she finally had the resources to face this intensity of challenge. Though often the experiential evidence seemed to contradict this, Jane felt this was the time and the place to renegotiate intimacy, to give it a name other than abuse and betrayal.

At each group session, I watched Jane's frozen and shocked expression thaw intermittently, reconfigure in ice, and then melt and open. This expansion and contraction needed to be tracked, its rhythm had to be sensed in order for awareness to emerge from the very place where denial once lived.

The breakthrough to the expression of what has been frozen out of fear is not easily done. The walls of resistance are mortared with self–protection, silence, and terror. It feels, from habit at least, much safer to remain hidden in the quiet invisibility that has been a shelter for so long. But Jane had the courage to admit that it was lonely in her protected place, and that it might be worth the risk to see if she could come out a little or perhaps bring another mature adult into her world. Sensing this, understanding her isolation, and truly wanting to break down the walls around her, Jane ventured into the group, tentatively, insecurely, courageously.

Frieda

Frieda was a skilled professional, a competent and successful woman in the world — witty, sophisticated, bright, and clever. The hurt she felt, the rage and fury that she squelched in order to function, was well–hidden behind her veneer of repartee, sarcasm, and a nimble mind. But she too was lonely, isolated, and sheltered by a world populated primarily by herself, her husband, and her therapist. Despite many years of consistent therapy, Frieda still felt shattered by the schisms she identified within herself.

Frieda was plagued by flashbacks to the early years of her abusive childhood, and when these flashbacks robbed her of her present–day reality, she retreated, took the phone off the hook, sought relief in isolation, and waited, agitated and distraught, for the storm to pass. And while this system of removal worked for Frieda, it cost her valuable work availability and seriously limited her relationships. There were certain places of intensity she reached within herself that she was ashamed and frightened to share with anyone. She was ashamed to be seen in this vulnerability, afraid to reach out and express the extent of her need.

Shame is, along with lack of trust, one of the primary interferences in relationship and intimacy for the survivor, and it was shame that overcame this strong woman in a group of other women. She felt shame for her anger and for the ways in which the trauma of her life had impacted her professional and intellectual development. She felt ashamed of her pain, which all too frequently made her feel physically incapacitated and helpless to heal. Despite Frieda's meticulously acquired skills and her well–researched knowledge of how to heal, including the use of touch, herbs, and networked resources, she all too often surrendered to the overwhelming physical pain that shut her body down, required her to use medications for pain control, and removing her from the life of vitality she so clearly deserved. Her bright expression and powerful compassion were a marked contrast to her helpless state of woundedness, splitting her relentlessly, confusing and shaming her. This splitting was hard for Frieda to bear and harder yet for her to reveal to others.

Frieda was horribly ashamed of her chronic pain syndrome. This tendency of the survivor to feel humiliation about the abuse and its symptoms is a generalized and deeply entrenched pattern for most survivors. It is not easily broken. Changing the pattern requires a profound attention and awareness. One of the ways I have found to influence this dynamic is by carefully noting the physical sensations surrounding the experience of pain and shame, staying with the physical process and letting that process itself inform you of the history attached to the feeling through image or through the sensation itself. In doing this, it is possible to separate, or detach, the history from the feeling.

This is hard to do alone and yet trauma and abuse frequently shatter the family collective and riddle all mirroring communities and intimate relationships with fear. How then to renegotiate relational suffering when it cannot really be done alone and almost all others are suspect reminders of past wounding? This is a place of great difficulty for many survivors, and it was so for Frieda.

When Frieda came into this mature group of women, the entire formation of individuals resonated with her past, and she attended the meetings dreading her own rising need for invisibility and the enormous possibilities of betrayal and abandonment that seemed to her to lurk within every exchange. Physical pain was her escape, her sanctuary, and also her cross to bear. It was a poor comfort for her fear, a self–abusive retreat from exposure to others.

Frieda had grown up as the target of enormous expectation. Always bright, her scholastic achievements became the source of both family pride and a relentless demand for more as a way of demonstrating worth. And so she did always demonstrate more. Being intelligent, witty, upwardly mobile academically — these were really *not* difficult for Frieda. They provided her with nothing to push against. But being accepted, without these achievements, being valued as a feminine being, a creature of enormous sensitivity with a need for affection and affirmation — this simple sense of being loved, this eluded her experience, and Frieda was left poignantly wanting. Her needs in this regard were marked by violation. How could she believe it would ever be otherwise? The group, where indeed she was truly loved and appreciated for her struggle and her essence as well as for her achievements, therefore became challenging and somewhat threatening, too.

The group offered real friendship, an opportunity to work on unresolved issues, a boundaried time and space where support was available. It held the possibility of relaxing that part of Frieda that had always remained clenched, untouched. And for these reasons Frieda secretly perceived the group as simultaneously an enticement and a danger. She truly was not sure she was ready to open herself to so many caring women, to let down her shield of cleverness, to let in this big dose of acceptance.

Kathy

Small and strong, Kathy grew up in a chaotic environment fraught with repeated relocations early in childhood as her mother was forced to find a place to settle after running from her abusive, alcoholic husband. Eventually Kathy's mother remarried, and this forced yet another resettlement, and this time the move included the new husband's family of youngsters. Suddenly Kathy and her two sisters found themselves with three brothers, and life increased its confusion. Mom's new marriage brought *no* stability into Kathy's life.

Kathy was the forgotten one in a large and awkward community. Quiet, withdrawn, serious, and sensitive, she disappeared from sight in the dramatic comings and goings of this unmanageable troupe of six children and the many attached aunts, uncles, cousins, grandmothers, and grandfathers who became part of everything as the family sought to lessen the financial burden in ways that always seemed to add more people to the cacophony. Eventually Kathy's mom and stepdad took in developmentally disabled people to caretake and thereby earn a living. Home became intolerably overcrowded.

Kathy found her solace and her companionship in the humid, florid countryside around her Virginia home. Hidden under dense foliage, behind the camouflage of the spice bushes, she could daydream, pretend, or remember. Solitude was usually preferable to her, perhaps because it was such a rare commodity, but her solitude was always strangely tinged with loneliness. Kathy's eyes sought something or someone to cling to, but that need had no expectation of being perceived, so it lay upon her face, flattened, without even apprehension or pleading, just a countenance of unmet need, stripped of hope.

Hidden under and behind the ferns whose growth seemed monstrously to overcome her tiny self, Kathy sank into the temporary feeling of protection, so fleeting yet profoundly comforting, inundated with the faint scent of the earth and its fecundity. Being encompassed itself felt wonderful to her and allowed her to relax more deeply than she could even in her own bed at home. Now, at last, she could think her thoughts and feel her feelings without interruption or distraction. It was here, settled and silent, that Kathy allowed herself to feel the fear and disgust she harbored toward all the patriarchs in her family — her father, her stepfather, and her grandfather. She was haunted by strange, unresolved memories of her father, whom she barely knew. She saw his shadow fading from the doorway as in an after–image, usually just as she drifted off to sleep. Her stepfather left her feeling extremely uncomfortable, and her grandfather had an eery quality, an odd, menacing charm that simultaneously pulled Kathy to him and repulsed her. Her mother warned her repeatedly with a stern look on her face, "Don't stay too long with grandpa, especially if no one else is around." There was no further explanation.

And while it felt good finally to give herself the freedom to let these feelings unfold like an accordion that had been kept latched in the attic and is finally played, there was a sadness to her solitary music. Though she couldn't know it at the time, Kathy longed to tell these feelings to someone who was actually listening, preferably her mother, and to hear in response an attunement, a responsiveness that reflected a comprehension of her feelings and, most important, her organic need for comfort and protection. This she never received, and her mother, her sisters, her cousins, and her aunts seemed all like women at a distance, unreachable, slightly frightening, and *very* removed. Their conversations, their interests, their attractions, and their choices all appeared foreign to Kathy. She assumed she was the misfit since they all seemed engaged, contented, and in agreement. They went busily about their lives and Kathy watched them. She watched and retreated from them, and so they called her "the quiet one."

But Kathy actually had a great deal to say, and her family would be surprised to know that she craved discussion, particularly with women, particularly with people who actually listened to her. Truly aware and in touch with this need, and willing to honor it at last, Kathy came to the group knowing she needed this community of women *now*! Her husband, her children, and the friends who labeled her "too intense" were not the appropriate audience for her conversations and process in regard to her emotional and psychological development. For this she needed a peer collective, people like her, who wouldn't consider her struggle odd or "too much."

Clear that a group was what she wanted but not quite sure that this particular configuration of women would all work together to answer each other's transformative needs, Kathy entered the group with not only great expectations but also with a great deal to offer. Her longing for connection was very present for her, and her need to communicate was, at last, something she no longer felt compelled to squelch.

Teri

Teri was a woman of unquestionable dignity and spirit. She was not afraid to speak and hid neither her strength nor her fragility. The trauma she had experienced was enormous — sexual abuse, the disintegration of her family, her mother's vicious dominance, her brother's drug overdose, her father's affliction with Alzheimer's disease, terror and horror.

In part to contrast the way in which her family of origin had been bombarded with suffering and forced repeatedly into chaos, Teri was a dedicated mother who gave up career and many of her personal interests in order to be available for her two children. Teri felt forced into frequent confrontations with her wounded self, the part of her being that had few resources. When she was reduced to her wounded self, her responses looked very much like her mother's — hysteria, screaming, confusion, disorientation, and despair, followed by withdrawal.

Much more honest than anyone else in her family of origin, however, Teri hoped the group would give her support and insight into this and other ways in which her childhood trauma, now over, followed her into the present. Teri needed a place to talk about this struggle, but she also needed some creative ideas on what to do, from survivors of abuse and trauma, not from the average parenting class or newspaper column on child rearing.

Her community had consisted of church members or parenting groups, not people who acknowledged a primary commitment to healing. Teri needed a group of her own, a place where she, to a certain extent, was just like everyone else, where she didn't have to hold anything back but could say it all without fear of judgment. Her willingness to come to the group was made more striking by the fact that her family had negated Teri's struggle for selfhood and would not empower her in it.

There was something about the need to be compassionately witnessed that was true for everyone in the group — a need to be seen, at deep levels, and for the truth to be known in an articulated, undeniable way. When movement was used in the group, I functioned as a witness for the others, and this permitted an unfolding of feeling expressed through action, a deepening of awareness that would not occur under other circumstances. Teri, like all the others, came to the group for an experience of compassionate, nonjudgmental witnessing in a community where there was some silence, some possibility of being seen and heard, and where the truth could be reliably witnessed. Her openness to being seen, and thereby to receiving help, was extremely courageous, and her courage infected the others with possibility.

Susan

No one needed community more than Susan. Now almost 70, Susan had searched diligently all her life for a way to free herself of the abuse she had suffered as a child. Not only sexual abuse but physical abuse at the hands of caretakers and abandonment by her invalid mother, had left Susan starved for consolation, affection, acceptance, and recognition, particularly from women.

For the others in the group, Susan was a gift. Each of us longed to connect with a woman of stature such as Susan, someone who had raised children, earned a living, succeeded in maintaining a good partnership, as Susan had, but who had honored her need for recovering from abuse and trauma and who could therefore honor and affirm the hopefulness of our struggle. This Susan could do because clearly her expression and admission of her process had kept her young, vital, active, and available.

This linkage between women, this yen for a sisterhood or collective, must be ancient. It is hard to believe that it springs only from trauma. It struck me in this group, and in others I have facilitated, that when women come together in groups, a priestess–like quality is generated in all of us, and we learn from each other and listen to each other in ways that seem to be unique to women and rather awkward for men. Susan embodied and encouraged the power inherent in the coming together of women of stature.

It was this priestess–like quality of women joined, and in particular of women expressing themselves, that made Susan a strong force for the group's existence and continuity. Her years of healing taught her that this bonding and the possibility of healing that it offered was not common. She recognized it in our group, and it deserved support. In addition, Susan had a quality that younger women often look for in an older woman but so rarely find — the sense of being emotionally attended to by a senex, of being heard by a mother figure. Susan sincerely wanted to hear about her younger sisters' experiences. There was a willingness to listen and a genuine, heartfelt sense of inquiry in her responses. Because many of us who have been abused have also been emotionally negated or abandoned by our mothers, there is a need to feel connected with an older woman, not only to be heard by her but also to learn about her, for there to be a relationship of truth and reciprocity that travels back and forth between generations of women. Susan gave us that option, and we needed it. So did she.

Melanie

In many ways, Melanie often felt she did not belong in the group, though sexual abuse was most certainly part of her history, along with emotional and psychic abuse, abandonment, and betrayal. She had found a place for herself in middle class America, and she was never sure that the medium of expressive therapy or the level of intimacy necessitated by the group's candid interactions really were right for her. Melanie felt safe in her suburban hideaway, in her kitchen, and in her lacy, feminine bedroom. She felt safe in her church, and with her churchgoing friends who shared her religious beliefs, which were a real comfort to her.

Shy, overweight, limited by illnesses and surgeries that restricted her movement, bound to the life of the home and the tasks of mother and grandmother, Melanie felt oddly out of place, frightened, and yet also curious about the idea of intimacy between women. In the back of her mind lurked a dread of homosexuality, as if the closeness between women would inevitably lead to a physical bonding that would threaten everything in Melanie's lifestyle. Though she would never say it, Melanie worried that lesbianism might be the outcome or perhaps even the intention of the group's closeness.

Melanie was always conflicted about the difference between her responsibility to herself and her responsibility to her children and grandchildren. The way she had been betrayed by her mother and father, who had given her away at birth, had devastated her so much that Melanie would *never* put herself before her children. She sacrificed herself over and over for them, and often for other people as well — helping them move when she was physically incapacitated, caring for the grandchildren at the expense of her own activities, and opening her home when privacy was her primary need. Melanie was so used to these sacrifices that she didn't acknowledge them, nor did anyone else. It was just the way "mom" was. She was afraid, though, that the group would pressure her to change, and she didn't know what change would do to her relationships.

But Melanie could not deny certain unresolved issues that, despite years of therapy, did not cease troubling her. She had no self–confidence in regard to men, for instance, and though she had been divorced for five years and yearned more than ever before for a partner, a companion, she was unable to develop a mature relationship with a man. She still lived and looked as if she were a married housewife taking care of the home and others devotedly.

And it wasn't only a lack of confidence that held her back. Melanie entered an almost altered state around men. She found herself, much to her dismay, behaving rather like a teenager. She blushed, her eyes were downcast, and the slightest sense of recognition from a man sent her mind into a tizzy, as if an adolescent inside of her was jumping up and down, shouting on the telephone, "He likes me! He likes me!"

Melanie, at 60, wondered at her own developmentally skewed behavior, and she hoped the group could help her see into this conundrum. Then there was another thing that really concerned her — her anger, no, her rage. Melanie did not know how to express her rage. She was already seriously concerned about her high blood pressure and heart palpitations. Tumors and fibroids, benign but chronic, were repeatedly forming in her body. She needed a way to get her anger out. She could not scream, she could not shout. She was held back in a way she could not comprehend. Maybe the group was worth risking to change some of these patterns. Perhaps the loud message of her body was worth her attention, worth a risk.

How the Group Worked: The Story of the Loving Hand

The group had met four times, and while the women were not really comfortable with each other yet, they were nevertheless familiar enough with each other's presence and sufficiently aware of each other's commitment to sink below superficial comments and experience the associations and connections that their coming together generated. The healing dynamic that had brought them into each other's company was at work, and now it was up to the individual women to use that dynamic consciously for their own process and evolution.

Being aware of this, Jane could not ignore the feelings she experienced in a group when Frieda had tuned in to Teri's distress and reached out to her. Teri was on the brink of tears, though Frieda was the only one to see it. Frieda had literally extended her arm across Jane to make a contact with Teri, and Jane had felt triggered from the moment of Frieda's outreach.

Jane didn't really know why, but when Frieda's hand moved across her vision, Jane felt deeply disturbed, frightened, and angry. How difficult and unnerving to have such enormous feeling from an apparently small event — the movement of an arm. The magnitude of Jane's feeling, the intensity of her internal experience, told her that she was triggered[1] by Frieda's action, though she didn't know why. Actually, the "why" was relatively insignificant; it was the "how" that told the story.

Frieda then moved her entire body to go behind Jane and be closer to Teri. Frieda rearranged herself to sit next to Teri and she cradled Teri's head on her shoulder. Teri sobbed in relief and allowed Frieda to comfort her while she expressed her distress over recent events in her household. Teri had lost her temper badly at home, causing everyone there to be traumatized by her behavior. Teri felt shame, guilt, and incredible grief over this.

Jane sat, removed, triggered, isolated, and, as the focus was on Teri, Jane was not noticed, nor did she draw attention to herself. It took her until the following week to begin to address the mysterious feelings she had in response to this episode and to gather the courage she needed to tell the group of this invisible process.

As Jane spoke in the group the following week, describing what had occurred, I noticed, by observing her body and her voice, that a piece of her past was longing for renegotiation. Asking her permission first, to make sure she cared to address this process this way, I asked Jane to pay careful attention to her sensations and, with my guidance and support, to allow these sensations to speak to her and reveal the story of her response to Frieda's gesture. Thus this tale unfolded.

When Jane was young, probably four or five years old, her mother would wash her in the bathtub. She would harshly and painfully scrub Jane's tender little girl genitals, using her long, red fingernails. Frieda's hand coming forward, moving through space, suggested to Jane her terror as a child each time her mother's hand came toward her.

Frieda's hand had, in that moment, become Jane's mother's hand for Jane, uncontrollably, unreasonably. What Jane felt first was rage and a desire to destroy that hand that had caused her so much humiliation and discomfort. But Jane's work on herself gave her the capacity to know she wasn't angry at Frieda's hand, but at another hand, another person, her mother, now dead.

Another habit of Jane's mother was to twirl Jane's hair in her hand whenever she was talking to someone. Jane's mom would sometimes even ask Jane to stand close to her, so she could twirl her hair while speaking to another person. Jane felt used by that hand! Her mother was displacing her nervous energy at *her* expense, abusing her body to experience a release. This memory came immediately after the feeling of rage triggered by Frieda's hand moving toward Teri.

Of course all this had nothing to do with Frieda or with Teri. All this was Jane's response to the hand, seeing it, and remembering on a feeling level, on the level of body sensation. The environment of healing, of being with women and focusing on recovery from trauma, was conducive to this recollection and this unravelling.

Jane's feelings as a child when her mother's hand, with its brightly painted fingernails, came toward her with a far–from–loving intent, were terror, rage, shock — all of these resurfaced in Jane's body as she watched Frieda's hand extend itself to Teri, comfort her, even stroke Teri's hair lovingly, gently. And, of course, what was also inherent in this experience was Jane's grief that her mother's hand had not been extended lovingly to her, but threateningly.

Jane watched these feelings, startled and confused, feeling troubled and inadequate. In the group she was silent, masked, never revealing any of the emotional chaos that coursed within her, effectively blocking the present, separating and isolating herself from the group. Jane not only hid from the group, she assumed that Teri's process was not interruptable and that she could not share the space of attention with Teri.

In her individual session with me, just two days after the group meeting, Jane talked about her experience. I suggested she bring her powerful and still unfolding process back to the group, seeing this as an opportunity to increase Jane's connection to the other group members and to make more real and solid her relationship with them. She did this, and it was not easy for her to do it. Jane was dominated by terror whenever she thought of being truly close to the other women in this group or in any group she had participated in. But with my encouragement and support and eventually with the support of the entire group, she was willing to venture a step further into the territory of intimacy.

As she described her internal experience, it was clear to me that Jane was not simply telling a story. She was reliving a series of sensations that were associated with previous abuse, but which were displaced into the present. With the rest of the group as witnesses to this transformative but gentle process, I knew that Jane would be permitted to go into layer after layer of sensation, unravelling a series of traumas. As the group validated and supported her, Jane teased apart the past from the present, allowing the feelings themselves a different evolution than was possible in the midst of trauma.

Experiencing and honoring the completion of these feelings, Jane discovered an expanded sense of her self, her own greater occupation of her body and a heightened awareness of who she was in the here and now. The horror of her wounded child-self, which had been frozen within her for so long, melted in the light of awareness, expression, and acceptance, and Jane became even more the beautiful, wise, and vibrant woman she is, and a little less of the helpless, terrorized, unsupported child.

Movement Process

The group had met for an initial six–week series. Everyone agreed that this was not sufficient time to explore the complex issues of intimacy, nor was it a sufficient period of time to feel really safe with each other. Everyone agreed to contract for another six–week series, and we also agreed that there was a strong possibility that an additional six–week period, after the upcoming one, and perhaps even one after that, would be necessary to find some degree of completion, closure, or satisfaction with our mutual experience.

In our first meeting in the second six–week series, we tackled immediately the issue of trust and intimacy, contrasting it with the phenomenon of caretaking, which all of us knew as a frequent substitute for intimacy. We talked in a general way for about the first half of our two–hour time frame, and then everyone felt they would like to explore the subject further individually, using movement. Each member of the group wanted to work on her own, and so they proceeded to find their individual spaces within the large studio. I found a comfortable place that was out of the way so that I could function as the witness, an essential role in Authentic Movement.

As we located ourselves in the space, a sweet, almost sacred silence filled the room. This exploration had a spiritual potency to it — the quest for personal truth was entering a deeper dimension, a simultaneously simpler and yet more profound arena, the world of the body. Despite our varying levels of experience with movement, all of us knew intuitively and experientially that the body never lies. It tells the unmitigated, deepest truth, and therefore its revelations always evoke refreshing insight and surprising awareness.

As survivors, many of our insights and revelations have resulted in the discovery of abuse memories, things we didn't particularly want to recall, and so the fear of that possibility lurks in every therapeutic intervention, in every opportunity to delve more extensively into our histories, even into ourselves. As mature survivors who have been hard at the task for a long time, we also knew that those discoveries bring liberation. So the atmosphere was tinged with both trepidation and excitement, curiosity and awe.

One of the things we had been talking about in our general discussion was a review of Jane's experience of Frieda's Loving Hand, and the images of that discussion were fresh in Melanie's mind. Jane had discussed her distaste at her mother's twirling of her hair, and Melanie had recalled, just as Jane was speaking, how often her hands went to her head and to her hair when she was in a therapy session, or when she was feeling distress, pain, anger, or grief. Finding a comfortable place on the floor, Melanie sat with her legs spread widely to support herself and began to run her own hands through her hair. Sadness welled up inside her, and she felt an overwhelming desire to comfort herself, to caress her lovely silver hair gently, and to rock slowly back and forth, which her position allowed her to do easily. When Melanie was a little girl, appearances were extremely important in her family. Good grooming included a torturous procedure with rags and irons, a precise twisting of the hair to make Shirley Temple–like ringlets that would cascade around cherubic faces.

Often, Melanie would have to sleep on contraptions that would insure she had hair ringlets for church or weddings or gatherings in which she could be seen and not heard! Melanie had only herself to provide consolation for this worthless agony, suffered for the sake of others, to please people with whom she had no real relationship and from whom she received no benefit. Her mother had no interest in her feelings about this. Looking at Melanie now, who at the age of seventy was amazingly beautiful, one wondered how anyone could have tried to improve the looks of a little child who must have been exquisite without interference or alteration? Rocking, and caressing her head, now bountiful with thick gray locks, Melanie comforted herself in the present for the losses of the past, and knowing she was doing this, her suffering indeed was relieved, and the movement process was completely satisfying for her.

As witness, of course, I did not know this story until it was told in words. The story came afterward, when all of the women had completed their movement experience (which lasted only fifteen minutes) and shared their internal processes with each other. But, sitting in my space from which I could observe only Melanie's back, I could feel the magnitude of her renegotiation and the poignancy of her cultivated ability to self-nurture. Her slow rocking and her hair's rhythmic movement in response to her hand's sifting of the strands, slowly, made a soothing choreography, honoring grief, honoring the way the spirit of a child withstands the dominating, unconscious, and narcissistic selfishness of adults.

In the center of the room, meantime, Jane was doing quite another dance. She had been feeling her strength, and revelling in the courage she had manifested in opening herself to the other women, a huge step forward for her into the land she feared so much, the domain of intimacy. She was moving with strength and striding forward, and as she did so, she fearlessly made the sounds of her strength, courageously expressing and declaring her presence and her fullness. Her strong legs moved relentlessly forward, and her arms moved to accompany them. Hot, she pulled off her outer sweater hurriedly, eager to return immediately to the movement of strength. Later, she described this movement as a locomotive or a train determined to reach its destiny. Midway in her process, she was aware of how much noise she made, and she began to modify her movement and her sound. She was taking up so much space, and everyone else was so quiet! Surely she must have been doing something wrong, or perhaps even harming someone, disturbing someone who was hoping for utter silence, peace, and calm. But even despite these cautioning internal voices, Jane continued her large movement, her big steps forward and her sounds, she just turned the volume down a notch on her inner radio, but she didn't stop.

In contrast, Kathy was over in the corner, her legs propped against the wall, and pushing, with a slow steady rhythm, against the wall, first with one leg, then with the other. Her hands were placed on her head, but unlike Melanie, she was not moving them, they were just resting there. Then, after a long time, she turned over on her stomach, took her feet away from the wall, folded her arms in front of her head, and rested her head, face down, on her hands. Her legs behind her moved again in a slow, steady rhythm up and down, rather like a child having a tantrum, but without the speed, without the screaming, without the drama. This is a quiet tantrum, one you wouldn't even notice unless you paid attention to it.

What was Jane's story and what was Kathy's story, as they responded to the internal call of their bodies? Yes, that's precisely what Authentic Movement is about — listening to your body and becoming one with its choices for movement, for action. Authentic Movement is not at all about performing, even though there is often a witness. But the witness is never an audience in the evaluative sense. The witness represents neutrality and maintains a grounding space. The witness keeps the time, she creates a ring of safety, she observes and honors, all of which are crucial to the health of the process.

The group's exploration with Authentic Movement always has a time limit on it, and after the time has been used, there is an interval of integration and re–entry, and then we come together to hear each other, not to discuss really, but to listen, to share in each other's journeys, and occasionally to make some supportive comments.

Jane described how much she learned about her tendency of holding back from this process. She acknowledged how she loses herself and her center, but not completely. The fact that nothing actually stopped Jane's progress forward was not lost to her. She acknowledged that as well, with much deserved pride. Kathy talked about resistance and her awareness that she herself slows her process down, moving with the resistance more than with noticing the movement that would bring her out of the resistance. Wisely not judging herself, but just noticing, witnessing herself, in fact, Kathy simply became aware of her resistance and made a commitment to herself to inquire further into it.

And so each woman's movement is her own exploration, her own attunement to her own body. If we learn to listen to ourselves so precisely, isn't it more likely that we will listen to others with the same respect, the same attention? And if we nourish ourselves so fully by paying such close attention to our movement initiation, our body's unforgettable and pure story, isn't that tantamount to loving ourselves, isn't that the same as giving ourselves the love we feel we have been denied for so long and for which we have been so arduously searching everywhere? This may indeed be the answer to the homespun koan that what you have been looking for is right in your own backyard. In fact, it is even closer, it is right in your own body!

At the end of the meeting, we talked about the possibility of doing Authentic Movement in dyads the following week, coming out of the isolation of our individual movement process and moving and witnessing for each other, in groups of two. The suggestion itself tells me that the group is steadily, organically moving toward greater intimacy, and I have a feeling of great good fortune at being so honored as to witness a group of mature women working courageously to find their own wholeness, their own truth, their own integration. After having been torn asunder, we are mended and made new. Is this not indeed a profoundly spiritual process?

Maturity

The struggle continues, and the work is never done, but the journey of recovery from trauma reaps the bounty of compassion and spaciousness for which many spiritual practitioners work hard and long. Mature survivors let the layers of reaction sift down. They honor their feelings and witness their sensations. There is a wisdom we come to that embraces the work of our healing and allows us to be very kind to one another.

Mature survivors have no tolerance for abuse. They know it when they see it, and they name it as such. And they take action against it, without hesitation. Mature survivors protect their children, are open about their feelings, and enjoy their sexuality.

The mature survivors I know value life and are willing to risk in order to live their own truth. You might say that conscious survivors earn a certain degree of enlightenment as their overtime pay. Our work is ceaseless, but we have a sense of purpose. Resolution rests in our love of our own spirits and our willingness to honor spirit in others.

Resources I

THE TOOLBOX

This is the most important section of this book. The process of healing from trauma is organic. If it is supported, healing will unfold in an inevitable way, and each individual will experience a unique empowerment. But in order for that crucial support to be solidly in place, certain tools often need to be found and used. One of the main tools, of course, is a trustworthy, creative, skilled, and aware therapist. See the section on SELECTING A THERAPIST for suggestions on how to find this resource.

Among the other tools or resources you will need are a support network of friends and an array of activities that allow you to meet your needs as you heal. Often in my own process I was without a therapist and sometimes I was fairly isolated, but I always had a few people I could connect with and I *always* had creative resources.

Everyone's healing process is unique. The guidelines I suggest in this book are not to be considered as etched in stone, incontestable, or utterly and absolutely authoritative. Please feel free to disqualify some of the tools and replace them with others. Things like finding the right therapist and building your support network seem essential to me, but I am a firm believer in each individual's ability to be at the center of their own healing process and to orchestrate what works for them into a symphony. My own journey happened without the direction of one specific therapist. Because of my need to work holistically and in a body–centered way at a time when there were few therapists with that orientation, I made my own way, often alone, with just my body and my writing tools to accompany me. While this worked for me, it was sometimes lonely and frightening and I think it is possible now to take this journey with companions, and I encourage my clients to do so. I am grateful that I can be the companion or guide whom I could not find for myself.

Selecting a Therapist

You can begin your search for a therapist by interviewing the candidates. Find some therapists who interest you and then find out what each therapist uses as an interview procedure. Some therapists will offer free consultations. Others will not have this option. Some therapists will offer an interview with the understanding that if you work with them, that interview becomes the first session, and it is paid for.

Follow your *own* inner guidance and intuition in selecting a therapist. This person is going to play a key role in your life. You need to feel safe and comfortable with this individual. He or she must be stable, dependable, and available for you, responsive to your needs and sensitive to who you are.

When you phone or interview a therapist try preparing a list of questions. You will want to ask about background and training in terms of how that dovetails with your needs. For instance, if I were looking for a therapist, I would look for someone who I knew would be supportive of my deep interest in movement and creative expression. The therapist I would select should be aware of and respect the role that creativity plays for me in the healing process. My therapist could not be ignorant of alternative healing systems or the spiritual component in healing.

It is important to decide whether you prefer to work with a man or a woman. You can answer this question by imagining yourself working with a male therapist, and see how you feel. Then imagine yourself working with a female therapist, and notice what you feel. Only work with the person you feel is comfortable, comforting, and inspiring.

Just as the therapist is important, so is the therapist's office. The space itself needs to be a place where you can feel at home, free to speak and move (or not move, if movement is threatening), free to be yourself. For example, I have created an office environment that is soothing to me, and I believe that the people who feel comfortable in my environment will be comfortable with me. My office is a large, uncluttered space. There are no chairs. My clients and I sit on the floor, or on pillows, and we are free to move around. There are tools in the room that reveal my orientation. Drawing and coloring supplies are at hand. There are Swiss Gymnic balls (large balls for sitting, exercising, rolling, and stretching) in a colorful display of red, blue, yellow, and green. There are symbols of my commitment on the walls — a poster of the Goddess Ishtar, Native American art objects, a wall chart about Jin Shin, an Amnesty International calendar, pillows of different sizes, music, and musical instruments. There are several tables for the practice of Jin Shin and CranioSacral Therapy. The room represents what I use to heal and what heals me. I display my credentials clearly to validate my training. This is who I am. This is what I do. What does the person you are interviewing have in their space? Does it feel good to see these things, or is there something about the office that disturbs you? If there is, don't be afraid to acknowledge it.

Your therapist's license or credentials should be evaluated in conjunction with his/her experiential background. If, for instance, you are looking for a body–centered therapist, you will definitely want to inquire about their licensing in bodywork and their experience in using bodywork in cases of trauma and abuse. Are they licensed in psychology or counseling? What preparation do they have? What do they know about trauma? What do they know about sexual abuse, if that is your presenting issue? Don't be afraid to ask these questions, and remember, above all, what counts is how you feel when you are with this therapist, and in their environment. What feelings arise for you? Pay attention to all of them! Don't feel pressured to choose a therapist on the spot. Take your time.

Once I went to a woman who seemed perfect. She had a Ph.D. in Psychology; she was licensed; she was a registered dance therapist, and she was also a Social Worker. I had seen her work with and teach family systems at a conference, and I was impressed with her creativity. The only thing I didn't like about her was the fact that she was extremely overweight, which made me uncomfortable. I made an appointment to see her and went to it eagerly, hopeful that she could help me at a difficult time. She had bowls of candy all around her office, which I found distressing. She had a smile on her face that didn't change. I sensed a passivity that was hard to name, but real to me. However, I made the mistake I often used to make — I disregarded what disturbed me, I minimized it, I certainly didn't mention it, and I proceeded to work with her anyway, thinking "THIS SHOULD BE OKAY; I SHOULD FEEL GREAT ABOUT WORKING WITH HER." And from time to time it was okay, but in the long run, this therapeutic relationship didn't work. This therapist didn't have the maturity I needed, the resourcefulness and the creativity necessary for the relationship to endure. A part of me knew this beforehand, but I discounted that sensitivity and intuition. I learned a great deal from this process, and what I learned is contained in my injunction to you to identify your concerns and value your needs ahead of time. Selecting a therapist involves looking at your relational issues and your relational patterns. My relational history was a pattern of putting aside what concerns me and just going ahead. This therapeutic relationship was part of that habit, but it was also part of the process of my becoming more conscious of this trend. If you have a history like mine, it can be offset by being clear about what you need ahead of time, and committing yourself to not settling for anything other than this. It also helps to be clear about what is unacceptable to you, and declaring it. You need not worry about hurting someone's feelings by honestly expressing yourself. In other words, when selecting a therapist, value yourself and your awareness above all else, respect your own ability to find what you need. Don't accept anything that doesn't seem just right.

Here's a checklist of what to consider when selecting a therapist.

1. Identify if you'd rather work with a man or a woman.

2. Ask about the therapist's interview process and fees for interviews. Be clear when you go to the first meeting what your responsibility is in terms of payment.

3. Find out about the therapist's training, both experience and education, licenses, areas of expertise, and knowledge of trauma.

4. Do you feel comfortable with this person?

5. Do you feel comfortable in this person's space?

6. Is this person in a position to be available when you need to see them and talk to them? How busy are they? What is their policy regarding phone contact?

7. Look at the therapist's disclosure statement. The therapist should supply this, but if not, ask for it. This statement should thoroughly inform you of the therapist's background and training, their agreements regarding cancellation of appointments, charges for administrative services such as insurance billing, charges for phone contact and consultations, report writing, etc., and the disclosure statement should also inform you of your rights.

8. Does the therapist have a supervisor, someone they go to who gives them feedback about their work? I am wary of therapists who do not have supervision since I consider working in therapy to be so full of the complications of projection and transference that supervision seems to me essential, regardless of how long one has been practicing.

Building Your Support Network

I think the overall healing process goes more smoothly if you have a therapist you can count on and a support network in place. The support network means friends and resources, activities and involvements that over time have proven to be satisfying and comforting, releasing and reliable, inspiring and accurate.

Friends and Other Resources

The friends in your support system don't have to number in the hundreds. In fact, they don't even have to number in the tens. Just a few dependable friends are all you need. Even one or two is sufficient. What counts is that your friends are people whom you COULD call in the middle of the night if you needed to, people with whom you don't have outstanding unresolved disagreements, people whom you respect and trust to tell the truth. I feel VERY concerned about working on trauma with someone who has *no one* like this in his/her life. That degree of isolation is a sign of severity that needs to be addressed before the trauma issues are addressed. In order to really work directly with the trauma issues that have disharmonized our lives, we need to feel safe somewhere, comfortable talking to someone, and not alone all the time.

When I speak of activities and resources, I am talking about healthy things you have done, and healthy things you can do to feel better when you are going through a difficult period. These are your resources — the things that move you out of your trauma patterns into your healing patterns. Examples of these healing activities are walks in the woods or the park, gardening, bicycle rides, aerobics classes or other exercise classes, swimming, taking a bath, going out for tea, buying yourself a book you've been wanting to read or a pen you'd like to use or art supplies, reading, writing in your journal, jogging, spending time puttering around your house, etc.

Make a list of these kinds of things that are resources for you, and put it on your refrigerator or on your bathroom mirror to help you remember the resources you have. You might want to do the same with a list of your friends, your therapists, emergency crisis numbers — all the numbers you can call when you need supportive companionship and guidance. Keep these lists available because if you have fallen into a trauma vortex, you might need some reminders to help pull you out.

I have found that nature and water, in particular, have the capacity to shift my mood and the condition of my nervous system rather profoundly. I use hiking or walking in nature, swimming, and other exercise, and creativity (writing and movement, especially) as my primary transformative resources when I am feeling caught in trauma. Each person will have their own configuration of activities and outlets that work for them. The important thing to do with these lists and these resources is to USE THEM!

Among our resources may be animals we love, our dogs, cats, or birds who live with us, or whom we know. Animals can be sweet companions of the spirit and their supportive roles in our lives should not be discounted. Maybe being near animals comforts you. If you live near a lake where there are ducks or fish, it may bring you solace and communion to visit there. Don't hesitate to allow nature and nature's creatures to be your companions in healing. If your friends have dogs you enjoy, call and ask to take them for a walk or a run when you feel their companionship can help you.

Using Art to Heal

Many people think of the arts as the terrain of just a few — the talented, genius–like, eccentric few who paint or dance or write, and who are very different from the "average person" who is not creative at all. I heartily disagree. I believe we are all deeply and profoundly creative, but the results of our creativity may not always be museum pieces, gallery pieces, public performances, or books. So what? I believe it is possible to be very satisfied and fulfilled with the art you create for yourself in your living room, or wherever you create it, and that sharing it with one other person or with yourself is quite wonderful.

Unfortunately, our culture is designed for a star system. Certain individuals can do star quality things, and everyone else watches. Some people create and the other people pay to be entertained, to be passively entranced. My sense of art is quite different. I believe we all have entitlement and capacity here. I believe art is participatory, collective, and communal. I don't think only the highly trained or the special few are creative and the rest of us must just watch or listen.

But, in order for us to access our creativity, we have to give ourselves permission to be ourselves, we have to feel the humility and joy of the artist's childlike, playful energy that we all have. We have to allow our feelings a form in some tangible way. We have to be willing to come out of the stubborn withdrawal that holds us back from expressing ourselves. Each of us will do this most easily with the art form or the expressive medium to which we are uniquely attuned. For me it is movement and writing, the body and the word. But for my friend Julia, for instance, it is color and shape, the visual world through painting, collage, pen, brush, oils, or watercolors. For one of my clients, it is performance and theater. For someone else it is the art of teaching. For my husband it is considering the environment and creating strategies for saving our lives from death by pollution. In this book you read about Luke's expression through photography, Lily's communication of self through dress design, and Kate's wood carving. Jeanette Bailey sings, and David writes plays. There are endless possibilities for creative manifestation.

What is important is not which of the arts or which of the expressive media we choose, but that we give ourselves the space we need to explore that creative direction for our own healing. We can't just talk about our creativity, we have to actively use it, engage with it, live it. My enthusiasm for the arts and creativity comes from experiences. The energetic releases that occur when healing from past trauma are so monumental that no relationship, no conversation, no talking, and no exercise will be sufficient by themselves. We need to employ creative outlets in this journey to wholeness. Most importantly, using the arts as tools for healing makes the whole thing much more fun!

Each individual can have an artillery of resources at their fingertips they can access with discrimination whenever they need to come into wholeness, whenever they are feeling unbalanced by their trauma history or just need to express themselves. It is my strong belief that art is an essential part of that artillery of resources. I will give examples to explain this, and I will offer some exercises to help you find your particular creative resources if you haven't been able to identify them yet.

The first step in using art to heal is to remember not to compare your creativity to the creativity of others, particularly people like movie stars, dancers, published and successful authors, etc. Your work may well be as good as theirs, but as long as you hold their "perfection" and "brilliance" as the model, you are setting yourself up for failure. Comparison in any regard is usually invalid, as no two people, no two artists, and no two works of art are alike. I would much rather use other people's work to inspire me rather than to deter me.

The most important starting point if you want to use art to heal is giving yourself the space to be the artist you are. I call this Structured Unstructured Time And Space, by which I mean, a time you allow yourself that has a limit (such as an hour or two hours), but within which you are free to be creative with the media you choose.

For me, this time is usually an hour or two in which I do genuine movement process (another way to describe Authentic Movement) and write. I often start with genuine movement, and I have my writing tools (pen, paper, colored markers, computer, typewriter) nearby, though the room is uncluttered and spacious. I have musical instruments and taped music available, but I tend to do my work in silence. Sometimes I play music afterward, to heighten my sense of resolution and closure. During this Structured Unstructured Time And Space, I explore my feelings in the moment and write whenever the process suggests that option. Sometimes I am exploring a particular topic (such as why I feel angry at my husband, why I feel stressed, why I am so sad when I think about my daughter, what is it about my interactions with my friend that arouses my sense of alienation, etc.) and at other times I am exploring a creative challenge (exploring the use of movement in the understanding of shame, finding appropriate movement possibilities for the expression of joy, exploring a period in my life when I was involved with someone or something, a political movement, for example, or a relationship that didn't work out and about which I still feel confused), and at other times I am simply exploring the way I feel in the present moment. I could easily see using this Structured Unstructured Time And Space for other media (clay, sculpture, pen and pencil drawing, voice) in exactly the same way.

The medium you choose becomes the vehicle through which you give your feeling form. When your feeling has form, it is no longer held within you, it is no longer blocking the fluid movement of energy in your system. It is active rather than passive. When you release feeling in this way, you expand internally. You give yourself more space to grow.

When feelings, particularly long withheld feelings, become dynamic in a healthy and transformative environment, they are no longer burdens, no longer obstacles. We are less stuck (and we always feared we would be stuck with these feelings forever!). Through this process of using art to heal, of giving ourselves space and permission, these feelings become part of the flow of life, which is where they belong. And we can see our feelings now, out there. If we are writing, we can find them in the form of words. If we are using color, we see the feelings become transformed into pigment and shape. And in their new forms, these feelings become subject to the laws of life, they move and grow and change. They are no longer frozen in the past, untouchable and forbidding. Free to evolve, these feelings change into other feelings, and we are lightened and often enlightened. It is a delightful, challenging process, and it adds vitality to the very difficult and ongoing job of healing from abuse.

It has been a joy to discover the many uses of art in the healing of trauma. Trauma is such a weighty subject. People don't even like to hear about it. Everyone would like to forget about it, avoid it, or deny it. But, unfortunately, we are living in a world that is inundated with trauma, and ultimately each of us must free him- or herself from the tentacles of trauma. Doing so in the atmosphere of creativity has made all the difference to me. It brings a smile to my face and ignites the candle of hope in my heart. Art nourishes my soul and gives me the knowledge of coming out of trauma into myself, into my health. Above all else, the use of art to heal reconnects me with the essential spirit that I am, the buoyant, creative, lively, and rather humorous human being I have always been, despite the heavy curtain of trauma that veiled me from myself for so long. Included at the end of this book are some of the poems and prose pieces, the writings that came out of my periods of Structured Unstructured Time And Space that I created for myself on the healing path. Please use these writings, not to compare yourself to, but to stimulate you to make your own statements using your own media.

In using art to heal, I suggest you encourage yourself to proceed by getting yourself the equipment, the supplies, that are part of the process. This does not have to involve spending a lot of money. If you want to work with color, get yourself the paper and the paints, the pens or crayons or watercolors or pencils you want and have them available for yourself. If you are going to write by hand, get yourself the pen that allows your writing to be fluid and the paper that allows you to write in the way that feels natural to you. While these may seem like small matters, I have found I feel more supported and empowered with these supplies available. They increase my sense of pleasure in the process of healing from trauma.

Computers, typewriters, easels, expensive framing, etc., can all wait until you deepen your involvement, or you may never need them. Once you have found your commitment and passion with an art form, you can plan and budget, if necessary. You will find appropriate ways to get what you need. Don't let finances, or the lack of them, stop you. People have always created with what they have. Drumming began with sticks and boxes; writing began with storytelling. It is exciting to determine that nothing will prevent your expression.

In using art to heal, it is also important to have a space that is designed to serve the purpose of this process and that really allows you to explore Structured Unstructured Time And Space. There is an exercise I have used often and quite successfully that allows me to create this kind of space for myself.

Finding Your Creative Space: An Exercise for Beginning

This exercise begins with a visualization, but it doesn't end there. It is very important to follow this exercise through with committed action.

First, find a comfortable place to sit. Have pen and paper nearby so you can write down what you discover. Visualization exercises such as this one are as valid and as useful as you allow them to be. They are not mere fantasizing nor are they indulgences in escapism. They can certainly be used that way, but that is not the intention with which I suggest this process to you. This exercise, and the others like it in this book, are doorways into your deeper truth, the truth of your potential, and they require your cooperation and commitment if they are to become actualities. As actualities, the results of exercises like this can transform one's life. They have transformed mine, and that's why I share them with you.

When you find a place where you can sit and remain undisturbed, close your eyes and relax. Feel comfortable and safe, and allow yourself to honor this as a time for exploration and discovery. Make yourself available for the unspoken within yourself, the undiscovered, and the possible. In this pre–visualization time, when you are preparing yourself to perceive your own truth, feel the delight a loved child feels upon waking, when they know they are the center of the day, abundant with new and exciting discoveries.

As you accept this space of permission and possibility, suggest to yourself that you can and will see your creative space, the room or environment that is the container for your expression, the place in which you will be able to experience and realize who you are as an artist. Let the place emerge as a picture or movie before you. Let it come into focus like a negative becoming a positive in the darkroom. Feel the magic of that moment of seeing, of allowing an image to become real, of manifestation. Enjoy this process. When you see your place, put yourself in it. See what you are doing and notice how you feel. Don't analyze this. Don't interpret what you see. Take it for what it is — your creative space. Enjoy this imaginative and fluid time with yourself.

Stay there for as long as you like, and when you feel ready, allow yourself slowly to open your eyes. Take a deep breath, and then, right away, without hesitation, write spontaneously and completely, describing what you have just seen. Now, reread this writing, and see what you can do to make this vision a reality. It is very important at this juncture not to pass the whole thing off as impossible because of something you don't have (let's say you saw yourself in a barn–like space and you live in the middle of Manhattan — where you will get a barn?). Believe that the necessary elements of this visualization can be made manifest (maybe you'll have to find a cheap loft, or use the big room in the back to get the feeling the barn image suggests). See which elements you have perceived are essential to your creative space — that's what's important here. If you have seen a place that's diffifult to get to, like that barn in the country, it may represent a future reality. What can you manifest that resembles it in the meantime?

Whenever I have envisioned my creative space, it is a large room with an open, airy view that lets nature in (sky, trees, water, if possible), with my supplies (writing tools, music) close at hand. That's it. And under a variety of conditions, I have been able to provide this for myself consistently. I have found this space in apartments, in basement flats, in studios, in kitchens, on decks, wherever I am. You can do the same. It doesn't have to be extravagant. It can be very simple. Usually people have all they need in their own homes to make a creative space. What's essential is that once you have made it conscious, make it real!

Once you have established your creative space, your environment for self-exploration, you need to allocate your times to be there. Sometimes this is the greatest challenge because it requires demarcating a boundary for yourself. Shut off the phones, don't allow interruptions (at my office when I need my creative space, I put up the SESSION IN PROGRESS sign — after all, this is MY session), and take your time, take your space! People I have worked with have made their spaces out of attics, garages, sewing rooms, and closets. Don't feel defeated. Make your space. Don't let anyone or anything stop you.

Allowing a time and a place in your life to be just with your creativity, with your expression, is a renegotiation, particularly if you come from an environment of trauma and abuse. When a child grows up in a dysfunctional family, with the accompaniment of yelling and screaming, of irresolution and conflict, where problems aren't solved in community, where power is unilateral and dictated, then the child believes they deserve no more than this, they believe that they are unworthy of anything better. So those of us who were brought up on this diet of abandonment and neglect tend to feed it to ourselves even though we are adults and know better. When we isolate time and space in our lives to nurture our creative essence, to feed our unfolding process, we give ourselves self-respect, playfulness, and communion, all the elements missing from our troubled childhood households. It was, in fact, out of this kind of relationship with myself that my sense of what I wanted to do in the world ultimately grew. The creative dynamic that was once my means of coping with trauma became also my means of connecting with who I really am and what I really want to become. It is because of the intimate bonding I have had with creativity that I trust imagery so much. I trust metaphors and I trust the mythic awarenesses we have at different points in our lives, moments when we see through the illusion of mundane reality into our true purpose.

So, this visualization of your creative space could well be a stepping stone to living your dream. Create your space, and go to it, and take seriously what you experience in this Structured Unstructured Time And Space, where you can begin to build a profound link to who you really are and see into your own past and your own future.

Awakening Healthy Expression Through the Arts

Now that you have envisioned your creative space and done something to make it a reality, you can begin to explore what you really want to do there. Whether your space is a converted sun porch or a corner of your bedroom, you can use it for any number of expressive and integrative experiences. It is essential, of course, that you have arranged to have your space solely for this purpose for a specified period of time so that you don't have to be concerned with interruptions. It may take a while to feel what it means to have designed time and space to be with yourself. You may need to just sit in this space, to feel it pulsating with your own energy, your own intention to heal, your own belief in your creative purpose and power. Soak in that intentional awareness, and appreciate yourself for creating this.

Once you feel at home in this space and integrated with its purpose, there is a general orientation for you to underscore. Above all else, do what feels appropriate and authentic to you in this space. Let all action or inaction, doing or non–doing, passive or active beingness, initiate from deep within yourself, from that core place of motivation that sits in the territory between your navel and your spine, the deep seat of original action. The suggestions that follow are just to give you options, a full plate of possibilities, for what you might do in your creative space.

Genuine Movement Process

Genuine movement is a simple but deeply authentic way of experiencing your body's reality through movement. It is one of my basic ways of getting in touch with myself. I have referred to it throughout this book. It is also synonomous with Authentic Movement. Genuine movement process can be a solo activity, a two–person activity, or a group experience. It is simple and anyone can choose to do it safely, with some guidelines.

Genuine movement process has a series of steps:

1. Find your space. Settle in it. Take your time.

2. Relax in that space, and allow movement to arise of its own volition.

3. As movement arises, allow it to complete and to flow into the next movement.

4. Continue this movement process until there is no movement left to complete, or until the time frame allocated for this process is complete. Allow your movement to find organic closure.

5. After movement, rest. Integrate the entire experience energetically by just being with it. Don't try to understand it or figure it out. Accept it.

6. If someone else is there as a witness, describe your experience to them, if you wish, or just connect with them.

7. If no one is there, you may wish to write about the experience, allowing it to unfold and integrate within you.

8. If you are working with a friend, or in a group, you can switch roles in agreed–upon intervals, so that one person moves and the other person witnesses.

While doing this movement process, feel free to allow sound to evolve just as movement evolves. This reminder applies to all the creative processes I am suggesting here. Generally, I am encouraging you to break down any ideas you may have about what creativity SHOULD look like, and allow yourself to become more of yourself in this space you have created. Writers don't have to sit still at the computer and think. They can get up and move around. They can make noises. Dancers don't have to have perfect bodies and stand at the barre and follow a routine of exercises. Singers don't have to be contraltos or tenors. They can moan and shout, they can mumble and make unintelligible sounds. The power of art is in its individuality. The power of expression is in its truth.

Embodied Writing

Writing spontaneously and writing from a body–centered orientation has always been natural for me, even when I wrote secretly as a child. Then, when I was afraid to be seen as the powerful and vibrant young person I was, the dynamic aspect of my creativity was hidden; it was internalized. Now that internalized activity can safely come out into the space I have created for myself. When I write I also dance and sing, or make sounds. To me all of these expressive forms are in the same family, the family of my being and the family of my body. I am very happy when I am free to write, move and make sounds, and when there is no restriction on my creativity. I do this privately, with consciousness and awareness, feeding my sense of health and buoyancy, allowing myself to be who I am, within a well–boundaried and safe structure of my own creation.

Embodied writing works very much the same way as genuine movement. In fact, writing often comes after a genuine movement process for me. On the other hand, sometimes writing leads me to dance. But whether I move first or not, when I create, I give myself enormous freedom and encouragement, just like a good mother supporting her brilliant child.

Those of us who learned to write from strict teachers who had an investment in the way our penmanship looked and in proper grammar, have to throw off the burden of correctness. For me writing is very much like mushing in mud or using clay or finger paints. Like drawing water from a well, I tap into the well of myself and draw language out. I let myself write whatever I need to write and I let myself write however I want to write. If I am writing by hand, I use unlined paper and I have a variety of pens with different tips and different colors so I can write big and sprawling, like an Oriental calligrapher, or I can write intensely, carefully, recording the details of my observations, the specifics of my feeling. I can write in lines of words that make a design of their own, creating poems out of impressions and insights, or I can write down my dream from the night before or make up a fable or short story out of a relational experience. I can write a letter, which I may or may not send, and I can make up fantasy characters. This is MY writing.

If I have a writing project I want to complete, like writing about my relationship with my father or writing an application for a program I want to participate in, I will do spontaneous writing *first*. I like to warm up to writing playfully. It's muscular, like any exercise. Writing is a careful orchestration of feelings and thoughts that integrate themselves, come together, and arrange themselves. I steer the ship (whether it be with pen, typewriter, or computer, or even with my voice, dictating into a tape recorder) through the waters of feeling and enjoy the cruise. Writing is both work and play, like all the arts. I enjoy both aspects.

The Spontaneous Epistle: One Form of Embodied Writing

Letter writing is a wonderful releasing form of embodied writing, and a good way to begin to write. Through letters you can have all the conversations you have restricted. And if you do choose to send any of the letters you write, you will provide a greater opportunity for healing because letters are usually received and read in silence. The person to whom you send your letter has the option of thinking about its contents, and taking time to feel your intention, your meaning, and to process their response. Think of what you haven't said to your mother or what you have always wanted to tell your daughter. Think of what you wanted to say to the man who left you or to the woman who abused you. Now let yourself say it. Let it come out freely, in the language of feeling, let that communication pour forth and BREATHE while you are doing this; breathe and feel what your body is telling you as you release this language. Feel the space in your body as you unburden yourself of these long-withheld sentences, answers, and questions. And know that as you do this articulation, you are doing it for yourself, because you don't deserve to carry this unspoken material around inside your body any longer.

Write and write and write for as long as the energy pours out. This is what embodied writing is about — it is about language as a tool for recovery, transformation, and communication; it is about giving yourself the space to say it all. When you are complete with this process, take a deep breath. Feel the space you have created inside you as well as the space you have created outside, the container you have created to both allow and hold your creativity. Enjoy this experience of feeling what it is like to be so fully involved with yourself. Feel how empowering it is to have given yourself the freedom to express yourself this way, and feel how healthy this outlet is, how transformative.

Depending on how you feel, you may or may not choose to reread your writing immediately after completing it. You may want to take care of yourself by consulting your list of resources or maybe by going for a hike or taking a bath. You may want to share the writing with someone else, or you may not. You may want to reread your writing after your hike or your bath, or you may want to consider sending it to someone. Give yourself all the space you need to know what to do with this energetic healing process. Or, don't do anything at all with it. Just enjoy it. Feel how you are changed by having said these things that have been pending inside you for so long. Feel how much stronger you are now. Accept this stronger you. Appreciate this stronger you who chose to do this, who allowed this transformation. Put this book down now and feel the power of this possibility of communicating, even if only to yourself, the truth of your own feeling.

Color, Shape, Form, and Structure: The Visual Arts as Healing Tools

What is your experience with color? Look around you. Color is part of life. Take in the color around you. How do you feel about it? Is it the sudden red of the house down the road that inspires you or the molten combination of green and gold on the rock? What impact does color make on your feeling? If it's a gray day, do you feel the grayness inside yourself? Does it remind you of being indoors and isolated, of the pain in your family that made you want to stay inside, that seemed to imply that you could not play with the other children? How does color express your feeling, how does it work as a medium for your experience? Can you use that medium?

For most of us, when we were growing up, color was the one thing we could use without too many restrictions. Children are given coloring tools to play with to occupy themselves, to distract them. Children are generally allowed to play freely with color and to make their imprint in color. So it may be easier for us to play with color now, except for the fact that as grownups we think the time is over for such foolishness.

Yet color remains available as a medium for expressing our feelings now just as it was then. Watch a child with paint or colors of any kind. See how spontaneously and freely they shape the color to suit their energetic moment. And think of all the child psychologists busily interpreting children's art to see what these children are thinking. Such is the power of this medium to reveal the truth.

I once kept a journal book that contained ONLY my expression in color and form. With shapes and pigments, I would weave my feeling. I got enormous satisfaction from this process, and a physical release akin to running up a mountain. The intensity and concentration that evolved as I told my story with color and shape amazed me later and still does whenever I look at this journal.

I point to the work and commentary of the renowned Alice Miller to illustrate my point here. Her book, *Pictures Of A Childhood*, published in 1986, remains a milestone document to support the incredible power of art in transforming the suffering of abuse and trauma.

> I had to make the discovery, and experience it over and over again, that creativity has to do with a process which is not furthered by formal training. It was even true in my case that every attempt to learn a technique blocked my capacity to express myself. On the other hand, the delight I took in the

freedom I had gained was sufficient to impart an ability I had not previously possessed, an ability that emerged from play, experimentation, and wonder. All together, this added up to what is usually designated as experience, something that always came my way only indirectly and circuitously.

Little by little, I came to terms with the fact that, as far as my painting was concerned, I could never plan ahead or think about what I was going to do. If I did, the child in me rebelled and immediately became defiant. Only as I learned to follow her instead of forcing her to achieve did she share with me a new and precious knowledge about myself and my history that came to fascinate me more and more. It was difficult for me to comprehend that I had been ignoring this knowledge all my life.

By publishing her book of paintings and describing the way her uninhibited use of color allowed her to further her maturation, insight, and evolution, Alice Miller made a great contribution to healing. Many people listened to what she had to say because by the time *Pictures Of A Childhood* was published, Alice Miller had already been acclaimed as the brilliant author of *Drama of the Gifted Child, For Your Own Good: Hidden Cruelty in Child–Rearing* and *the Roots of Violence,* and the astounding *Thou Shalt Not Be Aware: Society's Betrayal of the Child.*

Here is what Alice Miller has to say about the role that the free use of color played in her understanding of herself:

> There is no longer any doubt in my mind that as I am doing my spontaneous painting, the repressed knowledge of events that took place long ago is breaking through.

> I am fascinated by this ongoing dialogue between me as a grown person and the little child in me, a dialogue that was initiated as a result of my beginning to experiment with colors and then continued thanks to the aid of my writing. I have been able to give that silent child of long ago the right to her own language and her own story. Now she refuses to be dissuaded from remembering, from perceiving what really happened and reporting it with ever growing clarity.

Templates and Stencils

Everyone's story is rich with healing information, but these jewels cannot be found without a search. This is where the arts come in. Writing, drawing, painting, movement, sound, clay — all these media are ways to reach out while reaching in, and they are ways in which we can meet ourselves. For people who were raised not to believe in themselves, getting started can be the major obstacle to self-discovery. What follows are some jump starters, templates, and stencils you can use as you begin to unmask your artistic side.

The concept of Structured Unstructured Time And Space is based on the theory that we need a pressureless, supportive environment in which to explore the unconscious, but we also need a lamp and/or a guide to see into the darkness. The pressureless, nondemanding component is the Unstructured Time And Space, and the format, guideline, or choreography, the boundaries of the investigation, are found in the Structured Time And Space. Use the designs that follow as the format for your exploration in language, color, movement, or whatever medium you choose, but within these boundaries or guidelines, let yourself be free. The exercises to find your own Creative Space and The Spontaneous Epistle are also templates for you to use. Once you've tried several of my exercises, you'll be ready to make up your own.

Before exploring more exercises, let's review some principles and attitudes about art that could free you. The intention or state of mind with which you enter any of these challenging experiences is very important. All of these exercises have the potential to introduce real change into your life. That's exactly why I have created them, and that's exactly why I have done them myself, often over and over again! There are no exercises here which I haven't done myself; and I know that each one has shifted my reality. Before doing any of these exercises, make sure you are in a position of receptivity to change — and don't put yourself down if you're not! Feel the support you have created for yourself. Acknowledge your resources and feel your own safety and trust. That will make the whole process move smoothly.

In regard to writing in particular, these are some awarenesses I have found that are contrary to what I learned about writing in school, but which inspire my own creativity with language:

1. You can write to completion.

2. You are not writing for someone else.

3. You can write spontaneously and fluidly.

4. You don't have to shape your writing (outlines, etc.). Your writing will shape itself.

5. You can discover the form of writing that suits you by writing. You don't have to decide form ahead of time in order to write.

6. You don't have to hold anything back when you are writing.

7. You can write the way no one else has ever written.

8. You can write for yourself alone.

9. You can just start writing, without even knowing what you are going to say, and your natural intelligence will arise.

When we talk about some templates and stencils for genuine movement process, we will see that each sentence above applies for movement just as it does for writing. Simply substitute the word "movement" for the word "writing."

1. You can move to completion.

2. You are not moving for someone else.

3. You can move spontaneously and fluidly.

4. You don't have to shape your movement (choreography, etc.) Your movement will shape itself.

5. You can discover the form of movement that suits you by moving. You don't have to decide form ahead of time.

6. You don't have to hold anything back when you are moving.

7. You can move the way no one else has ever moved.

8. You can move for yourself alone.

9. You can just start moving, without even knowing how you will move, and your natural intelligence will guide you.

Do the same thing with painting or clay and you'll see that you are free to be the artist you are if you just give yourself permission, time, space, boundary, and support.

All of the TEMPLATES AND STENCILS for writing and movement involve coming to a place of centeredness or settlement BEFORE doing the exercise. In this time for focusing and declaring intention, we join body, mind, and spirit and commit them all to a creative journey designed to bring you into a deeper and wiser, more expanded and more fun loving, honest sense of self. Accept the unpredictable outcome of the journey, and realize that this journey is , part of a larger process, that there will be many journeys, and that, perhaps, the outcome of this journey will only be understood in the light of the overall process. Accept self; accept the unknown; accept that healing is your direction. Now, proceed.

The Faces

These writing suggestions come from a belief and an understanding that we store information in code within ourselves, within our bodies. We are each an ocean of buried treasure, but we have to make our own treasure maps. The treasure is often in the form of images we have retained, imprinted, and encoded into the receptive walls of memory. Only we ourselves can extract these images, decode them, and use them for the purpose of transformation. Faces whose impressions we have retained are likely containers for treasured and useful information. Here are a few exercises about such faces. These exercises are geared to writing, but you may decide to make paintings, drawings, or sculpture.

The Face of Someone You Can't Forget

Sit quietly and comfortably in your writing space, with your writing materials close at hand. Stretch out, if you like, or curl up in a chair or on your bed. You may be more comfortable sitting before your desk or your computer, or you may want to begin by lying down, with the room soft and dark. Ask yourself to recall the face of someone whose features or characteristics have stayed with you, marked themselves indelibly on your consciousness so that the mere suggestion of remembering, now that you are alone, brings their image before you in remarkable detail.

See this face and feel how powerful it is to see it without reacting to it, knowing that this face demands nothing of you now. Uncouple action from feeling and allow yourself just to witness the feeling. You may see the face of your beloved grandfather who was always a source of support and comfort. If you do, take in the details of that face and allow that countenance to nurture you now as it did long ago. Or, you may see the face of someone who attacked you suddenly, and whose wrathful features have haunted you as a threat to which you long to respond. See that face and repeat to yourself that the face is not threatening you anymore. With calm and precision, separate the past from the present, and really look at this face.

You may see the face of your sister, causing you to release all the feelings about her you haven't expressed, or you may see the face of a former lover, a child, a dear friend, or a neighbor who always frightened you. Just accept the face that presents itself, and study it now as you never could before, witness it, and see it as distinct from you.

When you feel ready, write (or color or sculpt) spontaneously from the experience of witnessing this face. Let the words move through you and onto the page without resistance. If you stumble and find yourself wordless, just be wordless until something arises, and something will. Write this face unto completion, including all the details of your feeling as well as the line, color, form, and shape of the face. Rest, and, if you feel like it, read. Given your time boundary, reflect on this face and this writing as it forms a part of your overall healing process. Come to an awareness of the roles this face and this writing play in your unfolding, and, as your time draws to closure, feel good about having reclaimed some part of your own mystery. Then let go of the entire experience, knowing it will integrate with the larger picture of your development in time, if it hasn't already. You've done your job for now. If the craft of writing is important to you, you may choose to edit this piece, thereby refining even more the separation of this face from your own, and the understanding and implication of this face, this person, in your own process.

The Face of Someone You Can't Forget can be used as a template for other Face exercises. What happens if you consider The Face in the Crowd or The Face of A Child? What about The Face of Kindness? The Face of Restriction? The Face of Freedom? Try these, and if the face metaphor is releasing, make up your own exercises in The Faces Series.

Finish That Sentence: Ending Communicatus Interruptus

Each of us has someone or many people in our lives with whom communication is incomplete. At unexpected moments, we may find ourselves going over incomplete conversations trying to finish them, saying what we didn't say before. Sometimes these revisions of the past become obsessive, and we wonder why we are so preoccupied with remaking the past. This exercise provides an opportunity to bring this repetitive pattern to closure and to see more specifically into the role of this obsession in your overall process. It is my firm conviction that these repetitive or even obsessive patterns hold energetic information that, once released, can invigorate us with new clarity and insight. It takes patience not to become utterly frustrated by repetitive patterns, thinking they are going nowhere. This exercise can be the key to the end of the perseveration.

Sitting quietly, in a way that allows you to become centered and clear about your purpose in doing this exercise and clear about your healing orientation, see the face of someone to whom you have something more to communicate, some incomplete conversation from the past that longs for resolution. This may be someone who made assumptions about you or something you did that you long to correct and clarify. This may be someone to whom you want to apologize. This may be the face of someone who died and to whom you never said good–bye. This may be a child you aborted without a farewell, or a perpetrator whom you wish to forbid entry into your space. The dialogue you are now ready to complete will emerge in the form of the face of this person. See the face, and repeating to yourself that this face is not a threat to you now, allow yourself to witness your feelings just as you witness the face. Trace the process of the feelings through your body, without reacting. Listen to the story, and wait for your own understanding. Understanding is not a quick reaction, it is a calm response.

Notice the details of this face. See the lines and colors, the shadings and the way the hair falls. See the environment in which this person appears to you. Is the environment outdoors or in a room that is rich with meaning and symbolism? Maybe you see your baby brother in the cradle or your grandmother sipping tea. Let the richness of what you see, the full potent image, make itself known to you, and take it in, see it, and see it with all the many dimensions of meaning that are present at once. The meanings will organize themselves for you as you write. Trust this. This part of the process is pure witnessing, pure perceiving, pure allowing, pure patience. Let your nervous system relax as these feelings continue their journey through your body, and take in what you are learning from yourself.

When the witnessing process feels complete, write (or color or draw) spontaneously. Let the expression tumble freely from your hand. These experiences *do* have a physical aspect. There is an instinctual level to writing, for instance, which most people do not allow because we are trained to write on demand, out of fear, with the pressure of assignment beating us over the head. This is *not* that kind of writing. This is writing to reclaim self. This is writing to declare personal truth, and to piece together the magnificent jigsaw puzzle of your life. Tell the story of the face. Let it go wherever it wants to go. When you are done with this work, rest, breathe. There is labor involved here, a birthing of sorts. Stretch out, relax, and then, if you feel drawn (which you probably will), reread what you have written. Let it sink in and eventually it will become clear to you what the role of this experience is in your healing.

The Obstacle

This foray into spontaneous creativity is designed to help you identify what keeps you from moving forward. Follow the steps I've described in the other exercises to begin — the steps involving coming into your space, making sure you will not be interrupted, finding your place of comfort and relaxation within your space, settling and centering and focusing on intention. This procedure is almost the best part of the process! It feels so good to come into this place of safety and wholeness. From this relaxed clarity, follow this guided visualization, and see where it takes you. When the visualization process finds its closure, write or draw or color.

See yourself leaving from the doorway of your house. It is a perfect day — whatever that means for you — a spring day, or a bright, autumn day, a hot summer day, or a crisp winter morning. It is a day you want to be in, and you have a destination, a place where you want to go, and you head there. Perhaps you are walking vigorously, or maybe you are riding your bike. Maybe you hop onto your motorcycle, or strap on your cross country skis. Maybe you put on your snowshoes or maybe you jog out, your dog beside you. Whatever is your favorite mode of movement and transport, you are doing it, out your front door, and down the road toward your destination. See the visual panorama around you, the town passing by or the fields, the country road or the city streets. You are moving past all of them, undistractable, on your way to where you are going. Suddenly and unexpectedly, you encounter an obstacle of such magnitude that you cannot continue. You are stopped dead in your tracks, unable to proceed. You are stymied, and, for a moment, disappointed, and then you remember — you are determined to get where you are going. Nothing is going to stop you! But how to overcome this obstacle?

See yourself reflecting on the situation and witness, with attentive eye, the process that allows you to overcome this obstacle. Watch all this unfold naturally and organically. Track your capacity to be undaunted in continuing, and allow the truth of your own unique way of overcoming this obstacle to reveal itself. Perhaps your creative skills show up as theatrics or physical strength. Maybe they show up as trickery or deception. Maybe they show up as engineering or construction skills. But whatever those skills are, recognize them. Those are the skills you need to acknowledge, nurture, and support in yourself. Whether those skills be skills of the spirit, skills of the intelligence, skills of the body, or all three, those skills represent your creative genius. Now, name it!

Once the obstacle has been overcome and the goal achieved, take your integration time, your space for rest and acceptance, and when you feel ready, express spontaneously, recording this meeting, so that whenever you need support again because you doubt your ability to overcome obstacles, you can reread this and remember who you are.

And the List Goes On

Creativity can be used as a way of grounding, a way of touching into who you are, a vehicle for finding your center, for connecting with yourself. In your Structured Unstructured Time And Space, sit and relax and say TODAY I AM ... Let the introductory statement complete itself in writing or in color, in movement or in sound. Here's one of my responses to this introduction:

TODAY I AM A WRITER

Today I am a writer. My mind is in love with words and expression. Today I honor how interested I am in the way people move and speak and interact. Whatever I see, I describe, because that is my function. Today I am a writer. I honor my curiosity and how it shapes my attention. Today I believe in myself as a writer and I let myself focus on my writing, on the way words are crafted through my being and become an assemblage of expression that represents my particular view of life, experience, reality.

Today I accept my writing ability and I support it. No one can write as I do and that's just fine with me. I do not compete with anyone. I don't need to succeed externally. The measure of my success is my internal experience.

I write as I am, and as I am, I write. My grace, my beauty, my awkwardness, my childishness, my maturity, my skill, my effort,

my joy and my embarrassment are all OK with me. In my writing,
I let myself be.

I can make sounds in my writing. I am with myself. Today this
woman writes her truth and accepts it and does not degrade it
and enjoys it and does not turn away from it. Pen to paper. This
is a beginning.

The Healing Challenge

Pick a challenge, any challenge, and address it with your creative
tools. This is a direct application of the therapeutic aspect of art.
Here's a list of possible healing challenges you might consider. In
selecting yours, be as specific as possible:

- Losing weight
- Gaining weight
- Forgetting about weight
- Insomnia
- Career development
- Fear of intimacy
- Stopping an addictive behavior (smoking, drinking, coffee,
  obsessive talking, drugs, workaholism etc.)
- Fear of authority

In this exercise, your first job is identifying the challenge itself
and then just accepting it for what it is. You don't judge the challenge or start thinking up solutions, you just see it, name it, and let
it be there. Orienting towards healing and trust, but without determining how to solve your problem, you proceed into spontaneous
expression, and write (or paint) for a predetermined period of time.
Then review your expression, and learn from it. Here's what one
woman wrote when she picked the challenge of fear of authority:

> Fear of authority robbed me of my sleep last night. It robbed
> me of love and it robbed me of closeness. I couldn't relax enough
> to be with my husband, even when he was willing to help me. I
> was so distracted by my fear of authority that I couldn't even

see straight! I had failed to get my car registration in on time and I had blown the consequences for this all out of proportion so that I was in a panic, and nobody could get me out of it. To others it must have seemed laughable, but to me it was a labyrinth from which I would not extricate myself.

I was slung in a bag of terror. My eyes were drawn inward, curled away from the light of reality and simplicity, looking in at each other, afraid to look out. This is all about my father. This is all about his bigness and the way he oppressed me. This is all about my weakness to push him out of my consciousness. This is all about the past.

Oh my poor eyes, cramped in that tight space of fear, not seeing, strangled. When I was little I was far–sighted and afraid to cry. My eyes would leak, but they wouldn't open and let my tears gush forth with the terror and grief which I must have felt constantly. My father filled every moment of my life with fear.

Why do I continue to allow authority to terrorize my life? What danger am I in now, with all this support around me? I am in no danger now, but the frightened child within me still feels unprotected. After all these years of therapy and healing, she is still not safe. I must honor that.

I soothe that little girl's eyes now. I soothe those eyes with gentle strokes, with a gentle touch, honoring the fear, acknowledging the terror, not damning it or hiding it. In this soothing of my eyes lies the answer to the needs of this humiliated and terrorized child, this vulnerable and defenseless being who still waits for her healing to be complete.

There is a sentence that runs rampant in my head: "They are coming after me," and all the "theys" are my father, though sometimes my mother is one of the "theys" with her tormenting demands. These were the women for whom my vulnerability was a bother. They too are part of the "theys" but all the "theys" are in the past. It seems to me that authorities ignore the vulnerable ones and don't listen to the pleading of the poor, but in order for me to deal with that, I have to separate my past from my present. I have to see that now I am strong enough to take care of my own vulnerability each time I feel afraid of authority.

After writing this, the author spent some time doing relaxation exercises for her eyes, which ached. In fact, she had been troubled all her life by various eye conditions — farsightedness and watering eyes as a youngster, astigmatism as an adult. She had pain in her eyes and they tired very easily. By taking her writing seriously and giving her eyes the attention they were calling for, she probably prevented further deterioration of her vision, and just as importantly, she attended to an aspect of her wounding that revealed itself somatically by becoming devotedly self–nurturing, by giving herself the attention her writing indicated. She said that this eventually relieved considerably her tormenting fear of authority, which had so ruled her life that she went into a panic whenever she saw a policeman, even if he were driving a police car behind her and she was driving perfectly. It may seem an indirect route to address such a fear through eye relaxation, but it worked! Creativity presents unique and unexpected solutions that prove effective, and that's what this is all about!

THE FACE OF SOMEONE YOU CAN'T FORGET, FINISH THAT SENTENCE, THE OBSTACLE, TODAY I AM, THE HEALING CHALLENGE, THE SPONTANEOUS EPISTLE, and YOUR CREATIVE SPACE are just a few examples of formats you can use to inspire spontaneous creativity. Eventually you will come up with exercises or formats of your own, designed especially for you. But until that time, here is a list of titles from which you can make exercises. These are toys for you to play with — aren't all toolboxes toy boxes? Spontaneous writing, genuine movement process, using art to heal — all of these are ways to play (or work) with something that is really quite serious. And the fun doesn't detract from the profundity of the process — it helps make the pain bearable and meltable. I may leave my movement work feeling saddened, or relieved, or overjoyed, or enthusiastic, or reflective, but I'm inevitably lightened of my burden and much more compassionate toward myself and others, being more deeply aware of the enormity of suffering we all bear and must transform to live successfully, healthfully, and vitally.

Try these tools as stimulants for writing, painting, movement, sound, or sculpture, and if you want to share the results with someone, send them to me:

- The Gift

- Why Do I Write?

- Portrait of Myself

- The Face of Love

- A Journey Into My Heart

- Myself A Year From Now

- Fear

- My Body

- What I Really Need

- Support

- An Interview with Myself

- The Place Where I Am At Peace

- My Town

- Going Home

- Sex

- Touching

- Reaching Out

- Endings

- Transitions

- Major Turning Points In My Life

- Being Sick

- An Image of Joy

Explorations in Movement:
Genuine Movement Process

To reiterate the intention described at the introduction to this section about embodied writing, the purpose of genuine movement process is not to train you to be a performer with a professional dance company. On the contrary, most professional dance companies perform *someone else's* choreography. They move the way they are told to move. They learn technique, and their bodies look like someone's image of a professional dancer. Genuine movement discards all those images and turns in an entirely different direction. The purpose of genuine movement process is to discover the way your body *wants* to move and what it wants to say and to let that happen, naturally, spontaneously, and in a supportive environment.

Genuine movement process, or Authentic Movement, results in a beauty that is quite distinct from the way dancers are supposed to look. The body is allowed to become itself and the elegance and grace of that organic unfolding is indescribable and unpredictable. It is also inimitable. You will become more of who you are if you allow yourself to do genuine movement process frequently, to enter it on your list of resources and tools, and use it. This is a gift to yourself.

I think it is worthwhile to go over the list of attitudes and intentions that support the authenticity of this process. As I mentioned earlier, this is a slight adaptation of the list of attitudes for spontaneous writing. You can continue to revise this list of intentions as they might apply for painting, drawing, sculpture, or whatever art form you care to make real for yourself. They are:

1. You can move to completion.

2. You are not moving for someone else.

3. You can move spontaneously and fluidly.

4. You don't have to shape your movement (choreography, lessons, etc.) Your movement will shape itself.

5. You can discover the form of movement that suits you by *moving*. You don't have to decide what to do ahead of time in order to move.

6. You don't have to hold anything back when you are moving.

7. You can move the way no one else has ever moved.

8. You can move for yourself alone.

9. You can just start moving, without even knowing where you are going with this movement, and your natural intelligence and your natural body will guide you safely to completion.

There are a few cautions, or awarenesses, with Authentic Movement that don't apply to embodied writing. Since you are moving your body, you want to clear the space so that there is nothing for you to run into. This will allow you to feel even more free when you move. Clear away tables, chairs, scatter rugs, and miscellaneous objects. People often do genuine movement process with their eyes closed. This seems to facilitate a more profound going within, and this also suggests the need to clear the space. Some people like their movement space to be carpeted. Others prefer a wooden floor.

Genuine movement process and working with color (paints and clay, etc.) tend to be more regressive than spontaneous writing. By this I mean, these media seem to more quickly and directly bring us into the child-body, arousing childhood feelings and experiences in a subtle but sometimes overwhelming way. It is possible in movement or while using color or clay, perhaps because of the pliability of the media and their association with childhood activities, to feel enveloped in the emotions and body sensations of childhood quite readily. For this reason, working in these forms requires a careful adherence to the boundaries of time, and a disciplined attention to the rest, centering and relaxation aspects of these exercises. While we want to be able to travel with grace between the past and the present, clearly distinguishing them and noticing the sensations associated with the past, we want to do this carefully, and without overwhelming our delicate nervous systems. So, before we begin a genuine movement process, we want to emphasize intention and purpose, and reiterate the boundaries of time.

Working with a friend when the media are suggestive of regression is wise and allows the process to be more grounded and integrated. My friend Marilla and I do genuine sound and movement process together on a weekly basis. We alternate, depending on our needs, in moving and witnessing each other, and sharing the process, supporting one another in coming to our own individual truth and wholeness. Companionship keeps the entire experience from being isolated or frightening and makes it grounded and friendly. Working with a collective, such as an Authentic Movement group, can be helpful. See the Resources section of this book to discover how you might locate such a group.

The Dance of the Jaw and the Pelvis

Come into your movement space and find your center there. Where do you want to be today? Do you want to sit down? Perhaps lying flat on your back would feel better? Or, would you like to curl up, sit with your legs folded in front of you, or lie down with your knees up? Whatever position feels the most satisfying, let yourself be in it, and from this place of comfort, relax, center, unwind, be in your body. Here remind yourself of your intention in this Structured Unstructured Time And Space. Remember your time boundary (move for fifteen or thirty minutes, rest, then write — or whatever agreement works for you), and recall your resources. Remember that you can stop this process whenever you want to and that you are in charge. Breathe deeply. Claim your time, your space, your body, and your being. Feel the specialness of this choice to be with yourself now.

From this place of awareness and clarity, imagine that you are entering experientially the internal geography of your jaw. Imagine that you are a beam of light coming from the eye of awareness and that that awareness moves gently across the territory of your jaw. Slowly, step by step, explore the world of your jaw in movement. Allow your jaw to tell you its story, to speak to you. Feel the holding of your jaw, and its wish for release. Feel the release of your jaw, and its need to hold. Take your time. And if your jaw wants to open, and if you want to sigh or sing, or release any sound, let it come out with permission and welcoming. Let your head move to accommodate the needs of your jaw. Let your entire body respond and become part of the dance of your jaw. Make room within yourself to hear the entire story of your jaw, from beginning to end. Take a deep breath. Relax, and see if there is more to tell. When your jaw is finished with its movement and with its sounding, rest, and make a space to tell the story of the pelvis.

Let the same light that entered your jaw, enter your pelvis. Feel it enter at the hip, penetrating through the territory of the pelvis with warmth and gentleness, erasing tension, and letting the tale of the pelvis unfold. This is a long journey. Don't feel that you have to tell the entire story today, during this time with yourself. This is a beginning. You will come back to your jaw and your pelvis many more times.

Let the pelvis move as it needs to, and let the rest of your body accompany the dance of the pelvis in a way that is organic and genuine. Don't make a dance out of this, let the dance become itself, let the movement unfold from the truth of your pelvis. When this movement process is complete, rest. Integrate. Feel the way your jaw and your pelvis are different now. Hear them and their after–resonance, their energetic reorganization, and the rippling throughout your being as everything within you shifts to accommodate the new state of your jaw and your pelvis.

When the movement of the jaw and the pelvis finds closure, you may choose to write, or, if you have a friend present, to share your experience. Your friend will listen and support you, just as your journal book will absorb and document this transformation. Drawing or using color (felt markers, crayons, paints, oil pastels) flows easily after Authentic Movement and affords us a valuable manifestation of our experience. This process will most likely feel deeply satisfying and will give you new insight into yourself and your body's story. Let this enjoyment, whether or not it has a conclusion or an understanding, be felt and acknowledged by your whole being.

The Movement of Sanctuary

Come into your movement space and find your center there. Feel the soothing quality of all the steps that initiate genuine movement process, the ritual of claiming your Structured Unstructured Time and Space. Put your phone message machine on and turn down the ringer. Put your DO NOT DISTURB sign on the door, and identify your time parameters. Ah! Now! This is it. *MY* time and space. When you find your place of being in the room, allow yourself to move to describe and define the shape of your own sense of sanctuary, your own sense of safety and support. What does that movement *feel* like to you — how does it feel to embody the experience of safety and sanctuary, to have it so physically and inescapably *known?*

Let this movement unfurl and take you where it needs to go. Stay grounded while you move, and stay focused, listening for the news from your body, the secrets you haven't told yourself. When the movement is complete, rest. Then write or share with your friend.

An Endless Assortment of Options

These are but two possibilities in an endless assortment of options you can have in your creative space with movement. My favorite movement experience is the one in which you step into the unknown, simply exploring what is in the moment, giving your body its due, at last, to speak to you and to be heard. In the silence and the spontaneity, I find incredible satisfaction and information about myself. A beautiful strength and maturity comes from these periods of Structured Unstructured Time And Space. The classic wisdom of "Know Thyself" has real meaning and real content. I encourage you to enter these spheres of truth and thereby to become your own transformative testimony.

Just as I offered titles as tools for embodied and spontaneous writing, here are some titles you can use as tools for genuine movement process:

- I Move Feeling Support

- The Celebration of My Strength

- My Vulnerability Finds Form

- My Body Tells the Story of Today

- ❧ My Heart's Dance

- ❧ My Undying Soul

- ❧ The Story of My Legs

- ❧ My Arms Speak

- ❧ The Right Side of My Body Speaks to the Left Side of My Body

- ❧ The Left Side of My Body Speaks to the Right Side of My Body

- ❧ Right and Left Sides Speak Together

Resources II

ENERGETIC INTERVENTIONS, BODYWORK, AND ALTERNATIVE THERAPIES

What are energetic interventions and what is bodywork? How are they different? Are they ever the same? How do you know which one you need? How can you tell if they are being effective when you do use them? These are just a few of the important questions I hope to address in this section. The items on the menu are intriguing and interesting, so relax and prepare to read this compendium with curiosity, and perhaps the modalities that suit you just perfectly will jump off the page with their offering of renegotiation and reclamation.

Ever since people like Wilhelm Reich, Fritz Perls, Alexander Lowen, Alice Miller, Marion Woodman, and many others from the Land of Understanding Human Transformation, have presented their views on healing and recovery (not to mention the great influx of Eastern healing wisdom), the outline of what we can use to get healthier has changed considerably. No longer are we limited to sitting across from someone at a desk or chair and talking in order to survey our emotional condition, and no longer are we limited to taking drugs when our immune system seems inadequate to fight disease. No longer *must* we choose surgery for back pain, glasses for weak eyes, and inhalers for asthma. The options are substantially increased now, thanks to the work of numerous courageous, articulate, and creative individuals.

These new options, some of which derive from or are Eastern concepts, have particular value for the survivor of trauma and abuse because of their holistic underpinnings. The somatic aspect of recovery can be addressed more directly now, with less fear of the "hysteria" label, the disparaging "psychosomatic" byline, or the snide "nervous tizzies" tossed indiscriminately, at women in particular, as if nervousness, anxiety, or panic were negligible weaknesses, meaning nothing of significance.

The number and variety of alternative healing modalities can sometimes be disorienting for the person seeking help. How can we possibly know enough about acupressure, herbology, and yoga, to name just a few systems, to ever make an intelligent choice? It is easier to realize that the old doctor–patient arrangement is not working than to know with what to replace it. This section is designed to give you some feeling for what is available and what works best when recovering from trauma. It would be impossible to present a comprehensive review in this regard. So many new and renewed concepts have been brought to the forefront recently that I can't claim to know them all, as much as I try to remain aware and in–touch. But, what I will try to do, in addition to discussing a wide variety of healing possibilities, is to give you a reliable list of resources so that you can inform yourself about the healing options available to you.

Before beginning this section, I want to talk about a primary consideration in selecting a healing system to use. All of the systems and concepts I will present are good, but you can be certain that not all of them are good for everyone. The relationship between a healing system and someone seeking healing is highly specific. What works for someone may not work at all for someone else. Similarly, the practitioner you select should be someone with whom you are comfortable. Use the same general guidelines I gave for selecting a therapist in selecting a practitioner of any healing art, be it acupuncture or aromatherapy. The relationship is as important as the system. Never proceed with someone until you have cleared your doubts and your questions.

If you really believe that an adjunctive therapy will benefit you, and you are strongly motivated to add a modality to your therapeutic dynamic, be sure to include your primary therapist in the process of seeking bodywork or an energetic intervention. You are at the center of your healing process, and, at all times, you are the decision maker, but your therapist can be helpful in supporting you and orienting you and, possibly, in offering you referrals for other therapists. When your therapist is aware of all your therapies, she can more easily integrate them into her work with you.

To underscore the importance of the relationship between therapist and recipient, and also to highlight the relationship between recipient and modality, I would like to share with you a healing story from my own childhood. This story says a great deal about how remarkable healing can happen.

By the time I was three years old, it was clear that my eyes were not functioning properly. For one thing, my left eye watered copiously, and clinical investigations into the tear duct revealed no problem there. More importantly, my eyes crossed, making me quite unstable as I navigated our tiny three room apartment in the Bronx. The strabismus clearly was not improving and was a detriment to my well–being, so at the early age of three years I found myself wearing glasses. I wore them all the time — it was dangerous for me not to and by the time I was twelve, my mother had some real concerns about the fact that "boys never make passes at girls who wear glasses." However, we were poor, and after investigating the cost for the operation that was purported to correct strabismus, my mother gave up.

Coincidentally, however, across the street lived my friend Lola Spivak, whose mother was notorious for her unusual ideas about healing. Lola's mother was a tiny, wiry Eastern European woman, and people came from all over to stay at her house to undertake curious cures. I never really knew what was going on at Lola's, and Lola was awfully embarrassed about it. One day, my mother got into a conversation with Lola's mother about my eyes, and Lola's mother told my mother about The Bates Method, and a woman who practiced it not far from our house. The Bates Method, she said, were eye exercises to correct all kinds of vision problems, and the woman who could teach them to me charged only $5 a session. I could even ride to her house on my bike. I remember my mother and father taking me to this woman's house. She sat with us for a while and then said, looking directly at my father, "It is important that she not feel troubled. She needs to relax. She is carrying too much sadness for a child." Such language was incomprehensible to my father, I am certain, and while it was somewhat comprehensible to my mother, there was nothing she could do to implement the kind woman's suggestion. She merely looked away as the woman spoke. Nevertheless, $5 was nothing compared to eye surgery. My mother could swing that, and I could get there on my own. I was signed up on the spot.

Now, 37 years later, as I sit here writing without glasses, I wish I could remember that woman's name. Of all the people who knew me as a child, I believe she was the first one to see into the terror of my life and offer me hope. Her kindness was her wisdom manifest as she worked devotedly with me to provide some relief from tension and some guidance in well–being. I trusted her and, beyond trust, I allowed her to help me. I loved going to her house and because our connection was so resonant, I did the exercises consistently; and when she took my glasses away, I found I could see. The Bates Method is not highly regarded these days, nor was it ever widely respected, but I believe it is a truly holistic system with a profound theory behind it. It involves an understanding of the workings of the eyes the like of which I have never heard elsewhere, and a system of muscular and relaxation exercises that, from my experience, actually produce results. But what made it possible for a serious and deeply troubled adolescent girl to practice demanding eye exercises every day was the caring I felt from her and the safety she imparted to me — probably my only experience of true kindness in the close company of another person since my grandfather died.

The Bates Method, as imparted to me by this nameless woman who serendipitously came into my life, included not only exercises to strengthen the eye muscles, but visualization, subtle movement (a gentle swinging back and forth of the trunk of the body, with the eyes closed, while standing in the sun), game playing (catching a bounding ball after tracking it with the eyes), story telling (imaging black to rest the eyes), touch (a gentle massage of the cranium), and conversation about how one is doing and what one is feeling. These elements — movement, gentle touch, conversation replete with respect and sensitivity, trust and attunement, movement and laughter, are, to me, the hallmarks of a truly healing dynamic, and I find myself incorporating all of these elements into my work with others.

It was only when I came to write this section of this book that it occurred to me that the inclusion and the awareness of these elements stems from this experience with The Bates Method teacher who took my glasses away from me forever and allowed me to see one image, one vision, at a time. I knew when she touched me that I was safe. The proof was that I relaxed. It was such a relief to feel her touch, her presence. For the one hour a week that I spent at her house, I did not have to protect myself, I did not have to defend myself, I was not afraid. Who is to say what healed my eyes — was it the exercises, or her? Or was it actually me, finally free to respond fully to the gift of life? I think it was primarily the latter. And so it will be with any healing system, whether it is so–called traditional or so–called alternative. YOU are the healer, and that is that. You should settle for nothing less than comfort, trust, and complete re-laxation. This is what you need to heal. And please don't ignore what comes into your life in an apparently coincidental way. Seren-dipitous events can change the course of your life.

Why Seek Adjunctive Energetic Therapies?

Why would someone want to add bodywork or an energetic heal-ing system to their therapeutic process? Isn't that overindulgence? How many therapists does one person need?

Here are some general indicators that an adjunctive therapy might benefit you:

1. Your level of fatigue is consistently overwhelming.
2. You have chronic headaches.
3. You have chronic neck pain.
4. You have chronic jaw tension.
5. Your immune system does not work to protect you from disease.
6. You feel stress all over your body.
7. You do not feel mentally alert.
8. You cannot lose weight.
9. You cannot gain weight.
10. You cannot break addictive patterns, such as smoking.

11. You sleep too much.

12. You sleep too little.

13. You are sedentary and unenthused about activity.

14. You are lethargic, but with a yen to be active.

15. You are hyperactive, hypertensive, and uncontrollably nervous.

16. Simple foods make you ill without reason — such as bread, or certain fruits.

17. Your back is repeatedly a problem, causing a variety of discomforts. Vertebrae are perpetually going out of alignment, pain ensues, and you feel helpless.

18. You have chronic sinus infections.

19. You have chronic ear ringing.

20. Your digestion is never smooth.

21. Your menstrual cycle is problematic in all regards.

22. You have chronic pain throughout your body.

23. Exercise never feels good. Your body always hurts.

24. You cannot feel your center no matter how much you want to, and no matter how much you talk about it.

This list is not a complete one. The point I want to make by listing these symptoms is that often the signs of trauma are somatic. Unexpressed feelings can become somatic expression, and frequently a somatic intervention is necessary to meet the situation on its own turf. If your somatic symptomatology can be traced in some way to your trauma history (and it probably can), you will want to work with practitioners who understand that you are a survivor of trauma and/or sexual abuse and who are willing to consult with your primary therapist (with your permission, of course) to make sure that your overall healing experience is integrated. Thus, employing additional therapists becomes a way of constructing a thoroughgoing and high functioning healing network to support you in reclaiming integrated self–hood.

What about the expense of all this, you may well ask? Adjunctive modalities can be employed on an occasional basis and it is frequently possible to find good practitioners who have reasonable rates. Beginning or even learning practitioners can sometimes be more sensitive than long–term practitioners, especially if you give them enough information about you. They will charge less, be extremely careful with you, and frequently give you more time.

By being forthright about your financial limitations and resources, a cooperative plan can be developed between the therapists and you so that the healing evolution is orchestrated to achieve what you want to achieve. By being open with people, you can give them an opportunity to support you in your healing process. Some of the most helpful healing I have received came from people who reduced their prices to support me. In turn, I reduce my prices for people who I believe in and who truly need it. This is not to say that one should bargain to get the lowest price from therapists who deserve their full fee. But this *is* to say that one should *not* let financial concerns stop you from getting the healing you deserve. *I never have.*

The energetic interventions and other resources I am reporting here are primarily ones I have tried myself. I have tried to maximize the number of interventions that are "self–help" oriented, and therefore less expensive to utilize. Self–help systems also have the benefit of empowering you and decreasing your feelings of dependence on therapists. I have also tried to emphasize the interventions that are subtle and gentle, and those that are not will be indicated as more invasive, strenuous, and impactful. Of course, I am not recommending or suggesting *any* of these interventions, but sharing my experience and perspective, and providing you with information that might not otherwise be so readily available.

This is a resource section designed for trauma survivors. What I list here is not a thorough overview of all energetic interventions or all bodywork. Rather it is a selected list of those adjunctive therapies that seem to me to interface well with the process of healing from trauma, and particularly in the process of healing from sexual abuse. My guess is that this listing will grow and change over time, as I learn more and more about healing and about what is available. Please send me your thoughts, comments, and additions to this list. This is the foundation on which to build more and more resources. We can't have too many resources!

Before I begin this listing, I would like to make a general state-ment. Always remember, you are free to stop any therapeutic expe-rience at any point and you should do so whenever you feel un-comfortable. Speak up at the first hint of not feeling right, and don't question your impulse to do so.

Acupuncture

The practice of acupuncture is traditional in China, but it is con-sidered innovative and alternative in the West. Most Westerners probably first heard of it in the context of an analgesic for painless surgery. Sometime in the late 70's there were television broadcasts of Oriental patients laughing and talking while surgery was being performed on them. We associate acupuncture with needles, and we know that for some reason or other they are placed in specific locations on the body. But acupuncture is just one aspect of an en-tire philosophy of health and well–being that the Oriental physi-cian uses in a comprehensive and integrated approach to under-standing what people need to get better when they are sick. The function of the needles is to send messages to the brain, which stimu-late one's own healing process. The needles are placed at points along meridian lines in order to impact the energy of that meridian and its corresponding organs. This is the most simplistic descrip-tion of how acupuncture works, but even from this description you can see how crucial it is to work with a practitioner whom you trust and respect. The choice about what needles to use and where to place them should rest in the hands of a person who really under-stands you and your particular needs. As David Van Nuys said in his introduction to my friend James Howland's delightful book, *Acu-puncture Principles and Your Health:*

> It is not so much the needles which heal as it is the skilled practitioner who is able to elicit the forces of self–healing which lie dormant in the patient. The needles are but one tool among many which are even more subtle through which the acupuncturist sensitizes his/her patient to the healing forces within. This practitioner is himself/herself one who understands and practices balanced living and the harmony of mind and body.

Why choose acupuncture as an intervention in your process? Among other things, acupuncture can be used to reduce pain, to awaken energy, to help stop addictions (smoking, drinking, and other substance addictions), to redirect the energy persisting around chronic conditions (chronic lung congestion, chronic headaches, chronic back pain), to awaken the vitality of the immune system, and to create an experience of calm and well–being. Acupuncturists are certified in the states where they can practice. The wiser the acupuncturist, the more profound the treatment. A good acupuncturist will want to know a great deal about you and should ask for an interview to assess all the influences on your health and well–being. In China, mental, emotional, and spiritual needs were never separated from physical needs, and that understanding needs to be applied when acupuncture is practiced in the West as well. There are short-term, weekend classes in acupuncture for chiropractors and other health care providers that do not in any way resemble the training a certified acupuncturist receives. If you are seeking acupuncture as a therapeutic intervention, you will want to work with a certified acupuncturist, someone who also has knowledge of herbs and moxibustion (two important components of this healing dynamic) and someone whom you feel you can integrate into your overall healing process.

Acupressure

Acupressure is most definitely a self–help system. Like acupuncture, it originated in ancient China and was born from the simple origins that actually shape many of the touch therapies: One's hands automatically go to the places that are injured; a mother's hands will always reach out to touch the troubled places on her child, and simple motoric impulses such as these. The acupressure system is basically the same as acupuncture — fingertip pressure is applied to acupuncture points. Shiatsu is the Japanese version of acupressure. Several books listed in the Resource section will inform you about how you can learn acupressure yourself. Combining your practice of acupressure with some knowledge of Oriental considerations in health and healing will augment the awareness you bring to your self–help treatment. Cathryn Bauer, in her book *Acupressure for Women*, makes this astute comment in this regard: "Yeshi Donden, holistic physician to the Dalai Lama of Tibet, encourages his students to develop a perception of the universe as a place where healing is possible. This outlook is your best possible supplement to Acupressure self–care or any other form of health treatment."

Alexander Technique

F. Matthias Alexander was one of the earliest proponents of the inseparable wholeness of mind and body. His views conflicted with orthodox medicine then, just as other organismic approaches continue to rattle the cages of allopathy today. Entirely self- taught, and learning primarily from his experience with himself and others, Alexander developed exercises that enhanced the fluidity and ease of simple movements, such as standing, sitting, and rising from a chair. The Alexander Technique is of great value to those who suffer restriction in movement or who wish to move, speak, sing, articulate, and express themselves fully. The goal of The Alexander Technique, essentially, is the greatest lengthening of the spine possible in every action. The threefold foundation for this goal is:

1. Let the neck be free
2. Let the head go forward and up
3. Let the torso widen and lengthen

Needless to say, the ability to be lengthened in this way implies a kind of openness and confidence that trauma precludes. But The Alexander Technique is a gentle way to encounter a physical experience of structural and emotional expansiveness, and to address some of the metaphors our bodies find to cope with trauma. These metaphors include scoliosis, lordosis, postural patterns that produce pain and limitation (such as hunched shoulders, tucking the head in, contracting the pelvic floor and/or the stomach). The way these patterns can be renegotiated, I believe, is through gentle, nonjudgmental systems, such as The Alexander Technique, that point us consciously in the direction of freedom, expression, vitality, and healthy sensuality. The Alexander Technique can be experienced directly by sessions with practitioners who are certified by recognized Alexander training programs. Alexander practitioners are usually located in major cities, and particularly in places where the theater arts are studied and/or practiced. The Alexander Technique has been most popular with actors and actresses, singers, and dancers, who seek to improve their performances on the stage. As always, make sure the person you work with is someone with whom you feel at home. The Alexander Technique is partially an energetic intervention and partially bodywork. In its time of origin, it was regarded as a kind of physical therapy or physiotherapy. Another phrase to describe methods such as this one is psychophysical education. Somewhere on the border between personal and psychological transformation and structural reorganization, The Alexander Technique has the capacity to affect mental–emotional–attitudinal states via changes in deep-rooted physical patterns.

Aromatherapy

Aromatherapy is a subtle and fine art involving the inhalation and absorption through the skin of the intense and condensed scents of herbs and flowers known to have certain effects on the brain. The use of these oils in baths, topically in massage, and to permeate the room is subtle but highly beneficial, particularly for sensitive people. Information about aromatherapy is primarily available through books. See the Resource section for some of these. This adjunctive therapy is relatively inexpensive and can be done as self–help with just a little research. This is a fun-to-use adjunctive therapy. Men and woman alike to whom I have recommended aromatherapy report pleasant and useful results — not "total healing," but gentle shifts in awareness and mood that make a significant difference in the moment. Aromatherapists offer massages with essential oils. They may or may not be certified in aromatherapy as there is no regulatory agency supervising this benign healing system. Use your intuition and ask appropriate questions in selecting an aromatherapy massage therapist. You should feel comfortable with this person since massage therapy always involves disrobing. Never allow yourself to be put in the vulnerable position of lying naked on a treatment table (or even lying fully clothed on a treatment table) until you have verified for yourself that the person serving you is someone who understands trauma and whom you can trust to be sensitive to your needs and your process, no matter how subtly it may reveal itself. Aromatherapy massage, it should be emphasized, is not designed for deep tissue or muscle relaxation, though it may have that effect. It is designed to permeate you and your body with a healing aroma and to allow your mind and mood to respond to the smell. The aromas can be stimulating and awakening if your energy is low, but the overall experience of aromatherapy massage is calming. Using the oils on your own can serve a number of different purposes, including addressing particular symptoms such as depression, congestion, nervousness, or hay fever, as the literature indicates.

Art Therapy

Art therapists are trained in Masters Degree programs at many universities and are usually highly skilled professionals who can introduce you to the use of color, line, shape, and visual expression generally as a route to self-understanding, self-discovery, and integrated well–being. They have clinical training and a strong developmental awareness. Art therapy is particularly useful when cognitive work has run its course and seems to be stagnating, or when the next layer of healing emerges as visual experience that has no mirror in language or reason. Like movement therapy, art therapy tends to be regressive in nature, so you want to be sure to find a therapist you can trust to hold the ground for you and bring you to the present when the regression goes deep. Maintaining boundaries with regressive work of any kind is something to know about ahead of time. By simply accounting for the possibility of going too far, you can keep your immersion into creativity useful rather than frightening. Art therapy can be added as an adjunctive therapy, with all the participants (therapists and recipient) in communication about the work, or it can be undertaken on its own for a while, with a plan to eventually return to cognitive therapy. Some cognitive therapists (meaning psychotherapists, psychologists, counselors, and others who use dialogue as a primary modality) are also art therapists or may know about the use of art in process. If you feel drawn to this way of working, talk to your therapist about it.

Authentic Movement

The term "Authentic Movement" has been through many permutations since it was first coined and introduced by Mary Whitehouse around 1979. Most recently, it has been developed by Janet Adler, who focuses on the role of the witness in the therapeutic dynamic of witness and mover. These two women are important in the theoretical development of movement therapy. However, the use of Authentic Movement can and has been liberally adapted to a variety of situations with more and less formal guidelines as the circumstances require. Dance therapists are trained by the American Dance Therapy Association (see Dance Therapy). However, nondance therapists with an interest in and experience with movement have taken liberties with the concepts of Authentic Movement and use it when it can benefit a client's development. The formal guidelines for Authentic Movement involve a therapist/witness and a client/mover. The witness is empathic and actively engages in observation of the mover. Mary Whitehouse, who was the mother of Authentic Movement (differentiating it from the groundwork done in Dance Therapy by Marion Chace), described it as active imagination represented in the musculature of the body. She would sometimes engage in discussion with her clients when they were not moving, exploring with them the feelings or experiences of the movement process. Janet Adler, on the other hand, refrains from interaction, encouraging her mover–clients to be entirely with themselves. The genuine movement process that is described in this book is my own adaptation of some of these concepts, flowing directly out of my experience as someone who uses movement to heal and who seeks to make this experience generally available to other survivors.

Currently, Authentic Movement is becoming more widely known and more easily available to the general public. An Institute of Authentic Movement (see Resources section) has formed, and people can more readily deepen their involvement with this remarkable healing tool. The listing of books, articles, and agencies that follows this section contains references to some networks that can put you in touch with Authentic Movement services, hopefully near you. An article I wrote for my clients, to whom I was introducing Authentic Movement, may be useful here, and so I have included it.

Focus Within/Allow Movement to Arise
Some Thoughts on Authentic Movement

Being in the space of Authentic Movement is being solely in the body's truth. Society suggests we go about adult life leaving the body out of the conversation, leaving the body out of the action. Ironically, the modus operandi in "civilized" urban life is to leave the body out of the movement!

On the other hand, genuine movement process (or Authentic Movement) is a living, spontaneous, active experience, arising from the body. It is a window into our own indigenous, primitive knowing. In Authentic Movement, we allow parts of the body to communicate with one another. We learn to listen to the body's gestures. We learn the secret codes our bodies have created and the stories behind our motoric impulses. Authentic Movement is not just about moving. It is also about listening with presence and compassion to our own movement and to the movement of others.

To live within the knowledge of Authentic Movement is to live within the ongoing network of motoric spontaneity. In order to move spontaneously, we have to trust our muscles. In order to trust our muscles, we have to know them - not by their Latin names necessarily, but by and with our own experience.

Authentic Movement allows us to tap our beauty and elegance in the true, individuated sense. To find this beauty and elegance, we must sacrifice our addiction to externals. We can find it whether we are fat or thin, have long hair or short hair, blonde hair or no hair, whether we are old or young, whether we have a flat tummy or a ripe belly, whether we are tall or short, whether we have candida or cancer or multiple sclerosis. This beauty can become our constant way of moving and it is found by focusing within and trusting our muscles.

We cultivate this trust by knowing ourselves and enjoying our discoveries. The opposite of compulsion is trust. When we move compulsively, governed by externals, we abandon our motoric truth. By focusing within, we discover a marvelous world of connective tissue, of organs, blood, and lymph, of muscles responding spontaneously to their own initiation; and we discover that there is enough space for all these parts of ourselves to express themselves in a unified way. Your friends will be your nervous system, your hormones, your craniosacral fluid, and your blood cells. All parts of your body — your hair, your fat, your nails, your teeth — all will befriend you. You will move as one integrated being, as part of nature.

Where does the form and structure come from in Tai Chi, Yoga, Jazz Dance, Modern Dance, Ballet, etc.? These designs arise from a deeply internalized discovery of body truth, body wisdom. These systems are born of the body and an immersion in its voice. We are each capable of sensing our own individualized, self-arising movement process. Authentic Movement is the container for your own discovery of yourself through a genuine movement process.

Ayurveda

Ayurveda (from the Sanskrit AYUS meaning LIFE and VEDA meaning KNOWLEDGE), born in ancient India, is a self–help–oriented system. Thanks largely to the work of Dr. Deepak Chopra, the author of a series of books on the subject of Ayurvedic healing, we can add this important perspective to our growing understanding of health and well–being.

> The guiding principle of Ayurveda is that the mind exerts the deepest influence on the body, and freedom from sickness depends upon our own awareness, bringing it into balance, and then extending that balance to the body. This state of balanced awareness, more than any kind of physical immunity, creates a higher state of health. — *Deepak Chopra, M.D.*

To use Ayurveda, one must develop the practice of noticing one's own behavior, one's eating habits, one's sleeping patterns, and one's energetic rhythms as they are revealed in the rhythms of our movements, our walking and our talking, our food choices, and our tendencies or intentions in regard to the way we live our lives. The level of self–awareness required to use the Ayurvedic system as a self–help practice is not modeled in western life. I spent one evening inquiring into Ayurveda with a group of very conscious, healing–

oriented friends and it was not easy for us to answer readily the questions in Deepak Chopra's book, *Perfect Health*, to determine our "dosha" or body–mind type. Becoming aware of some of the most mundane details of human experience is not easy for people whose minds are elsewhere. All the self–help systems, including Ayurveda, require us to care enough about ourselves to change the way we eat, sleep and exercise in order to strengthen or balance our lives, and to change generally the way we relate to ourselves. Ayurveda, like other self–help approaches I offer here, asks us to spend time touching ourselves in a loving and healing way, to understand what we need in order to become harmonized, integrated, and whole. Ayurveda includes dietary suggestions (based on a person's nature or constitution), exercise (yoga), and self–massage. The foundation for choosing new alternatives is self–respect, self–love. This simple and basic relationship to self of compassion and caring is both the foundation of health *and* a rare commodity in our grief–stricken, competitive, traumatized, and materialistic society. We shift that emphasis back to self–love, each of us, one at a time, slowly, in the process of personal healing. Our life demands this of us through sickness, unhappiness, disease, accident, and trauma. Ayurveda is one practice that can help bring us back to ourselves in a very practical, daily way through our food choices, our movement choices, and our responses to others.

Ayurveda is a complete approach to living. It encompasses an understanding of our natures and our characteristic harmonizing and disharmonizing habits or tendencies. By understanding your "dosha" or body–mind type, you can discover which foods, exercises, meditative styles, activities, and responses will balance you best. This is not mere behavioral repatterning. This is a way to discover who you are at your core, and to strengthen that core of selfhood using the materials of life (including nourishment and activity) to become more and more who you are. Chopra's premise is that through this approach, longevity is achieved. My intention here is to encourage you to consider Ayurveda not only to live longer and be more beautiful, but also to experience the option of coming from a place of balanced being–ness into the world, into your relationships, and into your life. This is the jewel of human experience, and before we destroy ourselves with pollution and imbalance, let us try the option of health, each of us, individually. You may not choose to take on the Ayurvedic system as your guiding viewpoint for your life and health, but its influence can be integrated into your lifestyle, as *you* decide to orchestrate it. Some of the choices Ayurveda offers are simple and virtually cost–free. For trauma survivors, integrating this system and the resultant dietary and lifestyle shifts can become part of your overall discussions with your therapist(s). I would heartily encourage all trauma survivors to keep a journal as they make these or any other basic changes in their lives, noting the influence of all these many factors on their overall attitudes, their nervous system responses, etc. I, for one, would be profoundly interested in learning about these discoveries.

Bach Flower Remedies

In the early 1900s, in England, Dr. Edward Bach set out to find a perfect cure for disease. His research, to which he was deeply devoted, resulted in the Bach Flower Remedies, "a simple and natural method of healing through the personality by means of wild flowers discovered by a late Harley Street specialist, for the lay healer and the home" from *The Twelve Healers and Other Remedies*, by Edward Bach. This can most definitely be a self–help system. Dr. Bach designed it to be accessible, and his pamphlet contains "instructions regarding the finding of the herbs, preparing the remedies, dosage and administering." Essentially, Dr. Bach found that certain flowers contained healing properties, and if the flowers were gathered, distilled, and potentized, they had a marked affect on attitudes, moods, feelings, and overall states of mind, which resulted in a shift in health. Now the flower remedies are available in health food stores and directly from the Dr. Edward Bach Healing Centre in England. (See the following Resource section of this book for more details on flower remedies.)

Dr. Bach's discoveries were based not only on his comprehensive understanding of the nature of healing, but also upon his overview of the medical establishment and its relationship to wellness. In his book *Heal Thyself,* he says:

> For many centuries the real nature of disease has been masked by materialism, and thus disease itself has been given every opportunity of extending its ravages, since it has not been attacked at its origin. The situation is like to any enemy strongly fortified in the hills, continually raging guerrilla warfare in the country around, while the people, ignoring the fortified garrison, content themselves with repairing the damaged houses and burying the dead, which are the results of the raids of the marauders. So, generally speaking, is the situation in medicine today; nothing more than the patching up of those attacked and the burying of those who are slain, without a thought being given to the real stronghold.

Believing as he did that the source of disease was not material, Dr. Bach developed a system whereby a prepared essence of flowers was taken in a liquid form, in drops under the tongue, with an awareness of homeopathic conditions, and that completed the treatment. First there were but twelve remedies, then thirty–six, and recently new flower remedies are being discovered by researchers in the field. By reading the literature carefully, you can determine which remedies are appropriate for you. A popular and useful Bach Flower Remedy is called Rescue Remedy. It combines several flower remedies and is used in the treatment of shock, panic, sudden accident, and under any shaky circumstances — hearing surprising news, unexpected events, etc. There is also a Rescue Remedy Cream, which can be applied topically to traumatized areas, such as when there is a fall or impact to the body, creating bruising or abrasion. A few drops of any remedy may also be added to bath water for healing effect. They are not expensive and are interesting explorations into transformation. They would be good choices if you are seeking a gentle awakening or a gentle shift in understanding or have chronic attitudes (like insecurity, despair, isolation) that you cannot easily change. Someone recommended a flower remedy for me once when my menstrual cycle was stagnant due to emotional causes related to my experiences of sexual abuse, and within a short time after taking it, my cycle became healthy, regular ,and balanced again. This is but one example of the way in which these gentle, benign, but effective remedies can be useful to help us face the many obstacles we encounter on the path of healing from incest, rape, and all the shocking horrors that afflict us in this modern age.

Bates Method

The Bates Method is probably being described here for the first time as an energetic intervention, but I believe that is what it is. Dr. Bates, who wrote his treatise on vision before 1940, had great insight into the body–mind process in terms of the eyes. His book, which is now the primary way to find out about his method and which outlines the exercises that comprise The Bates Method for Better Eyesight Without Glasses, describes how the eyes are affected by trauma and stress and what we need to do to heal them. He tells us precisely what damages vision and what vision *actually* is, while giving us the means to correct our vision and to improve it. As I described earlier, The Bates Method, and the person whom I was fortunate enough to know as a practitioner of it, completely corrected my severe strabismus and eliminated the need for the glasses that I had worn since the age of three, and which I fully expected to wear the rest of my life. The simplicity of the process, and the natural restoration of my sight, was the most delightful thing, and the smooth way in which it occurred will always remain with me as an example of what healing is all about.

Bioenergetics

Bioenergetics evolved out of the work of Alexander Lowen and John Pierrakos, both of whom were students of Wilhelm Reich. We are indebted to them for the verbalization of the concept of "grounding" which is used extensively in body-centered therapy and in bodywork. They are also to be credited for introducing and supporting the very idea of body-centered psychotherapy. The term "bioenergetics" itself comes from a biochemical theory that energy is involved in all life processes. In the practice of the Bioenergetic approach to psychotherapy, this idea is extended to the personality. Bioenergetic interventions focus on the breath, and on stimulating the awakening of energy. Bioenergetics frequently uses aggressive stimulation to evoke energetic change. Change is formulated in terms of charge and discharge. Bioenergetics, like other systems I mention in this listing (Rolfing and Holotropic Breathwork, for instance), can crack the shell of armoring and defense against pain and vulnerability. Because these systems are aggressive, I suggest extra caution in considering them. Explore with your primary therapist if they are appropriate and timely.

Body–Mind Centering

Bonnie Bainbridge Cohen established The School for Body–Mind Centering in Massachusetts in 1973. The purpose of the school is the exploration of learning through and about the body. To quote Ms. Cohen: "This involves identifying, articulating, differentiating, and integrating the various tissues within the body, discovering the qualities that contribute to one's movement, how they evolved in one's developmental process, and the role they play in the expression of mind." Centering suggests the orientation towards the integration and alignment of all these systems through various means (touch, visualization, movement, creativity, dialogue, meditation) to find a place of wholeness. Practitioners are trained to assist people towards this experience of wholeness.

Ch'I Kung

Ch'I Kung is an ancient Chinese art that literally means "breath work." It consists of exercises designed to expel toxins from the body. The exercises open the energy meridians and have a strong impact. They should be practiced carefully, with the guidance of an instructor, or, if that is not possible, by paying close attention to your experience, stopping when you are uncomfortable, and being very attuned to your own needs, body, and feelings. Ken Cohen, a teacher of Ch'I Kung, comments: "The breath is obviously our clearest indicator of psychological health.... If a student tends to hold on to past trauma, he may have trouble exhaling. If he has a low self–image and finds it difficult to integrate new experiences, he may have trouble inhaling. As the breath becomes deeper, relaxed, and balanced, there will naturally be emotional responses. This is another reason for gradual, step-by-step progress." Strong breathing techniques (Reichian breathwork, Holotropic breathwork, etc.) all have the potential to create an uproar! Stay in touch with your therapist and your resources if you are drawn to these practices, and *go slowly!*

Craniosacral Therapy

Craniosacral therapy is the child of Dr. John Upledger, founder of the Upledger Institute. Here is his story about how Craniosacral Therapy came to be: "I first became involved during a surgical procedure in 1971. I was assisting a neurosurgeon in the removal of an extradural calcification from the posterior aspect of the dural tube in the midcervical region. Our goal was to remove the calcified plaque without incising or disrupting the integrity of the dura matter. My task was to hold the dural membrane still with two pairs of forceps while the neurosurgeon removed the plaque without cutting or damaging the underlying dural membrane. But the membrane would not hold still. I was embarrassed because I could not carry out such a simple task.... It became apparent that the movement of the dural membrane was rhythmical at about 8 cycles per minute. This rhythmic activity was independent of the patient's breathing and cardiac rhythms. It was another physiological rhythm. It appeared to be an ebb and flow of the fluid that is contained within the dural membrane." Thus was craniosacral or cerebrospinal fluid discovered and the craniosacral system of therapy born. The craniosacral system is a fluid system that vitalizes the entire being. It is evaluated by the palpation skills developed in a craniosacral therapist. These therapists are trained in courses taught by the Upledger Institute. Craniosacral Therapy can be instrumental in relieving the pain of headaches, decreasing stress, increasing vitality, solving unsolvable structural problems, reducing fevers, relieving the conditions of head injury, and a wide range of other applications of great significance to survivors of trauma of all kinds. It is a gentle noninvasive system, though subject to all the conditions of caution I mention throughout this compendium.

Dance Therapy

Dance Therapy is a form of psychotherapy that uses movement as the major form of intervention. Dance Therapy grew, to some extent, out of the modern dance movement, a new art form that attempted to align more closely the experience of feeling with the experience of movement. Dancers themselves became free to explore their own spirituality and emotion. It was within this current that Isadora Duncan, Ruth St. Denis, Ted Shawn, and Martha Graham made their contributions. Marion Chace, the originator of Dance Therapy, was a student of Ruth St. Denis and Ted Shawn. So, it was this dancing that adhered more precisely to an authentic emotional experience that led to the formulation of dance as therapy, and then, later, movement as therapy. Dance therapy began in the early 1940s in mental hospital wards, with Marion Chace leading the way into the unknown. From there, it wove into the developing thread of psychotherapy and has continued to evolve. The American Dance Therapy Association trains, registers, and certifies dance therapists. This organization publishes a directory of therapists, journals, newsletters, and other information resources. See the Resource listing for more information.

Feldenkrais Method/Awareness through Movement/Functional Integration

These three terms are used to describe the practice of what Moishe Feldenkrais taught to allow people to come into a healthier structural, postural, and movement relationship with themselves. Feldenkrais was attuned to individuality, uniqueness of structure, and genuine observation. "People prefer to believe in miracles, such as guidance by the spirit of a dead doctor or some other farfetched explanation, rather than to verbalize their inner sensations," he said in his book *Body Awareness as Healing Therapy: The Case of Nora.* Feldenkrais wanted to help people get in touch with their own somatic experience, their experience of sensation, and their response to stimulation. His system involves touch and exercise, and a dialogue between client and practitioner. Practitioners are trained in carefully designed programs that involve working on themselves as well as on others. The Feldenkrais Method™ is particularly beneficial if you have structural pain and want to release it by becoming aware and recovering consciously. If you have been in an accident or had a sports injury, this approach can help you understand the patterns that were connected with the injury and how you can change them. This is an important way to link mind and body and to find the opportunities hidden in your physiological condition.

Holotropic Breathwork

Holotropic breathwork is a breathing process that was developed by Stan and Christina Grof. It involves rhythmic breathing and the use of certain kinds of music that are amplified during the breathing process. The combination of intense breathing and loud music leads to altered states of consciousness, resembling what happens when holotropic drugs are used. I do not recommend this process for survivors of trauma. Though the breathwork procedure is usually facilitated by sensitive people, that is not sufficient, in my estimation, to provide the safety and understanding necessary to navigate the delicate territory of the traumatized nervous system. While some people have commented that Holotropic Breathwork can be helpful in breaking down resistance and overcoming obstacles to feeling, I think this can be achieved through a gentle, titrated process more effectively and more permanently than in Holotropic Breathwork workshops. For further information on how this approach was created and is implemented, you should read the work of Stan Grof. His research on consciousness is not really oriented towards an understanding of the many dimensions of trauma and that is probably why his system is not useful in that application. Facilitators are trained in the breathwork process but are not necessarily therapeutically conscious, though some therapists have also trained to be Holotropic Breathwork facilitators. There is no real processing component to the program, and in that regard retraumatization can occur very easily. Before considering this approach to healing, I would suggest deep consideration and inquiry. By making these comments, I do not wish, in any way, to invalidate the sensitive psychotherapists who employ this approach.

Homeopathy

Like Dr. Edward Bach (see Bach Flower Remedies), Dr. Samuel Hahnemann discovered homeopathy as a result of his dissatisfaction with allopathic or orthodox medicine. Also like Bach, Hahnemann searched on his own, passionately and with determination, to find a way to truly help people suffering from disease, rather than offering, at best, temporary symptomatic relief. Hahnemann did his research and made his discoveries in Germany beginning in the early 1800's, publishing his *Organon of the Art of Healing* (which introduces homeopathy), in 1810.

Again, like Bach, Hahnemann's quest was for a true understanding of basic healing principles (What is disease really? What is true healing?). His search was for principles that were timeless, and indeed, his discoveries have increasingly more relevance. With all humility, I would like to suggest that I, we, all students of healing, are on this same quest. Having experienced the spectrum of trauma, many of us are seeking, in every way we can, the answer to the questions: "How do we heal? How do we get better? How do we recover?" Hahnemann's persistence and determination are an important inspiration for us to imbibe.

Through homeopathy, Hahnemann articulated his answers to these questions. The underlying philosophic points of homeopathy are (in brief):

1. Symptoms of disease are seen as attempts of the body to heal or signal distress, and they are respected as such. In fact, these symptoms are explored in great detail to find the most useful homeopathic remedy — to identify the true source of the illness, whether chronic or acute.

2. There are no diseases as such, but only diseased individuals, and therefore the individual's history and symptoms are of the utmost importance.

3. Illness is always dynamic in nature, so the remedy must also be in a dynamic state in order to cure.

4. A patient should be given only one remedy at a time.

5. Homeopathy is based on the Law of Similars — that like cures like. Homeopathic remedies can produce an aggravation of symptoms temporarily because the remedy is the same as the disease.

6. The preparation of homeopathic remedies involves diluting them to their molecular states and potentizing them, literally by shaking them, through many successions, to make them dynamic and energetically vital.

7. Disease is only possible when there is a disturbance in the life force of the organism. Only medicines in an energized, dynamic state can effect this vital life force and restore it.

This brief list summarizes the way a homeopath looks at the healing process. Homeopathic doctors conduct extensive interviews with their patients, to understand both the historic, genetic influences and the current symptoms. Usually only one remedy is given, and the organism's response to that remedy is carefully evaluated.

It is possible to educate yourself about homeopathy and to prescribe remedies for yourself, and purchase those remedies at your local health food store. They are available and accessible because no negative side effects have been found for taking the "wrong" remedy. Particularly in "first aid" kinds of situations — such as using Arnica for bruises or falls — having even a rudimentary knowledge of homeopathy can be very helpful. Books listed in the Resource 2 section are clearly for the purpose of providing this information and finding out how to get more.

For trauma survivors, the value of homeopathy is that it is attentive to individual process and gives great weight to psychological factors as well as physical ones. In homeopathy, moods and emotional states are a crucial area of inquiry in determining which remedy to use and when. Furthermore, homeopathic remedies are available for many of the symptoms of post-traumatic stress and for the wide variety of somatic symptoms (eczema, sinus infections, chronic headaches, chronic sore throat, difficult menses, etc.) that can be the result or expression of trauma. The homeopathic remedies are gentle in their impact and even when there is a temporary aggravation of symptoms, there is an awareness that the symptoms will go away, resulting in a longer-term relief.

A summary statement by George Vithoulkas, the internationally known homeopath, indicates its relevance for trauma survivors. He

describes homeopathy as "as highly systematic method of powerfully stimulating the body's vital force to cure illness." This says it
all, I believe, in terms of the intention of survivors of sexual abuse
and related traumas. Our objective is to reclaim our life force, the
life force that is inherent within us, by the gentlest and yet the most
powerful means possible so that we may truly put an end to the lineage of abuse and trauma. Homeopathy, at least, identifies this life
force, and aims to support it, and therefore I have found it useful.

Imagery

> . . . images are an expression of the body, and the body is the
> concrete expression of its images. — *Belleruth Naparstek*

The language of imagery elicits the body's experiential responses —the responses of feeling, thought, sensation, and emotion. Each body responds to the imagery it perceives in its own
unique way —through the formation of attitudes, through the
arousal of memory, through physiological sensation, through relaxation or tension. The body is gullible and naive as well as profoundly
intelligent. In this regard, it is very much like a child, open and
innocent, pure and honest. We are confronted with evocative imagery all the time, and we respond to it, whether we acknowledge
those responses or not. When descriptions of suffering are heard on
the radio, for instance (torture, terrorism), we contract; when someone is freed from captivity (a political prisoner, a kidnapped child),
we expand. Recently, while running errands in my car, I heard a
broadcast of recorded conversations from a Suicide Prevention Crisis Line. My heart responded by going out to the suffers, but my
mind responded too. It discovered a phrase, which it kept repeating as I continued my tasks: "Why don't we value human life?" I
meditated on this question for the rest of the day, and it stirred my
soul. This is how imagery works. It suggests something precise and
specific to whoever hears it. According to Belleruth Naparstek, who
has documented the impact of imagery on people with chronic or
life threatening illnesses (her book is listed in the Resource section),
the body responds to images as if they were actual events. Therefore, imagery has the power to significantly impact the way we func-

tion — the way our nervous systems react, the neuropeptides our brains produce, and the way our emotions are directed.

Like many of the approaches that I emphasize here, the use of imagery can be a self-help system. In addition, it is the way in which imagery so readily allows us to enter the world of our own truth that makes it a powerful ally. Through witnessing our responses to imagery, we can sink deeper and deeper into our own self-awareness, finding levels of our own reality that we had pushed away, out of reach, because of fear and because of trauma.

> It is the power of these authentic emotions that the imagery elicits, emotions that sometimes have no conscious memory in the normal, waking state, that opens the door for healing. And because images are experienced by the body as real events, we can, over time, transform our self-perception from victim to survivor. — *Belleruth Naparstek*

The use of imagery, then, involves an alertness to the body's internal language and the dynamics of healing. It is a refined and calculated healing art, demanding many levels of awareness to perfect. Finding appropriate metaphors for particular needs, and sometimes combining music, perhaps even movement or touch, to augment the power of the imagery (placing your hands, for instance, on your own lungs, to deepen breath), makes the whole process of developing and using appropriate imagery a careful one. But, given this, once developed, imagery has enormous potential to enhance well-being in all regards from the physical to the mental and the spiritual. With some practice and experience, you can have a great time developing images for yourself, making tapes with music, and playing them back to yourself, while you do deep relaxation to let into your cells the power of the authentic healer within you.

Imagery is best used in conjunction with deep relaxation and when there is enough time to truly acknowledge the content of the guided imagery and to integrate your responses. Use the books recommended in the Resource section to get you started. They contain good descriptions of how to construct appropriate guided imagery for particular needs. You can probably find a library that loans audio tapes with guided imagery for relaxation so that you can have a model of how this works. Since the body is so suggestible, pick the tapes you feel resonant and congruent with, and don't play them any longer if you begin to feel uncomfortable while listening.

The somewhat altered state you are in when deeply relaxed is hypnotically receptive, so you don't want to receive any suggestions that aren't just right for you in the moment. Let your body guide you here, and if the voice or the music on the tape you are listening to feels "off", don't hesitate — push that eject button. But if you do find guided imagery that consistently relaxes you, relieves your tension, lessens any symptoms you might have, empowers you to be yourself and to live the way you want to live, make a practice of using this imagery on a continuous basis — daily or several times a week, so that you begin to feel consistently the positive state that is truly your own.

A tried and true healing way to use imagery is to imagine yourself to be in a place where you feel completely comfortable and safe. Let yourself go there and feel all the qualities of comfort this place offers. This could be a place in the mountains that you've always loved; it could be your room; it could be an imagined place; (indoors or out), it could be by the ocean or by a creek, or by a special tree you remember from your childhood. Let yourself fully be in this place and notice how your body responds, notice your breath and your heartbeat, notice how your mind responds, and be a particularly good witness to the feelings that emerge, and let them have more space, more endorsement, more support then you usually give them. Let yourself remain in this place and absorb even more deeply the feelings of comfort and safety, of complete acceptance, the feeling of being without fear, for as long as you can. If this imagistic journey is successful in calming you, in deepening your breath, in freeing you of anxious ideation and fear, then put this imagery into your medicine bag. Use it whenever you have a panic attack, whenever you are intimidated by something in your schedule, whenever you feel inadequate to a task or to an encounter. Use it whenever you need it and you will have found the power and value of imagery.

Jin shin

Jin shin was brought to this country from Japan by Mary Iino Burmeister, who studied directly with Master Jiro Murai. Master Murai brought the art out of obscurity through his personal experience — a near death illness that resulted in the awakening within him of the flows of Jin shin. Jin shin employs a subtle but well organized system of holding areas of the body. Pressure is unnecessary, but an awareness of the movement of energy is crucial for the powerful implementation of this system. This ancient, intricate, and multifaceted art is gifted with a self-help component that is relatively simple to learn and practice. Jin shin provides symptomatic relief, instills awareness, and can make a significant impact on every form of disease, from physical to emotional. There is no certification process or regulation of practitioners but the gentleness and noninvasive quality of this healing art make it safe to learn and easy to apply. If you are interested in adding Jin shin to your medicine bag, exercise the same discrimination in selecting a practitioner that applies to all therapeutic interventions.

Since Jin shin first was taught in America, numerous people (including me) have adapted it and reformulated it for a wide variety of applications, combining it with other systems, and reinterpreting its usefulness. Jin Shin, Jin Shin Do, and Jin Shin Tara, as well as Jin Shin Jyutsu®, are available. See "Organizations" in the Resource section (page 294, 295) for information on how to contact these practices.

Martial Arts

I believe the martial arts can play an instrumental role in helping survivors of abuse and trauma recover their motoric capacities to protect and defend themselves from attack. Unfortunately, there are few programs carefully designed to integrate psychotherapy and martial arts training so, once again, it is usually up to the survivor to combine these elements by keeping a therapist on duty while martial arts training ensues. I encourage my clients to learn self-defense, and I have taken extensive time and energy to pursue these studies myself. I feel the strength of this effort and recommend to my readers that they explore the possibility of learning self-defense and using it as a healing modality. See the Resource listing which follows for more information.

Massage

Massage is simple, wonderfully beneficial, and an ancient system of healing. Ayurvedic principles include a self-massage program that I highly recommend for survivors of trauma. Dr. Deepak Chopra's books clearly illustrate this process and recommend appropriate oils for all the body–mind types. Self-massage is an important opportunity to be self-nurturing and can have strong healing impact on the nervous system. In terms of receiving massage from a massage therapist, it is very important to make sure that the massage therapist is certified, well trained, and sensitive. A program in Colorado called TraumaTouch Therapy™ trains massage therapists in the awareness of trauma, but many massage therapists are unconscious of how deeply arousing and disturbing massage can be. It is important to talk to your massage therapist *before* being massaged, before you take your clothes off, before you lie down on the treatment table, and get a clear understanding of the purpose and intention of the massage. Touch is one of the greatest opportunities for healing that we have. A nourishing, aware touch can work miracles, but a careless, and unconscious touch can easily retraumatize. Pay attention to your feelings whenever you are being touched by anyone, and stop the touching if there is any inkling of disturbance. Always honor this! If you would like to include massage therapy in your healing program either because of physical stress or to ease tension , talk to your therapist — perhaps she knows of massage therapists who are sensitive to trauma and attuned deeply to their clients' responses. Get referrals and recommendations from friends and people whom you respect and who have discriminating wisdom. The care you take in choosing your practitioners is the value you place on yourself, your body, and your energy. You can't care too much, can you? The only danger is in caring too little.

Meditation

There are many systems of meditation and you want to find the one that suits *you* if you want to meditate. Meditation can be profoundly healing, regenerating, and relaxing. I have tried various meditation systems, and in some regards I am still looking for the one that is perfectly attuned to who I am, though I think I am close to meditating in that way. Choosing your meditation practice is an intimate decision. Take your time. There are numerous Buddhist, Hindu, Christian, Jewish, Taoist, Vedantic, and metaphysical approaches to meditation and prayer. I think they probably all reach the same destination — the serenity and calm of attunement to self and Self, simultaneously, the achievement of union with a divinity that inspires us and encompasses, motivates, and fulfills us, seeing through your own mind. However you get there, you get there, and meditation practices are extremely helpful in healing from trauma when you find the right one. Feel free to search and to inquire. Ultimately, nothing soothes the nervous system and heals it like meditation, but it has to be the appropriate meditation. I will not recommend one here, but I will encourage you to search if you are so inclined.

Pilates

Joe Pilates developed an exercise system to restore the body's balance and stimulate a flow of energy to enliven and harmonize. Some of the greatest dancers in America loved this work. People like George Balanchine, Martha Graham, Jerome Robbins, Ruth St. Denis, and Ted Shawn were devotees of Pilates. What does this mean for survivors of trauma and people recovering from abuse? The answer is that Pilates is a route back to the center, a way to find, from within your body, the ability to activate movement in a manner that never leaves you defenseless and that allows you to navigate in time and space as if you belonged there — something survivors often doubt. The Pilates Method is yet another way to bring body and mind together in a dynamic integration. For survivors who can find Pilates studios with sensitive instructors, this is a route to reclaiming the body. I recommend that all my clients find some way of exercising that makes them *want* to be in their bodies, that allows them to celebrate the joy of physical action, of being alive and capable of movement. This is a renegotiation of trauma. Sexual abuse robs us of the knowledge of the beauty of embodiment, which is everyone's birthright. There's nothing to do then, when you realize this, but to reclaim the body. The Pilates Method is one good way to do this.

Rolfing, Structural Integration, and Deep Tissue Work

Rolfing is a system developed by Dr. Ida Rolf to free the fascia in a series of ten sessions designed to restore the body's natural relationship to gravity. Structural integration is the term Rolf used to define the principal aim of Rolfing, and those who are not trained by the Rolf Institute or who have created spin–off systems sometimes use that term for their work. Deep-tissue work is another way of describing the manipulation of the fascia through intense touch, which is common to this process. This work is very provocative and practitioners are not always trained to process the material that can arise from such intrusive intervention. While there is certainly an awareness of trauma in the study of Rolfing and its related systems, the therapeutic knowledge necessary for truly addressing the material that can be evoked from this deeply penetrating work is generally not available to bodyworkers. If Rolfing seems an important structural intervention in your healing process, I would strongly recommend that you not undertake this process without the involvement of your therapist. With a therapist on hand to support you during this critical unwinding, the process can be useful. However, I do believe there are gentler ways to get to the same place, using some of the other resources mentioned in this compendium. I used Rolfing extensively in my own healing process, but in retrospect I can see the damaging side-effects that I ignored while the process was occurring. You need to be a strong advocate for your feelings in a Rolfing process, and sometimes the process itself makes that difficult. I would recommend approaching Rolfing with care. Discuss it with your therapist and be very discriminating in your choice of practitioner. Look for someone mature, someone who can give you the space you need to move through the layers of your feeling along with the layers of fascia, muscle, and tissue. The Rolf Institute, in Boulder, Colorado, is a major training center for practitioners who are located around the world. See the Resource listing which follows for more information.

Shamanism

According to its foremost historian, Mircea Eliade, Shamanism is an archaic technique of ecstasy. Eliade calls the Shaman the "expert in the human soul," an exceptional being with an exceptional path. Shamans deliberately journey out of the body. Their lives are marked by crisis and transformation. Their path is an extreme one and their healing interventions are extreme, unusual, and sometimes mind boggling. There has recently been a great interest in Shamanism, and particularly in things like soul retrieval. This name alone is appealing to survivors of trauma who feel that parts of themselves, particularly their childhoods, have been lost. Like intense breathwork and other cathartic and invasive experiences, I recommend caution when exploring the shamanic realm for healing. This is not to imply that there isn't much to be learned and much that is valid in this approach, which I myself have investigated with good result. But to be honest and aboveboard, I must remind my readers that out–of–body journeys resemble all too often the dissociation common to defending against traumatic overload, and for survivors the distinction between ecstasy and dissociation may be difficult to determine. Whereas engagement in shamanic experience can be exhilarating and can open pathways to understanding that no other system can make available, this can happen at great expense to us. The delicate sense of groundedness that we build daily on the path of recovery must be protected. As I have stated so many times already, use your knowledge, your own powers of discrimination, to determine when to venture and when to wait. There are many shamanic teachers these days. I recommend you as your most powerful spiritual guide.

Sounding, Voicing, or Toning

> When we sing, we give thanks. And when we give thanks, then
> miracles begin to happen. — *Craig Carpenter, Hopi*

Liberating the voice for expression seems to me, as a therapist practicing in contemporary Western culture, to be a very difficult task. Of all the parts of the body, the throat, the voice, and the mouth are, collectively, the most restricted. This is said, of course, from my bird's eye view, as a witness to trauma and its impact, through my clinical practice. In CranioSacral Therapy , the thoracic diaphragm, the throat, and the mouth are called "The Avenue of Expression," and so whatever forces have inhibited our unique, individuated articulation reside in this domain. In our star system, singers, when they are successful, are considered almost as demigods revered for their ability to project the passionate expression we deny ourselves, and we heap boundless rewards on them for doing this job for us, while we remain close mouthed, tight lipped, jaw clenched, holding back expression.

In facilitating programs of Authentic Movement or genuine movement process, I always encourage authentic sounding or voicing, spontaneous utterances, or the like. I welcome articulation, song, chanting, or prayer, but it rarely evolves. Silence tends to officiate in the realm of spontaneity, even when sound is sought. For this reason, I think tools like toning, which invite the voice to participate fully by addressing its mechanisms directly, are quite useful. Toning is a system of sounding long, sustained notes, and letting those notes become, in and of themselves, containers of expression.

All singing, and especially toning, increase the breath in all regards. The deepening of the breath, in virtually every approach to well-being, is considered essential to promote healing. Books in the Resource section following this one give more information on toning, if you want to know specifically about this deeply relaxing and stimulating way to free the voice. People report enhanced vitality and motivation and a feeling of really being present throughout their bodies as a result of toning, not to mention the emotional release that is possible.

I have several more suggestions for finding your voice, and I want to stress the importance (and the fun) of doing this. One possibility for exploring the power and range of your vocal expression is by taking voice lessons. Whether you study with a classically trained singer or someone with a more modern approach, these classes will help you explore your feelings around oral expression and the possibilities for vocalizing. If the teacher seems judgmental or limited, unsupportive or critical, don't take it on — simply find yourself another teacher. Empower yourself to get the support you need to find your voice. Or, perhaps you have a friend who is a singer. Maybe she wants to trade voice lessons for one of your gifts?

My friend Marilla is a glorious singer and since I didn't sing at all, we agreed that she could experiment with her capacity as a voice teacher by giving me lessons. What a great time we had! And I learned so much from our sessions! I learned that I come from a long line of singers — my grandmother and my aunts were all singers, and yet I had no memory of hearing them sing; all I had were stories of how well they sang and one recollection of hearing my grandmother sing. So, in my family, singing was a lost art, yet buried deep within me was a longing to reclaim that lineage. Through our voice lessons, I also identified the songs and the voices I wanted to emulate — the ones that stimulated me, and the feelings those singers and those sounds (Billie Holliday, Leonard Cohen, Rosalie Sorrells, Appalachian voices, Eastern European voices) evoked in me. And I got to actually hear my own voice — my voice calling out to be heard, my voice looking for its tone, its place. I also got to see how my breath was restricted, where I actually breathed from, and to learn what could enhance that breath.

As we met regularly, I began to allow singing to be a part of my life. I found myself singing in the locker room at the Recreation Center, on the street, in the sauna — wherever and whenever the sound came through me. And to my amazement, people began to sing with me. I remember my surprise when I was practicing Leonard Cohen's "The Sisters of Mercy" after swimming, and I heard a woman, way over on the other side of the locker room, singing the song with me. It was a moment of pure delight, unexpected, reassuring; our voices found each other before our eyes ever met, and we joined in this prayer of hope, the naming of the angels — "The Sisters of Mercy."

I didn't become a renowned singer as a result of these lessons with Marilla, but I did learn more about myself, and a seed was planted for the future, for the continuity of this energetic support of my voice, my own particular sounds entering a world where they are heard.

Another suggestion I can offer from my experience is a combination of writing and voicing. I suggest that if you write poetry, you make audio tapes of yourself reading your poetry. And read with gusto, reach with expression, use your breath, be quirky, be outrageous, be yourself. And then listen to these tapes and honor your voice. Don't cringe, though that may be the old habit. Cheer your voice on. Applaud. And see if your voice doesn't develop resonance and depth, range and fullness, just from being heard, being received. The same suggestion can be applied to any writing that you do — prose of any kind, fiction or nonfiction, short stories or long stories, letters, journal entries — whatever you write, let it be heard, and let it be said in your own voice. You can add another art to this process, if you like. Do Authentic Movement to taped recordings of you singing or reading your writing. I did this and created an entire performance piece, which gave me completion and resolution. I did it all for myself and received all the satisfaction, though others benefitted as well.

T'ai Chi Ch'uan

T'ai-chi Ch'uan, popularly known in the West as Tai Chi, is an art of self-defense but has become, through usage, more a form of physical exercise, with numerous health benefits, and for Westerners seeking their apparently illusive center, a route to that discovery. From its self-defense origins, Tai Chi offers the practitioner a way to experience stability in the body. Like Yoga, there is a strong component within Tai Chi that focuses on the breath. Through the slowing and the deepening of the breath, relaxation is truly experienced, and combined with the focus required for the slow, rhythmic movements, a grounded, meditative state is reached, which ultimately soothes and quiets the nervous system, thereby providing real help for the trauma survivor, or anyone experiencing anxiety and stress, internal or external pressure.

Tai Chi is usually taught in combination with Chi Kung (see Chi Kung in this same compilation). The two together produce an over-all possibility of regeneration, making Tai Chi an available avenue for recovery. The added benefit, I find, in Tai Chi is that it is so stabilizing for the body. The low, crouch posture in which most (if not all) of the exercises are done, deepens my relationship to gravity, my felt sense of being supported by, and united with, the Earth.

The other reason I like Tai Chi is because it can be practiced alone, in nature, or at home. Once the "form" is learned, it becomes your own, and you can play with it privately, as well as deepening your practice by attending classes or reading books, or finding videos that illustrate the various moves. Again, like yoga, Tai Chi has the capacity to be transportable, and I can be independent in my pursuit of it, which is of great value to me. There is no demand that I align myself with a particular school or a particular teacher, and yet I can gain mastery by exposing myself to teachers and students as I choose.

In my limited experience, I have noticed that Tai Chi is usually presented by men and they are referred to as the "masters" of the discipline. Upon inquiry, though, I did learn that indeed there are women masters of Tai Chi, but they never seem to be discussed, and their names are not on or in the books available. Because of this, Tai Chi seems to be offered within a male framework, and while this did not alienate me in my own study, I was still aware of the male emphasis, the male model as the dominant one for demonstrating the correct form. I did with this what I have learned to do with all systems I find useful — I made it my own; I tuned into my body and shaped the process according to my own inner guidance.

If this appeals to you, then I encourage you to ask questions when you are in a class, to experiment (with awareness of your body, of course) with even traditional movements, and generally to play with the style that is so authoritatively presented, and make it your own. If this is done with respect for the way in which the system is designed to be helpful, I think the end result is that you will have more fun with what you are learning and will be less worried about "performing properly." Relaxing and "sinking" are considered the foremost elements of Tai Chi. My guess is that you will "relax" and "sink" more when you are having fun, when you are not worried about performance, and when you have said what you wanted to say and asked what you wanted to ask.

Tai Chi is also known as Metaphysical Boxing. It was discovered by a Taoist saint, Chang San-feng, between the 12th and 13th centuries. Let me quote from Cheng Man-ching's *T'ai Chi Ch'uan*, about these origins, to conclude this entry:

> While practicing mystical meditation in a state of semi-trance, he (Chang San-feng) is said to have perceived how all parts of the human body act in unison to effect metabolism and facilitate blood circulation under the guidance of a vital principal. Repeated experience convinced him that instead of any artificial exercise as a means toward physical invigoration, one should rather follow or obey Nature in every movement of one's corporal organs, whether internal or external.

Yoga

The word "Yoga" comes from the Sanskrit word "yuj," which means "to bind," or to focus, to bring together, to join. The union referred to is the union of mind, body, and spirit. By focusing attention on the alignment of the body in yogic postures and in breathing exercises, a peacefulness (through concentration and by releasing scientifically determined areas of the body-mind system), is possible. The purpose, originally, for this path of experience was Enlightenment — the union of the self with the Higher Self. In the West, of course, yoga has been used for many purposes — to improve appearances, as a form of physical exercise, for health, longevity, and stress reduction. Nevertheless, it remains a real path for self-discovery, self-awareness, and true relaxation.

Hatha Yoga comes in many forms, and many teachers have brought their particular style of yoga to the West from India. We now have what is known as "Iyengar" Yoga (yoga as practiced by the students of B.K.S. Iyengar, a dynamic and thoroughgoing teacher who has influenced and attracted many people to the path of yoga), Asthanga Yoga, Kundalini Yoga, yoga as presented within Ayurveda, yoga as presented by Swami Sachidananda, by Baba Hari Das, etc. There are also many Western students of yoga who have blended yoga with dance, aerobics, acupressure, and whatever they have found to make yoga less formal, less strict, and more desirable and available to Westerners.

What value does yoga have for the incest survivor, for the person with a post-traumatic stress response? The answer here is the same as the view I have tried to present throughout this book. You yourself know if yoga is useful for you. What I want to encourage in my readers is an awareness of how they can, intuitively and thoughtfully, determine their own course of healing. For some, yoga will be a good tool on the path; for others, yoga will not be helpful.

I have been practicing yoga for over twenty years, but I have adapted what I have learned from many teachers to form a routine for myself. The way I use this routine works with my life. I use yoga to stretch the stress out of my body, to bring me to a peaceful center, to open me out of my tension, and to regenerate the places that have been worn down by over-usage, such as my eyes. To create my own routine, I had to experience many approaches and experiment. I had to discriminate between what was good for me and what didn't suite me. I had to be free to make "mistakes" and take "bad" classes. I have not become a yoga adept, by any means, but yoga has a real place in my life.

Yoga is, practically, a series of physical postures. These postures should be entered gently, with full awareness of what your body is experiencing. Too much stretching for an unprepared body can lead to injury. Approach yoga with the same attitude with which you approach any therapy, because it *is* a therapeutic system, designed for physical, vital, and mental health. It is aimed at benefiting the neurophysical system and the endocrine glands. Each individual, of course, will have unique responses to this kind of therapy. Interview teachers, observe classes, be an educated consumer, and then pick what feels right to you.

The most attractive thing I find about yoga is its capacity to awaken our potential. For all the systems I have described in this book, this is the most relevant point. Which system appeals to you enough so that it becomes a way (a form, a structure) for you to expand your potential? Within the framework of a traumatizing and retraumatizing society, potential is squelched, diminished. What will counter that? What will turn our attention to the possibilities for health and awareness that wait within each of us individually? Yoga may or may not be such a system for you. If it isn't, look elsewhere. But if it is, let yourself have it. Use it. Play with it. Make it your own.

As I conclude this listing, I am aware of many systems that I have not discussed. If they are relevant, I hope you will add them, and if you feel inspired, drop me a note about your experience.

Books, Journals, Organizations, Centers, Networks, and Workshops

This is an alphabetical listing of books, organizations, journals, workshops, and centers where tools for recovery can be found. Having access to the greatest number of resources is, in itself, powerfully helpful and supportive when navigating the whitewater of trauma renegotiation. Knowing where you can find help means knowing you are not alone, even if your family doesn't understand your struggle and even if you don't feel connected to a community or collective of any kind. The network of resources is larger than you think, and even larger than this list suggests.

Each time I went to the bookstore or the library to update my resource listings for this book, I found more and more books in all of the fields I discuss. From aromatherapy to yoga, from acupressure to Tai Chi, it seemed to me that books were rolling off the presses faster than I could count them. I couldn't possibly read and evaluate all of them in time for this publication. So, I finally stopped pretending I could (an important step in acknowledging my human limitations). Therefore, I say with confidence that this resource list is not complete. It is merely what I know to be available and I have done my best to make good suggestions for you.

Whenever I have had a personal connection with a listing here, I have noted why I think it is valuable for you. I have kept these comments brief, but they may assist you in selecting which resource to access when. Or, what I say may allow you to know more readily which resources are *not* useful for you.

By the time this book comes out (given my recent experience), there will be even more useful books in the stores and libraries. Use these places as energetic support systems — go to the libraries and bookstores wherever you are and inquire, browse, look for what you want and need in the way of support, and my guess is that eventually you will find it. If you want to know more about what it means to be the child of an alcoholic, if you want to know about the history of sexism or what it was like in the town where you were born one hundred years ago, you can probably find what you are looking for, and your healing journey will immediately take on a new dimension. Librarians and bookstore clerks, I've noticed, seem to live for interesting questions. It takes the boredom out of their mundane tasks of filing and ordering. Ask them to help you and you will find yourself escorted by a friendly smile to the newest section of the bookstore, or invited to use the library computer to locate publications across the country or around the world.

I think it's far more healing to go to the bookstore or the library than to access either of those places on your home computer. Computers are extremely useful, but insofar as they isolate you and keep you out of contact with humanity (I mean faces, bodies, eyes, smiles, direct experience), they are limiting rather than enhancing. But if contact with others feels overwhelming and it doesn't seem easy to go to the bookstore and ask for the best books on, for instance, rape, then using your computer can be empowering rather than limiting.

However it is most beneficial for you, I encourage you to add to this resource section on your own. If you feel a deficiency in a certain field in my list (and you probably will), augment it. I invite you to totally outdo me in my compiling efforts and if you feel so motivated, send me what you've found, and in the reprints of this book, I'll be grateful to use your additions. It would warm my heart to make this book a cooperative effort in the name of letting trauma survivors know how many resources are available to them. Each resource is a friend, a helping hand, a gesture of inclusion to counter the overwhelming tide of exclusion we often feel as the result of trauma.

With all this said, I invite you to take full advantage of this section. Call the places which suggest help to you, write to the workshop leaders who may have training or literature to support you, buy or borrow from the library or from a friend the books that you sense invite your growth and healing. The course of my life and the pattern of my healing has been powerfully influenced by encountering books and articles and classes and educational programs that deepened my ability to understand myself and transform my pain.

Knowing this, I want to pass these opportunities on to you with belief and hope.

PUBLICATIONS

A Moving Journal: Ongoing Expressions of Authentic Movement
168 Fourth Street, Providence, Rhode Island 02906.

This journal contains articles discussing the application of Authentic Movement as a healing process and as a spiritual path, as well as Calendar listings of Authentic Movement classes, seminars, and training programs. This is an excellent way to plug into the Authentic Movement network. New and ongoing groups around the country are listed in this journal, and some of the most current thought in the field is expressed here.

A New Model for Health and Disease
George Vithoulkas, Health & Habitat, Mill Valley, CA and North Atlantic Books, 2800 Woolsey St., Berkeley, CA, 1991.

Written by a prominent and socially concerned homeopath, this book offers a view of the current state of health, worldwide, including the AIDS epidemic. This is a homeopathic view of the overall impact on our collective immune system of the widespread use of drugs, particularly antibiotics and vaccinations. Vithoulkas addresses what he calls "the destruction of the 'inner ecology' of the human organism." His statement about what will make a difference mirrors the intention underlying this book — we need a shift in consciousness to end the lineage of trauma: "One could say that suffering is manifested in our societies because of the very values we project and will only end if we change these values."

Abused: A Guide to Recovery for Adult Survivors of Emotional/Physical Child Abuse
Dee Anna Parrish
Station Hill Press, 1990.

Acupressure for Women
Cathryn Bauer
The Crossing Press, Freedom, CA 95019, 1987.

This is a good experiential workbook for self-help.

Acupuncture Principles and Your Health
James Howland
Auricle Press (available directly from James Howland at
18917 Lomita Avenue, Sonoma, CA 95476).

This simple book is a delightful way to enter the world of Oriental medicine.

Addiction to Perfection: The Still Unravished Bride
Marian Woodman
Inner City Books, 1982.

This is an excellent resource for uncovering the perfectionistic saboteur.

Ageless Body, Timeless Mind
Deepak Chopra
Harmony Books, July 1993.

A useful introduction to Ayurveda.

Allies in Healing
Laura Davis
Harper Perennial Publications, 1991.

Essential reading for partners of survivors.

Anatomy of Change, The
Richard Strozzi Heckler
Shambala, Boulder, CO, 1984.

Anatomy of Movement
Blandine Calais-Germain
Eastland Press, Seattle, WA 1985.

Aromatherapy for Women
Maggie Tisserand
Healing Arts Press, Rochester, VT, 1988.

Aromatherapy A–Z
Patricia Davis, Saffron Walden,
The C.W. Daniel Company, Ltd., England, 1988.

Art of Aromatherapy, The
Robert Tisserand
Healing Arts Press, 1977.

Awareness Through Movement
Moshe Feldenkrais
Harper & Row, 1972.
An explanation of the principles underlying Feldenkrais work.

Ayurveda: The Science of Self–Healing
Dr. Vasant Lad
Lotus Press, Santa Fe, NM, 1984.

Bach Flower Remedies, The
Edward Bach, M.D. and F.J. Wheeler
M.D., Keats Publishing, Inc., New Canaan, CT, 1979.

Banished Knowledge
Alice Miller
Doubleday, 1988.
Alice Miller's books are all powerful exposés of the inner workings of trauma in our relationships, our families, and our creative processes.

Bates Method for Better Eyesight Without Glasses, The
William H. Bates
M.D., Henry Holt & Co., NY, 1940, reprinted 1981.

Beyond Illness: Discovering the Experience of Health
Larry Dossey Shambala, 1984.
Larry Dossey's books open new dimensions of healing.

Black Butterfly: An Invitation to Radical Aliveness, The
Richard Moss, M.D.
Celestial Arts, Berkeley, CA, 1986.

Body, Self and Soul: Sustaining Integration
Jack Lee Rosenberg with Majorie L. Rand and Diane Asay
Humanics Ltd., 1985.

Body, Space, Image: Notes Towards Improvisation and Performance
Maranda Tufnell and Chris Crickmay
Virago Press, London, 1990.

This beautiful book can inspire you to create, move freely, and explore the domain of performance for expression and communication.

Body Stories: A Guide to Experiential Anatomy
Andrea Olson
Station Hill Press, Barrytown, NY, 1991.

A great introduction to exploring the healing capacities of sound and movement. This book offers a daily guide you can easily use in your creative space.

Body Awareness as Healing Therapy: The Case of Nora
Moshe Feldenkrais
Somatic Resources, Berkeley, CA, 1977.

Read this book if you want to see into the mind and thinking of Moshe Feldenkrais.

Breaking Down the Wall of Silence
Alice Miller
Dutton, 1991.

Complete Aromatherapy Handbook
Suzanne Fischer-Rizzi
Sterling Publication Company, 1990.

Compassionate Touch
Dawn Nelson
Station Hill Press, 1994.

Courage to Heal, The
Ellen Bass and Laura Davis
Harper Perennial Publications, 1988.

Courage to Heal Workbook, The
Laura Davis
Harper, 1990.

For the grassroots survivor, this, and *The Courage to Heal*, have become classic handbooks for recovery.

Dance Therapy and Depth Psychology: The Moving Imagination
Joan Chodorow
Routledge Books, London, 1991.

Dance Movement Therapy: A Healing Art
Fran Levy
American Alliance for Health, Physical Education, Recreation &
Dance, 1900 Association Drive, Reston, VA 22091, 1988.
The primer for learning about the history and development of dance
therapy.

Elusive Obvious, The
Moshe Feldenkrais
Meta Publications, P.O. Box 565, Cupertino, CA 95014.

Flower Essences: Reordering Our Understanding and
Approach to Illness and Health
Machaelle Small Wright, Perelandra, Ltd., Jeffersonton, VA.
This complete and practical book describes flower essences in an
easy-to-read and intriguing manner. Perelandra also publishes work-
books for people who would like to make their own flower essences
and even start their own flower essence garden. Perelandra also
prepares and sells the essences themselves. You can contact them
by phoning (703) 937-2153 or by writing to Perelandra, P.O. Box 3603,
Warrenton, VA 22186.

For Your Own Good
Alice Miller
Ferrar, Strauss & Giroux, New York, 1984.

Gateway to the Miraculous: Further Explorations in the Tao of
Cheng Man-ch'ing
Wolfe Lowenthal
Frog, Led., Berkeley, CA 1994.

Handbook of Self Healing, The
Meir Schneider
Penguin, 1994.
Meir Schneider has enhanced and developed his self-healing discoveries. Tapes about his approach are available from his center,
where you can also study and take workshops: Center for Self Healing, 1718 Taraval Street, San Francisco, CA 94116, (415) 665-9574.

Handbook of the Bach Flower Remedies
Phillip M. Chancellor
The C.W. Daniel Company, Ltd., England, 1971.

Heal Your Body
Louise Hay
Hay House, Incorporated, 1982.

Healing From Within: Psychological Techniques to Help the Mind Heal the Body
Dennis Jaffe, Ph.D.
Simon & Schuster, 1980.

Healing Voice, The
Joy Gardner-Gordon
The Crossing Press, 1993.

Joy Gardner-Gordon takes a comprehensive look at the history and scope of using the voice and provides actual exercises to begin the practice of Sounding.

Healing With Whole Foods
Paul Pitchford
North Atlantic Books, 1993.

If you want a comprehensive overview of the use of food for healing purposes, including safe ways to change your eating habits for general and specific purposes, this book will be helpful.

Healing on the Edge of Now:
A Practical Guide for the Use of Psychoneuroimmunology
Carl Brahe
Sunshine Press, Hygiene, CO.

Holistic Aromatherapy
Ann Berwich
Llewellyn Publications, 1994.

Homeopathy: Medicine of the New Man
George Vithoulkas
Arco Publishing, Inc., 1983.

Though rather formally written (perhaps because English is not

Vithoulkas' native tongue), this book lays out the process by which homeopathy evolved, through the thinking, questioning, and experimentation (often on himself) of its founder, Samuel Hahnemann. It describes homeopathic treatment and provides examples of how homeopathy works under various circumstances. This book also includes a highly abbreviated Materia Medica to illustrate for the reader what homeopathic remedies are. The basic tenets of homeopathy, which Vithoulkas describes quite well, distinguish it mightily from orthodox medicine, which homeopaths refer to as "allopathy." Allopathic physicians approach disease from a "fix it," symptom-based perspective and prescribe drugs or medications that are contrary to, or unlike, the disease itself, and which are often the exact opposite of the disease, such as antibiotics. Homeopathy, on the other hand, is based on the Law of Similars. Read this book, or the entry on Homeopathy in the Energetic Systems and Bodywork section of this book, to find out whether homeopathy might be useful for you.

How to Use Homeopathy
Dr. Christopher Hammond
Element Books, 1991.

I Never Told Anyone: Writings by Women Survivors of Child Sexual Abuse
Edited by Ellen Bass and Louise Thornton
Harper, 1983.

If You Want to Write: A Book About Art, Independence and Spirit
Brenda Ueland
Gray Wolf Press, St. Paul, Minnesota, 1987.
A fun and inspiring treatise to encourage you to write, now!

Imagery in Healing: Shamanism and Modern Medicine
Jeanne Achterberg
Shambala Books, 1985.

Imagineering for Health: Self–Healing Through the Use of the Mind
Serge King
Theosophical Publishing House, Wheaton, IL, 1981.

Incest and Sexuality: A Guide to Understanding and Healing
Wendy Malz and Beverly Holman
Lexington Books, D.C. Heath & Co., 1987.

I That Is We, The
Richard Moss, M.D.
Celestial Arts, Berkeley, CA, 1981.

Kahuna Healing
Serge King
Theosophical Publishing House, Wheaton, IL, 1983.

Lesbian Psychologies: Explorations and Challenges
Edited by the Boston Lesbian Psychologies Collective
University of Illinois Press, 1987.

Letters to a Young Doctor
Richard Selzer
Simon and Schuster, 1982.
A positive view of Orthodox Western medicine.

Light on Yoga
B.K.S. Iyengar
George Allen and Unwin, Ltd., 1983.
A good introduction, with excellent photos, descriptions, and yoga postures.

Light on Pranayama
B.K.S. Iyengar
Crossroad Press, 1985.
This book introduces you beautifully to yogic breathwork.

Love Yourself, Heal Your Life Workbook
Louise Hay
Hay House, Incorporated, 1990.

Lupus Novice: Towards Self–Healing
Laura Chester
Station Hill Press, Barrytown, NY, 1987.
This book provides a wonderful look at how holistic healing happens.

Mortal Lessons: Notes on the Art of Surgery
Richard Selzer
Simon and Schuster, 1987.
More about allopathy.

My Father's House: A Memoir of Incest and of Healing
Sylvia Fraser
Ticknor and Fields, New York, 1988.
This is an excellent story about how memory of incest can return.

No Safe Place: The Legacy of Family Violence
Christina Crawford
Station Hill Press, 1994.

New Concise Guide to Homeopathy, The
Nigel and Susan Garion-Hutchings
Element Books Ltd., 1995.

Perfect Health: The Complete Mind–Body Guide
Deepak Chopra
Harmony Books, Division of Crown, New York, 1991.

Pictures of a Childhood
Alice Miller
Ferrar, Strauss & Giroux, New York, 1986.
This inspiring book reveals the power of art in the healing process.

Pregnant Virgin: A Process of Psychological Transformation, The
Marian Woodman
Inner City Books, 1985.

Psychoimmunity and the Healing Process:
A Holistic Approach to Immunity and AIDS
Jason Serinus
Celestial Arts, Berkeley, CA, 1986.

Quantum Healing
Deepak Chopra
Harmony Books, Division of Crown, New York, 1989
(1990 for soft cover).

Self-Healing: My Life and Vision
Meir Schneider
Penguin Books, 1987.

This remarkable story of self-healing is valuable for people who believe they have anything "incurable."

Search for the Beloved: Journeys in Sacred Psychology, The
Jean Houston
Touchstone Books, Inc., 1987.

Exercises and explanations to deepen awareness and creativity.

Sensing, Feeling and Action: The Experiential Anatomy of Body Mind Centering
Bonnie Bainbridge Cohen
Contact Editions, Northampton, Massachusetts, 1993.

Staying Well With Guided Imagery
Belleruth Naparstek
Warner Books, 1994.

An excellent book to learn about the wide scope and application of imagery in clinical and personal settings. Belleruth Naparstek writes in a friendly way that allows virtually anyone to acquire the art of using imagery. Belleruth Naparstek's audio tape series, *Health Journeys*, is also available from Warner Audio Books.

Stories the Feet Can Tell Through Reflexology
Eunice Ingham
Ingham Publishing House, Inc., P.O. Box 12642, St. Petersburg, FL 33733, 1938.

T'ai Chi Ch'uan: A Simplified Method of Calisthenics for Health and Self-Defense
Cheng Man-Ch'ing
North Atlantic Books, 1981.

A good introduction, complete with photographs, to Tai Chi. People have been known to teach themselves Tai Chi using this book.

Therapeutic Touch: How to Use Your Hands to Help or Heal, The
Dolores Krieger, Ph.D., R.N.
Prentice–Hall, Englewood Cliffs, NJ, 1979.

There Are No Secrets
Wolfe Lowenthal
North Atlantic Books, 1991.
An introduction to Tai Chi.

Thou Shalt Not be Aware
Alice Miller
The New American Library, 1986.

Too Sacred to Cry: Psychic Trauma in Childhood
Lenore Terr, M.D.
Harper & Row, 1990.

Treating the Young Male Victim of Sexual Assault: Issues and Intervention Strategies
Eugene Porter, M.A.
Safer Society Press, 1986.

Untouched Key, The
Alice Miller
Doubleday, 1990.

Vibrational Medicine: New Choices for Healing Ourselves
Richard Gerber, M.D.
Bear & Co., Santa Fe, NM, 1988.

Victims No Longer: Men Recovering from Incest and Other Sexual Child Abuse
Mike Lew
Nevraumont Publishing Co., New York, 1988.

Wild Mind: Living the Writer's Life
Natalie Goldberg
Bantam, 1990.

Witness to the Fire: Creativity and the Veil of Addiction
Linda Leonard
Shambala, 1989.

Woman as Healer
Jeanne Achterberg
Shambala, 1990.

Writing the Natural Way
Gabriele Lusser Rico
Tarcher, Inc., Los Angeles, 1983.

Writing Down the Bones
Natalie Goldberg
Shambala.

Writing from the Heart: Inspiration and Exercises for Women Who and Want to Write
Leslea Newman
The Crossing Press, 1993.

Writing for Your Life: A Guide and Companion to the Inner Worlds
Deena Metzger
Harper, San Francisco, 1992.

Writing from the Body
John Lee
St. Martin's Press, 1994.

Waking the Tiger: Healing Trauma Through the Body
Peter Levine
Ergos Press, Box 1730, Lyons, Colorado 80540, (303) 823-9524.
This ground-breaking document, by my mentor, Dr. Peter Levine, is essential reading for the student of trauma. It is available directly from the author.

You Can Heal Your Life
Louise Hay
Hay House, Santa Monica, CA, 1984.

Your Healing Hands: The Polarity Experience
Richard Gordon
Wingbow Press, 1984.

Your Inner Physician and You: CranioSacral Therapy and Somato Emotional Release
John Upledger
The Upledger Institute, Palm Beach Gardens, Florida, 1991.

ORGANIZATIONS

American Dance Therapy Association
2000 Century Plaza, Columbia, Maryland 21044 (301) 997-4040.
Publishes journals and papers and holds conferences. Gives references for certified dance therapists throughout the country.

Association for Pre- and Peri-Natal Psychology and Health, The
1600 Prince Street, Suite 500, Alexandria, VA 22314, (703) 548-2802.
An educational, nonprofit organization dedicated to the in-depth exploration of the psychological, emotional, and social development of babies and parents from preparation for pregnancy through the post-partum period.

Authentic Movement Institute
Berkeley, California. Contact Neala Haze (510) 237-7297.

Awakening the Warrior Within
20 Rancheo Drive, San Anselmo, CA 94960, (415) 457–9009.
This California–based program is taught by my feisty and woman-wise martial arts teacher, Dawn Callan. Of the self-defense programs around, I can recommend Dawn as the most savvy about emotional dynamics.

Dr. Edward Bach Healing Center
Mount Vernon, Sotwell, Wallingford, Oxon, OX10 0PZ, publishers of the Bach Remedies Newsletters, The Bach Remedies Repertory, The Twelve Healers and Other Remedies, and other publications related to the Bach flower remedies. These tools are also available from Ellon Bach, USA, Inc., P.O. Box 320, Woodmere, NY 11598.

Emerson Training Seminars
4940 Bodega Avenue, Petaluma, CA 94952, (707) 763-7024.
Dr. William Emerson conducts a training program for health professionals and those interested in understanding and addressing the issues of pre- and peri-natal psychology. Dr. Emerson is an outstanding theoretician in the area of shock and trauma. His training covers not only an investigation into pre- and peri-natal trauma; it also explores the evaluation and treatment of trauma and shock,

and its impact on the developmental stages of life. Dr. Emerson has worked with adults and infants for over 25 years to heal birth trauma with the goal of creating a healthy repatterning. He has developed diagnostic and treatment modalities; he is also an author and an educator.

Ergos Institute
Box 1730, Lyons, Colorado 80540, (303) 823-9524.

Dr. Peter Levine, cited for his many contributions to my thinking, directs and teaches through the Ergos Institute, which offers classes, workshops, seminars and publications addressing the issue of trauma from a somatic perspective. Dr. Levine's trainings in Somatic Experiencing provide the groundwork for understanding trauma renegotiation.

Feldenkrais Guild, The
P.O. Box 489, Albany, OR 97321, (503) 926–0981.

Feldenkrais Resources
P.O. Box 2067, Berkeley, CA 94702, 800– 765–1907 or 510–525–1907.
Feldenkrais Work / Awareness through Movement.

Flower Essence Services
P.O. Box 586, Nevada City, CA 95959, (916) 273-6363.

Integrative Body Psychotherapy
A professional training program for therapists, combining breath work, family systems theory and gestalt psychology. You can contact them at P.O. Box 1603, Boulder, CO 80306. (303) 541-9316.

Jin Shin
Pamela Smith
1508 Jennings Ave, Santa Rosa, CA
Practitioner training from a teacher with extensive experience.

Jin Shin Do
Iona Teeguarden
PO Box 1097, Felton, CA 95018

Training in this system combining acupressure and Jin Shin. Iona Tee Guarden has incorporated various approaches to Oriental healing for a unique understanding.

Jin Shin Jyutsu, Inc.
8719 E. San Alberto, Scottsdale, AZ 85258
Classes, and general information about Jin Shin Jyutsu.

Jin Shin Tara
Stephanie Mines, Ph.D
PO Box 2309, Boulder, CO 80306
Training for therapists interested in a holistic approach to treating trauma.

National Center for Homeopathy, The
801 North Fairfax Street, Suite 306, Alexandra, VA 22314, (703) 548-7790.
Journals, newsletters, referrals, and general information about homeopathy.

**North American Society of Teachers of
The Alexander Technique**
1– 800–473–0620

Rolf Institute, The
205 Canyon Boulevard, Boulder, CO 80302, (303) 449–5903.

Somatic Experiencing: Training in understanding and working with trauma directed by Dr. Peter Levine under the auspices of the Ergos Institute
788 Old Apple Valley Road, Lyons, CO 80540, (303) 443–6622.

Traditional Acupuncture: The Law of the Five Elements
Diane M. Connelly, Ph.D.
The Center for Traditional Acupuncture, The American City Building, Columbia, MD, 1979.

TraumaTouch Therapy™
A training program for massage therapists and bodyworkers to increase their awareness of trauma and how to deal with it in a bodywork session. Colorado School of Healing Arts, 7655 W. Mississippi, Suite 100, Lakewood, CO 80226, (303) 986–2320.

Living
Art

Expression and Trauma

A Note Regarding the Living Art Section of This Book

What follows is a selection of writings that are focused on the process of healing from trauma and sexual abuse. These writings come from my personal notebooks, journals, and files of poems and stories. I offer them here in order to stimulate my readers to express themselves and to use the avenue of the written word as a way to find freedom from the bondage of what remains unspoken and unsaid as a result of trauma and abuse. Many of my clients wonder how to start expressing from the apparently endless well of the unspoken. It is important to know that it <u>is</u> possible to express all you need to express. Begin by speaking with pen to the pure white page, which is without judgment or interruption. My purpose in sharing these writings is purely to encourage you, to beckon you on to believe in yourself, and to say what you need to say. Don't read my writing thinking you can never express yourself this way. Read my writing so that you can write. Let my call to expression be met by your response so that a great sound is made everywhere, a sound so awesome that even perpetrators stop in their tracks to wonder at the beauty of it.

Find your own voice and use it — this is the way home.

The Fable

After the rape
She bled and healed
and bled
and healed
until she began to know light
as the outcome of pain.
Her father,
the rapist,
was a tornado of fury
who whirled down upon her
over and over.
Unlearning,
he grew inward,
battering the world with hatred
the way he had
battered his little girl.
She searched for him
in all the darknesses she could find.
In men grown sad and useless, she sought him;
In the inversion of the outcast,
and in the dance of the rebels,
she sought him
whom she could never know.
It took a long time for the girl to give up her search
and find herself.
It took a long time
for her to become her own quest
and to know her father as a cave,
a place where she could not live.
She became a woman
on the edge of life,
curious about softness,
the space within her
which she must reclaim.
Slowly she entered her breath
and carried her space,

little by little
finding her joy was with the space.
But her movement still carried the burden
of her father's heavy body
and she
who was becoming the empress of freedom,
the simplicity of this is what is,
the voice of
i forgive you and
yes, i am victory, began to see how
he had made her strong
and
astoundingly elegant.

Demolition Dance

i dance on the terrain of demolition
i have danced there for years
i dance there still
when i leap
no one lifts me
when i climb
i use my tongue
or my toes
i use my shoulder
my teeth
and no one meets me
at the edge of my leap
when i arrive
except my own truth
and i say
you are resurrected
rocking myself
kissing my tears away
and i say
when this peace is done
it will not be by words alone
it will be by flesh

I am

Airborne and Earthbound
i cry
for i am stranded
stuck
but not rooted
life giver
woman
defying the laws of gravity
saved by water
resisting metal
elemental
passion beyond man's capacity
or
understanding
stranded
singing dancing
torn asunder
penultimate integration
ageless
peering through
pierced childhood

(written in the ninth month of pregnancy)

Mother Daughter

There is no thread.
I spin loose in the world,
on a long tether,
swirling
timeless
until i return to a
Mother Divine,
having never known

the embrace of
a mother who is human.
i have been held
but not encompassed;
i have been fed
but not nurtured.
This is not a wail
but a keening,
a lament without complaint
as i
embracing myself
write
eat
serve
work
dream
create
bear children.
There is no thread.
i spin loose in the world
bear children
feel and see the pulsing life
dive deep into the heat and pain
of birth in many forms
spinning loose on a long tether
swirling timeless
until i return
to a
Mother Divine.

(pre labor contractions)

Poem For the Child Who Runs Me Round the Circle of Trees

O daughter
You who were born as I
Straddled the world
In crimson elation of earth-sprung pain,
You are a treasure of this life
Your beauty wipes my tears away
With a shout you lead
Child-struck, I follow

Seeing you grown, I
Crave the taste of wind
From your mouth
I grow greedy for your skin
And could crush you back into elbow's curve
To rock again into the midst of mothering

But I am grown into another treasury
An age of questing inward to erase a shadow
Your love is light to guide me
Until we as one are sent to fly
Into the sea of light from whence we came

All My Life Comes In On Me Now

All my life comes in on me now
The whole illusion
Scene upon scene
And then they are condensed
Into one drama,
The search for family and love,
And then my spirit comes
And shakes the fading scenes
Into crumpled material
To be thrown away,

But i am bursting with love
And there is no way out
But to Love.

Initiation

God has many hands and one eye
With love she heals the threadbare past
The Golden One, who holds all secrets lovingly
Offers me one at night's midway point
Psyche then rises from her search
To the eyes of her Beloved
And grace descends
I rise to dance from dormancy
Into the cool cool turning
Into the cool turning change

Night

The cold is more tender
Than a lover's first kiss
It embraces my eyes, my feet
i am alive and moving
i am living whole, unified
Breath, fluidity, laughter
Thought, sadness, despair
All are one
i shed not one tear
Which is mine alone
My words belong where 'ere they fall
My heart is given in love
i embrace my sisters and my brothers
Universe, i feel our Oneness
Mother of the Earth, i am not alone

Service

No one believes i am fragile
They see woman made whole by pain
Painting a magnificent life landscape, every day
No one knows the chiseling on the melting ice cord
Of my nervous system
Like a chipped crystal
In which you see facets of horror and a
Strange bloody ecstasy.
It is not what most want to see
Intimately
But i have become used to carrying this
Fragile broken chain inside my body,
I hear it clinking when i walk up the stairs,
My sleeping child in my arms,
And i hear it as i bend and stand,
Tending the bodies of the abused.
It is my secret wind chime —
This arrangement of ice and glass and crystal,
Shattered by the dreadful sounds
Of our secret animal rage and rebuilt
By a glass blower's delicacy and hard work
All the years of my life.
None can honor this imperfect nervous system
The way i do.
Nor can anyone's tears cleanse it
As well as i
The wounded healer — she of the dances and the
Screams of truth.
May i do this for you,
Oh my many brothers and sisters?
May i do this for you to remove one or two
Of the rocks from your path?

Let Me Tell You What I See

Let me tell you what I see
Without which speaking
I feel like dead wood on an ashen hearth.
Let me tell you with impunity,
To lessen the pressure,
To free the hour ahead.
Let me say it with care and craft
To prove myself worthwhile
And show the language of my heart,

And let it enter somewhere
So that it goes out of me,
Allow me this greed and need
I do for the reward of making.

The Woman Who Taught Me To See

When I came to her, I saw everything twice. She smelled of violets. The lights were soft for our eyes. She said I should be well treated — not made to cry uselessly.

She told me about black cats walking plush carpets into black rooms which issue music played by a black gloved woman seated at a black piano. She made me love the black of night wherein I safely slept, a child. I think her hair was red.

She stretched me from the eyes. She worked my muscles and set me in the sun to cure. She threw away my glasses. Her house smelled of garlic, herbs, and twilight. Her dresses sounded silk as she moved about me in slippers. She stroked my temples.

Leaving her was an assault of white bleached white. The city fell like rocks onto my softened face. I rode home on my bike, bearing her aromas — lemon verbena and violet. I rode home through one vision at a time.

I came and went — a sad young girl, and she must have sat down after I left to release my pain from her hands where she had gathered it in.

Low on Money

Low on money, I stock up on
Typewriter ribbons and fruit,
Eye delicate trinkets no longer appropriate
For my matronly form.
Food is something I'm entitled to, office supplies
And underwear.

The cool spring evening puffs a turquoise fog
Which fumes to the sky, encircles the moon
And becomes a rainbow halo.

I am not a bird; I am one of the poor folk.
I am not a creature of the night; I retire early.
I have accomplished no great feat of psychic power
Or physical austerity.
I am low on money.

I am sticking it out.
I am here in my fleshy illusion
On a cold spring night.

Walking in the wet grass
I see the moon beaming exquisitely
For free.

Poem at Day's End

It takes a long time for the day to end,
For the bitterness to finish,
For the good to be done, and the eating,
The serving and the cleaning.
And then comes the one round empty time
Wherein I enter like a bride
To utter fidelities to a dream.
I breathe within a greeting,
I find peace or fail at it,
More often the latter — my own errors coming home to roost.

At day's end I take off my appearance in my room
And cry for a while because I am lost.
In the quiet which reigns supreme
The cool comes to soothe my face,
The world is without and I am within.

Summer Night

Silence, like a dark prince
Embraces me
And holds me without desire
Night beings hum and incorporate themselves
into the silence
This unblemished beauty
Washes, washes
My soul
Breezes of love go through me
Go through me
i am permeable now
Transparent
Alone

The Nocturnes

(for Edgar Varese)

1. *Night is the cape of the sun flung over the city*
   It shadows me as I hurry home with my groceries
   Ringing its bell in my ear
   Night is two–headed, four–armed
   It grabs me by the waist and we go
   Falling, falling
   Night is the neighborhood I wander
   As through fields of abstract sound

2. *Night cuts through my house*
   The roses whisper above their thorns

Flags and scarves flutter in my room
I am ready to step into my shadow
But I do not move

3. *In the chill midnight*
   I skate my skin's surface
   Making wounds deep enough
   To bleed from an original source
   I am knee deep in silence
   My mind, in hibernation,
   Awaits itself

4. *My house is empty of me*
   I want
   To find where night hooks into tomorrow
   Death is a dazzling ornament
   Tempting me to a brilliant blindness

5. *Who comes? The garden gate creaks*
   Who comes? Winter scurries like a rat
   Who comes? The ragged mantle is buried, is burnt
   Who comes? Night separates like the red sea
   Who comes to ferry me across? Who comes?

   Frost drips down the window of my heart
   The gate is swollen with cold
   The cats delight in underbrush
   My eyes are weighted closed with the
   Pennies they rest on the lids
   Of the dead

   The frozen trees scrape the house of the old neighbor
   Far off a child cries in her sleep
   The moon rests in her lighter phase, slender sister
   But oh I am blind, blind
   Still blind and wondering
   Who comes?

6. *Give me nectar of night to drink*
   So I can see into the pool of darkness
   Silken night, I wear you as a veil

To cover my eyes
To see inside
Silken night,
I put my face into my hands
And hold it up before my eyes

7. *Night is an opalescent canopy*
   Over my inner vision
   Night is a rocky terrain
   Inhabited by many breeds
   In its sandy earth a seed slumbers
   Pulsing a constant undertone
   It will flower narcissus
   It will flower elder
   It will flower golden, as the sun

8. *Soul patters the black floor of night*
   Dancerly mysteries travel nether reaches
   A child sleeps, spring on the rise
   Coming to heal furious demonheads
   In the thundering center of night
   The peaceable eye opens wide

9. *I want to elope with sentences*
   I want to be an alphabet
   Or the hairs of a calligrapher's brush
   Or embossed paper
   But most of all
   I want to be the night
   On a winged unicorn
   Covering the world's industry
   With my luminous black skirt

10. *Night, I embrace you*
    Awaiting love like an exposed house
    Its gate swinging open

11. *Soon I will whisper*
    Step soft so as not to disturb
    The peace I occupy

Soon I will enter my quiet
Forget all but the Unforgettable
In that time the delivery of love
Will be simple
As eating sparingly
After Prayer

Green River

near Moab, Utah

The canyons are me
My body strewn endlessly
On a murky river
Burnt sienna, terra cotta, black
The growth around my openings
Tough,
Clinging to my muddy shores
Prickly, protective.
This majesty yet seems apart from me
I am not old enough
To feel the immensity of this
Silent wisdom
Towering and open
Open beyond open.
I feel my kindness here
My smallness
And my hope.
This Mother Earth
How she reassures me
By her Eternity
So personal, so enduring.
Akin to her, I feel
Unpredictable, like she
Trackable only by the
Attentive, the utterly present.
This mirroring astounds me.
I am She, the Earth, yet she is my mother.

What was done to me was done to her.
What is done to her is done to me.
In silent softness night enfolds me
Kissing me with breezes too gentle to be named
Zephyrs of delight caress my tired body
And soothe it
For the shaded coolness of a brief morning
Before the heat comes
To toughen the skin of the earth,
A beauty treatment for the hardy.
I must remark upon this journey into myself
I must not lose this communion
Ever
I must remember
The silence of my name
This sacred space
A wombing embrace.

Prayer for the Winter solstice

There was a time, I know
When the world flowed
As from a woman's soul
And the pattern of days
Was shaped like a woman's cycle
Responsive to feeling, taking its rest
Honoring the needs of children.
But a woman's way is soft
Things slide off the edges of her time
And focus is circular
Life moves slowly
Pacing the heart's rhythm.
When did the hunters, with minds like their spears, come
Sharp and determined,
To outsmart the cycles, the seasons,
To make things stable and firm and solid

So that there could be
Structure?
Whenever they came
It signalled the end of one time and the beginning of another.
Women's way receded
And the days grew shorter, the nights longer.
Women burrowed into the darkness,
Finding their way, with their hands
Reaching for the cycles, for the circular forms
For the children's souls, for the light.
Now we live in a great darkness
Which grows, progressively, bigger.
Children shoot children
Fathers violate daughters
Mothers violate sons
And disease runs rampant
Both the innocent and the guilty are slain
And spirit suffers the weight of a horrid, hard materialism
A scourge is upon the land
Darkness hovers in the air
Our breath is stifled
And few amongst us pray.
In this tomb of darkness where we lie in wait
To whom can we ask for delivery?
Great Mother
From whose belly we are all born
Eat the venom of our minds.
Dear Mother
Breathe us out
Into the
Everlasting Light
Lest we die here in our ignorance.
Put into our hands
The roundness of your vision,
Put into our hearts your undying child love,
And let us

Awaken,
O Mother,
Let us awaken
For the darkness threatens mightily now
And we are longing for the Light.

Grandmother

My grandmother is the incarnation of healing.
Long ago, she says,
My people were slain
Their blood could be seen
Soaking into the autumn mud
Somehow I was spared
But I walked amongst their bodies
I let my hair hang down
And I sent my endless tears
Into the earth
Into their bodies
Everyone was taken from me
And I wandered alone
Until I was taken in by the
Sanctuary of their compassion
Where I spent my last days
Now I have come back
To heal the land where my people were slain.
Because I am a woman
I can never be separated from my belief in
The future.
When you see me
You cannot see my strength
But you can feel it
I carry the light of all the
Souls of my people
The slain children's light I carry
The light of slain warriors I carry

The light of women, young women
Pregnant women
The healing women
The medicine women
All this light I carry
It is warm
It is the greatest comfort
It is the source of Life.

My tears are yet abundant
There is no need to stop them
I cry for all the terror of the helpless
I cry enough and more
I am the wailing woman
Grandmother of the Tears
Protectress of Children.

The light of my being
Reaches everywhere
Abused and abusers alike are healed
If they can but see my light.

There are no secrets.
The slaying of my people is a brutality
I have absorbed into me.
I have drunk the blood of my people
And eaten their mutilated flesh.
I carry no anger or fear
But I am strong beyond measure.

I have devoured the placentas of all beings
In the cave of my grieving
I have done this for you
All people are my people
I am the Grandmother of All
Let me sing my song to you
In the silence of my light
Have no fear
I will tell you now

There is no death
My light, my tears and my kiss are the same.
We return and return
Go in love
My child and my children
Go in love

Embroidery

This typewriter is my embroidery needle
Doing mysterious stitchery on pearl white fabric,
Black on white, white on black.
Machine, I would make you supple,
Make work a dance and us a couple.
May we sing together
These hours into purpose, reality?

The Dance Place

Dance of loss
Dance of shame
Dance that hums my father's name
Dance of joy
i move, i am
now
alone
space
arms
heart
my passion for this wind
which blows away my daddy's eyes
i kiss his head
farewell
farewell
a dark loss
falling from my chest

The Last Rape Poem

You see
this is the end:
a man
took me
and twisted me
this way and that
when no one was looking.
i begged him,
i said,
"if this is all you can give me,"
i said,
"here, take me then
and eat me
till i am gone,"
i said.
"here, devour me,
until i am dead."
"daddy," i said,
"finish me now, make
your mouth full with me,"
i said,
"here, daddy,
eat me,"
and i died.
i fell into the pit of years.
i forgot all truths.
i saw not the door nor the day nor the way.
i saw only my head
in the sewer,
my body
decapitated,
struggling to fight back,
still crying, alone, my head,
still crying
alone.
"but daddy," i said,

"daddy, do you like me?
will you come home now, daddy,
and like me?"

My Daughter and I Live at the Edge of Town

My daughter and i live at the edge of town,
in the shelter of a mountain ridge
which was once the home of a healing tribe.
In our small place we are sometimes quite afraid,
but at other times we abide in our peace,
and do what we must do
quietly
together.
Today the grey betwixt winter and spring
is spread all over our town
and we take it as a hint of
stillness and retreat.
On days such as these
hungry ghosts may run about and shout,
having lost their homes in the fog.
Therefore, it is good to rest within
and banish ghosts while cleaning shelves
and writing poems
and thinking of the way
this life unfolds on the screen of time's illusion.

This is my fortieth year
and today is like a winding river
revealing youth at one moment, age at the next.
Will some knowledge speak its truth
from within me, soon and surely?
Let my love of life
shape my face and my form.
Let me become what i truly am, inside.
Awaken souls, mine and my daughter's,
to the True Joy, the Light.

The Blouse

The shop where she saw the blouse was on a street in a walkable town. The windows were decorated with cups and books, towels and coffeepots. It was a gingham street on a bright day, harbinger of springtime, the season for which she hoped the most intensely. The blouse was crisp and finished, white collars and cuffs, a blouse her mother might speak of, reminiscing.

The girls on the street were tiny. They didn't walk — they ran, tilted, posed remarkable on high wooden heels. She sat down to watch them as a mother watches a brood of children.

She was on the street, not in it. She wondered if most people did things so that others could see them doing it. She felt invisible and there was evidence *that she did not exist. No heads turned when she walked by. Saleswomen did not come and ask if they could help her when she entered shops.*

In the cafe she thought about the blouse in between watching the girls and letting the myriad conversations hum by, senselessly. She liked the way that blouse looked, perfectly folded by the wide-hipped saleslady so that the arms disappeared. She got up decisively, walked across the street and bought it.

She carried the blouse off with a sense of completion, her purchase of a bright thing on a bright day. It hung in her closet, crisp, perfect cotton, unsullied by time. It is a simple thing to pretend in, she thought, and felt sad. It is a paltry thing to take such pleasure in, meaningless, she knew. I want that crispness in my heart, I want that brightness in my eyes, but all I do is buy it, wear it. She hung her head. It wasn't late enough, but it was dark. Down the street she heard the clanking of high-heeled wooden shoes on pavement. Someone must be going to town, she thought.

Letting Go

The past clings in rocky clumps to my new body.
Muddy accumulations of fear and distrust
Hang like strings of dirty, broken prayer beads
On the silver thread of my lengthening spinal cord.
Stretch, i say, looking out at the softening
Kingdom of Abundant Beauty.

Fear is short and love is infinitely long.
Love's reach is a dancer's dream —
The arch of the spirit for home.
World, mottled but glistening
i reach into your womb.
i embrace your ever-changing Illusion.
Dance me into shattering rhythm.
Send these vestiges of dead life
Into the gyrating emptiness,
The nothingness from which i came.
And i will greet this new day
with child's delight, reborn,
with nothing of the past
ever again to recall.

Co Dependency

i love the you
who doesn't exist
i love the
unrealized transformative potential.
my faith in you — that is what
i love.
i don't see the you
who has forgotten me,
the you too needy
to notice the pain you inflict.

your innocence and vulnerability

make me treasure you,
your fragility —
these make me hold back the truth —
that you are hurting me, hurting me
with the ignorance you deny,
and i take on the hurt
and lick my wounds when i'm alone,
building my disease
on the altar of my
sacrificial love.

Coming out of Co Dependency

when i drop what i want from you
and look
i see
a brilliantly torn asunder man
a thunderbolt of insight
asleep at the wheel
dangerously disembodied
i step back from you
taken aback
reeling
i step away and look
at you
a
fellow traveler
i find you
in my chest
curled into a hope
i carry you this way
because of the loving
you
help me
build my vengeance
into

elegant discrimination
you can
i can
take care of
myself
i am loving you

The Woundings

Fear is my father's name. He is not the Sun. He is the
darkness that dwells like a worm in a wound, to keep it from
healing. And then there is my Father, the Sun, who forever
has been shining down on my wound to heal it. My father is
a wanderer somewhere on this earth, a lonely man, with
ulcerated wounds, blind to the healing. Poor humans, we eat
at each other, and the Sun Light, our Father, licks our
wounds. In the night, an Angelic Divine Mother comes
with her ointments and fluids, and gently does she clean us
and care for us, so that our skin and flesh and cells might be
stronger to bear these woundings we inflict on one another.
Like are we unto Christ, crucified and resurrected, we of the
tears and laughter, all we wounded poets. And who of my
friends escapes this? Only those who have ceased to wound
another because she is healed, and I know no such human.
We are not one against another, rather are we wounded and
healed, healed and wounded, repeatedly, until we see.

Autumn Starts Tonight

Autumn starts tonight
With a cold wind.
i lift my heart to this page
The way the breeze lifts the leaves.
My passion is burnished gold,
Singed, tinged with a heat few dare to touch.

Sing autumn air, my messenger.
Rustle me to the ecstasy that quivers in
Explosive quiet.
Give me the release that brings me
Chattering to the brink of wholesome delivery.
i am gone quickly into a movement
That destroys mind's activity.
i go the way dry leaves dance
Just before they are crushed to dust.
That is how i will die — arching,
Fingers curled around an invisible strand of hair,
Lips sucking Mother's breast, which is
Offered without illusion,
Offered without threat of abandonment.

Autumn is Cold Desertion

Autumn is an unlikely season for resurrection.
It is bundled, stuck behind the woodpile,
Hysterical with color.
Autumn is random, a season between substantial thoughts.
It is whispering in trees which move repeatedly
Closer and closer to one another.
And i, in my sleep, remember closeness,
Remember bodies savoring other bodies in innocence,
Remember tribes, animals, a love which,
When felt,
Solved
Forever
The mystery of
Desire.

Autumn Harvest

This is the cultural loneliness
of our communal bodies,
hungering for a mother's touch,
a father's love,
through years of absence.
Desertion is seen as fog through the trees.
The sky's emptiness mirrors my untouched smoothness.
We wait and wait.
Behind our masks, we cry:
Sun, Earth, Mother, Father,
Shine your embrace onto our passion!
Let me cry into the womb of Eternity.
Mother, your redemption calls me
Like the beat of my own heart.

Snowstorm

i am under this slowly falling soft and glistening stuff
withdrawing into my blood
retreating into the thick silence of my own winter
hibernating to birth my forgiveness
hibernating to redeem myself with love
that round heartfelt syllable of truth
i spiral in on myself, dervish in
to uncover bitterness, resistance, fear
i will cast out all this rejection
and open my arms wide
and gather love in
and then let it go, free
bird of the winter
my soaring love of truth
unbound, uncontained alive

On Looking at a Photograph of my Daughter

What physical knowledge!
Nothing the body fears
And what it fears
It acknowledges
And so has freedom.
What joy of stance!
Striking a pose,
All flesh supple
To do the will of a
Moment's dance.
Such a gift of living!
No loss is there.
And now here
Birds sing
Where my daughter is not
And I am.

I Reside with Myself and No Other

i am made whole in my solitude
Becoming mySelf i am liberated from myself
And can walk into the crowd of Us
Alone and joyful
i reside with myself and no other
This is my pain
This my union

Winter is a Night of Pure Ice

Sleep is a serious thing
A place to go
for healing or treasure hunting,
A territory of artifacts

Or a respite from
Days of digging to unearth the Soul.
i do my work like a woman on the edge,
in my coat of many colors,
alone with the wind,
reaching my hands into the void
to extract demons and other curious entities
from the bodies of friends and strangers.
Winter is a night of pure ice — slippery and slick.
It is me alone, flat and frightened.
It is the poignancy of desertion, and
the nameless hope of union
hidden like a seed under the snow.
Winter is to nurture
the recollection of ecstasy,
as when my body became light
under the hands of love.
As when entered i was not defiled
But resurrected
To honor this womanhood,
this unending yearning
for beauty, for purity,
for my Mother Divine
who brings the Light,
who is the Light.
May She cover me with it
All over
All over
so that when i love
it will be a simple thing;
so that I may come and go
on this Earth
like a soft passing,
so that i may be all i ever wanted to be —
a Spring breeze
ruffling the hair of a child.

Mama

If you should pass from me
Before i have loved you well
i will wail in the night
For all the embraces
Still harboring release
So mama, I choose to love you now
And papa too, wherever he may be
Till we are given a chance
To care for one another again

Autumn Evening

The Arabic moon, a perfect teenager,
Sits serenely above playing children,
On her throne of impending night.
The dusky blue evening sweeps down upon us
From the sky of utmost peace.
While i glory in the wonder of this
Cold struck time
With its hush of the rustling dead,
My inner eye seeks within, probing, probing,
For while all the world beckons
i am yearning for the dream of my own truth.

Resurrection

From this hunk of mud and gravel
into which my father ground me
comes a spirit of my devotion
a body of meat
which dreams of celebrations
night upon night of celebrations
singing free like the voice of my sex.
And in the fires of my rage

let my surging die
until i am forgotten
and all this wounding
is ash,
is ash.

**

i pray over my father's sleeping form
caressing his absence
until i shake myself awake
to travel.
he has become weary
and must rest
while i
meet goddesses
and build villages
and nurse children
and prepare garments
to adorn the moments of my
many transformations.

***

when dark comes, it's true, i sleep,
but in my sleep i stir the cauldrons of healing,
blending the energies of fire and earth.
my eyes are focused inward so i can
chant the words i know by heart
but have no memory of learning.
This night is crucial
to the changing Earth
and i am the midwife
to a journey
none know yet
that they will take.

****

Friend, i am beside you but you know not my name.
You have been my father, son and lover,

you have been my rapist and deceiver,
you have robbed me and struck me hard,
you have thrown me into the night
beaten and weak,
and left me to die in backwater towns, alone,
with nowhere to turn,
and i have found myself resurrected.
Goddess within me,
Goddess my name,
Goddess my body

*****

On this very earth,
solitary
unvanquished
invincible —
blue energy,
the heat of God.
i am she
whom you have forgotten,
she whom you cannot bear to face,
not even in your drunken absence.
i shower you
with the currents of my love
so that you quiver
in a brightness
too ardent
for your fallow life.

******

Goddess within me
Goddess my name
Goddess my body
On this earth
Solitary
unvanquished
blue energy
the heat of God
i am she

whom you have forgotten
i shower you
with the currents of my love

Birthday

i wake to a beautiful morning feeling a combination of
despair and hopefulness, fear and enthusiasm. The world i
am in is on the brink of either disaster or transformation —
or both. My own personal evolution and the evolution of the
world (humanity) seem linked. i grope towards a self–
understanding coupled with knowledge or attunement to
my environment/community. Neither of these understand-
ings is easy to come by, and frequently i question my own
value and ability, my work and my search. How dare i
grapple with these issues? Yet, right now, this week before
my forty–fourth birthday, i feel rising within me a yearning
for my union with life, my acceptance of the present, and
my willingness to love. My work with people is central to
my growing capacity to love. May it expand infinitely. i
thank each and every soul who has touched me deeply —
those who have hurt me as well as those who have been
tender with me. As i gradually step out of the false concepts
i have had about myself, i enter the realms of compassion
and endless possibility. Slowly i come to believe in joy and
the richness of experience which molds me to perfection.
Which path shall i take on my quest? This question is
confusing me now. But whichever path i take, i will arrive
at my own True Self and merge in the simple ecstatic
oneness of being. This is the sex at the core of my desire.
This is the sensuality of my touch. May i awaken to con-
stant presence with the essential goodness which speaks for
me now. Holy are our lives when we affirm the genuineness
of our yearning. May my father find his shelter on this earth
or in any of the realms where he resides, and may he be free
of his torment. May i find sanctuary and peace in my own
Self. May we all reach the home of Truth.

Ritual

i offer the shame and fear
which coagulates my core
to this dancing floor
this wood
streaked with sun and shade.
i offer this twisted shape,
turned to hide,
stubborn and unruly,
to God, my Essential Nature,
the all embracing Void,
my Nothingness.
My passion bows, disappears
and enters
the electric feminine
consumed
by Pure Goodness,
finally.

Flesh, Not Flesh

This is flesh
This is not flesh
This is the matter of lust
This is the stuff of transcendence
This star heat
For centuries kept sacred
In Shiva's boudoir
In the flask
Hidden behind the brocade and gold
The bottle sealed with a vajra
Elegant and decadent, the material of new life
Degraded and uplifted
The form of
Crystal, the form of
Silk, the form of
A tongue

Inside a bell which is
Rung to begin
The night
The smoothness of annealed steel
The fire of hell
The softness of heaven
Your fear
Keeps you on the other side
Safe
In my tears

Death

Long dead days
i dreamed of death
and called it God.
Now death is gone
and i find this
emptiness
which is me
and i must love her.
i dream
one long night
that i have a lingam
it glistens
magic wand of the truth
and i put it inside me
penetrating myself deeply
with the wisdom of
holy desire.
dream my dream
women of the lost tribe,
dream my dream
and we
as eternal undulation,
Shakti,
will live
forever.

The Room

*It is always summer in Los Angeles and the sadness of the
Jews fills the air with bittersweet longing. In the California
Jewish ghetto, in the 1950's, everyone, even the old people,
are upwardly mobile. The boys will become professionals,
the girls will marry them, and the wizened elders will
ascend to heaven to celebrate with centuries of villagers
their long-awaited release from fear.*

*In a small room facing the street, on the second floor of an
apartment, a girl looks out the window and feels the difference between the limited futures represented by the houses,
and everything beyond the window which is vast, exquisite.
The simple act of looking out the window is what she
returns to over and over in her privacy. Her room is bare
and she keeps it clean, finding pleasure in whiteness and
order. The room is aborned only by the beauty of the world
beyond, not the one of traffic and conversation, but the one
of flight and sky. She is enticed by a glorious universe and
its beauty presents itself to her right there in that room,
repeatedly, when she stands and looks out the window.*

*The contrast between the smallness of the room and the
exotic, unknown explodes in the moment. The outside
universe steps into the girl's room like royalty, and she,
feeling quite undeserving, enjoys the multicolored entertain-
ment as it unfolds in never-ending scenes. She wonders if
she can ever share this ecstasy? Which Jew down the street
would care to listen to her tales of nonsectarian bliss? She
loves the people in the houses. She sheds their tears again
and again. But something delicate and dancerly calls to her,
beckons beyond their tragedy, and she is committed there.*

*It is quiet. Shabbos morning. Men in dark suits come out,
their hats angling, ties loosened, hands in their pockets, and
walk with a wide, easy gait down the streets. Wives and
children follow, moving like satellites about the planet Man.
Shabbos. Families. Slow movement. Time and space inter-*

twine. *Los Angeles streets could be village roads on Shabbos. The girl watches from her perch. The tree growing into a sheltering maturity outside her window watches with her. She takes it in — the people below, the vastness above. She takes it in.*

Then silently, with sighs, tears, and an inner stirring, it comes to epiphany within her, and she is full with beauty. In her invisible adolescence she knows that life has been made good and beautiful on earth, and the loveliness of this knowledge is too great for language, too silken to be touched.

"This small room," she thinks, looking about her, "how much feeling is contained here, how much I have gathered with my eyes in this place." Something draws her into expansion, releasing the containment. Others might call the quiet event mysterious or vague, but the girl knows reality is present in the room. It expands within her body, filling it with light. It makes her lose sight of all boundaries and being alone in the moment she joins everyone and everything, silently merging.

Ripening

i accept this body
i touch its fullness with love
everywhere this flesh is celebration
my body is sweet
a feast of ripening
a woman's place
basket of delectables
smooth pillow
neverending softness
reach into me
and take all you can hold

INDEX